EMULSION TECHNOLOGY

Theoretical and Applied

Including the Symposium on Technical Aspects of Emulsions

SECOND, ENLARGED EDITION

1946

CHEMICAL PUBLISHING CO., INC.

BROOKLYN, N. Y.

U. S. A.

Copyright
1946
CHEMICAL PUBLISHING CO., INC.
BROOKLYN   N. Y.

Contributing Editors

W. R. ATKIN, M.Sc.

N. H. CHAMBERLAIN, PH.D.

W. CLAYTON, D.Sc., F.I.C.

R. M. K. COBB, CHIEF CHEMIST, LOWE PAPER CO.

J. W. CORRAN, B.Sc., PH.D., F.I.C.

F. G. DONNAN, C.B.E., M.A., D.Sc., F.R.S.

R. DOREY, B.Sc.

A. C. FRASER, M.R.C.S., L.R.C.P., M.B., B.S.

H. FREUNDLICH, PH.D., D.Sc.

L. G. GABRIEL, B.Sc., M.I.P.T.

M. P. HOFMANN, CHIEF CHEMIST, BARTLETT, SNOW CO.

R. I. JOHNSON, B.Sc., A.I.C.

L. A. JORDAN, D.Sc., A.R.C.S., F.I.C.

J. B. SPEAKMAN, D.Sc., F.I.C.

H. P. STEVENS, M.A., PH.D., F.I.C.

W. H. STEVENS, A.R.C.S., F.I.C.

F. C. THOMPSON, M.Sc.

V. G. WALSH, M.B., B.CH., B.Sc.

S. WERTHAN, COLLOID CHEMIST, N. J. ZINC CO.

R. M. WOODMAN, M.Sc., PH.D., F.I.C., A.I.P.

G. M. SUTHEIM

iii

PREFACE TO THE SECOND EDITION

THIS edition has been enlarged with a comprehensive section on the *Theory of Emulsions and Emulsifying Agents*.
Another new feature is an up-to-date list of emulsifying agents classified in the following groups: anion-active, cation-active, non-ionic and miscellaneous emulsifiers. It lists in addition to the commercial and/or chemical name, the chemical composition, the type of emulsion it helps to produce, physical properties, suggested uses and manufacturers of the emulsifying agents.

In this enlarged form, the book embraces every aspect of emulsions and emulsifying agents.

THE EDITOR

PREFACE

THE symposium on emulsions, held by the Leather Trades Chemists, brought together some of the foremost European colloid chemists. The papers, presented at this symposium, were published under the title of Technical Aspects of Emulsions. This useful book ran to three editions and is now out of print. Because of the numerous requests for it and because of new developments in emulsion technology, it was decided to bring out a new edition with certain revisions and additions—the latter by American specialists.

Thus there have been included: a section by M. P. Hofmann, an authority on the use of colloid mills and homogenizers, a section by R. M. K. Cobb, an authority on paper treating emulsions, tying in the theoretical and practical, and a section by S. Werthan, a specialist on water emulsion paints and other coatings; all these serve to round out the theoretical and practical aspects of emulsions.

There have also been included authoritative data on methods and formulation of many practical commercial emulsions in the following fields: drugs, cosmetics, beverages, foods, polishes, waxes, coatings, paints, etc., as well as a comprehensive list of all important commercial emulsifying agents.

This unique assembly of data and technique of the scientific and industrial phases of emulsions should prove of particular interest to all those concerned with the investigation, production and utilization of emulsifiers and emulsions.

H. BENNETT

CONTENTS

SECTION   PAGE

PREFACE   v

FOREWORD TO TECHNICAL ASPECTS OF EMULSIONS . . .   xi

1. ON THE MECHANISM OF EMULSIFICATION   1

2. THE FUNDAMENTAL PRINCIPLES OF PRACTICAL EMULSION
   MANUFACTURE   7

3. THE USE OF HIGHLY DISPERSED EMULSIONS IN THE TREAT-
   MENT OF TOXAEMIC CONDITIONS   33

4. EMULSIONS IN THE PATENT LITERATURE   39

5. INDUSTRIAL EMULSION FORMULATION   66

6. THE DESIGN OF EMULSIFYING MACHINES   88

7. EFFECT OF THE MODE OF PREPARATION ON THE DISPERSION
   OF SOAP-STABILISED EMULSIONS   119

8. PROBLEMS CONNECTED WITH THE PREPARATION AND AP-
   PLICATION OF EMULSIONS USED IN AGRICULTURAL SPRAY-
   ING   127

9. SOME OBSERVATIONS ON A TYPICAL FOOD EMULSION .   176

10. EMULSIONS AND EMULSIFICATION IN THE WOOL TEXTILE
    INDUSTRY   193

11. THE STABILITY OF EMULSIONS IN THIN FILMS   207

12. EMULSION PAINTS   214

13. EMULSIONS IN THE LEATHER INDUSTRY   230

14. RUBBER LATEX   240

15. SOME PHYSICAL PROPERTIES OF DISPERSIONS OF ASPHALTIC
    BITUMEN   253

    APPENDIX   279

16. THEORY OF EMULSIONS AND EMULSIFYING AGENTS . .   329

    INDEX   349

ix

FOREWORD

To Technical Aspects of Emulsions

By Professor F. G. Donnan, C.B.E., M.A., D.Sc., F.R.S.

(Professor of Chemistry and Director of The Chemical Department, University College, London, W.C.1)

THIS volume contains the papers read at the second Symposium held by the British Section of the International Society of Leather Trades' Chemists. I regard it as a great honour that I was asked to preside at the Meeting, which was held at University College, London. The subject chosen by the Committee, namely the "Technical Aspects of Emulsions," possesses very great importance. It is now thirty-six years since my attention was first directed to emulsions and their formation and stability. In the intervening period, I have seen the scientific interest and the technical importance of this subject grow steadily from year to year. Not only does the study of emulsions throw great light on important aspects of colloid science, but emulsions in themselves offer scientific problems of the highest value. Need I refer to the fact that it was a quantitative study of the sedimentation-distribution of emulsions which led Perrin to his classic evaluation of the Avogadro constant and the proof of the validity of the kinetic-molecular theory of matter? And, if I may be allowed a somewhat personal reference, it was the study of oil emulsions in the Muspratt Laboratory of Physical and Electro-Chemistry at the University of Liverpool which enabled Lewis to carry out the first quantitative test of Gibbs' adsorption law, and which enabled Ellis and Powis to show that finely dispersed hydrocarbon oil emulsions in water behave in many respects as "suspensoid" sols. Indeed, the important discovery of the "critical" zone of zeta-potentials arose out of this work.

The great importance of emulsions in many industries and many technical processes requires no emphasising on my part—the papers contained in this volume bear striking witness to the truth of the statement. Readers of this book will learn much concerning the application of the science and technical art of emulsions and emulsification to many industries—leather, wool, agriculture, food, rubber, paint and varnish, road-making, etc. They will also acquire valuable knowledge concerning the machines used in making technical emulsions, and concerning the patent literature of the whole subject. There is another very important aspect of emulsions and emulsification which must on no account be forgotten, namely the part which they play in physiology, medicine, and pharmacy. Does not the absorption of fats in the intestine and their transport to the living cells in blood and lymph depend on the formation of emulsions? I think I am in no way overstating the case when I say that the large audience at the Symposium listened with the deepest attention to the striking contribution on "The Use of Highly Dispersed Emulsions in the Treatment of Toxæmic Conditions," made by Dr. Walsh and Dr. Frazer. If I may express a non-expert opinion, this paper appears to foreshadow a very important advance in the treatment of disease.

Last, but not least, I should like to refer to the very interesting contribution made by Professor Freundlich, dealing with the emulsifying and de-emulsifying actions of ultrasonic waves, *i.e.,* sound waves of very high frequency.

In conclusion, I desire to congratulate the British Section of the International Society of Leather Trades' Chemists on their initiative and energy in organising these Symposia and publishing their results. This is work of the highest value for the advance of science and the progress of industry based on science.

May I be forgiven a note of national pride if I say it is a sign that the British Section is very much alive and alert, and worthy of its great Master, Henry Procter.

F. G. Donnan.

The Sir William Ramsay Laboratories of
Inorganic and Physical Chemistry.
University College,
London, W.C.1.

SECTION 1

ON THE MECHANISM OF EMULSIFICATION

By Prof. H. Freundlich

(The Sir William Ramsay Laboratories of Physical and Inorganic Chemistry, University College, London)

DURING the last few years, following the pioneer work of Wood and Loomis,[1] a great number of experiments have been made with ultrasonic waves, *i.e.,* acoustic waves of so high a frequency that they are inaudible. Generally, frequencies of some hundred thousand cycles per second are used. In the present work, frequencies of about 200,000 cycles per second have been used. The highest frequency one is able to hear approximates to about 15,000–20,000 cycles per second. These ultrasonic waves are produced with the aid of a piezo-electric quartz-plate between two electrodes connected with the poles of a Tesla-coil vibrating with a high frequency. The top electrode, made of brass, has the shape of a ring, and the bottom one is a block of lead. Both the quartz-plate and the electrodes are in an oil-bath. As soon as the quartz begins to vibrate, stationary waves are set up in the oil; the fluid is violently agitated, rising in fountains from the middle of the plate. These ultrasonic waves are a source of strong mechanical energy, which causes local high acceleration of molecular motion. If it is desired to transfer this energy to other systems, it is only necessary to dip a test-tube, for instance, containing the material under investigation, into the oil-bath, just above the vibrating quartz-plate; the waves are transmitted through the walls of the tube to the interior.

1

Wood and Loomis have found already that mercury is rapidly dispersed in water under the influence of these waves. This emulsifying action has been further investigated, as well as the influence of the waves on the stability of emulsions of greater dispersion. These investigations, mainly due to my collaborators, Dr. Söllner, Dr. Juliusburger and Mr. Bondy, will now be described briefly.

No difficulties are encountered when emulsifying mercury in water (H. B. Bull and K. Söllner [2]). The results are best, if the amounts of mercury and water are kept within certain limits; a too large or too small amount of mercury is not advantageous. The particles formed are not very small; their diameter is, as a rule, between 0.5 and 1.5μ. These emulsions are, therefore, not very stable, and the particles settle in the course of 24 hours. In some other cases, [3] for instance, with Wood's metal in certain organic liquids like bromobenzene, etc., very stable colloidal solutions have been produced, but, so far, the conditions under which they are formed are not clearly understood. The influence of salts and emulsifying agents, such as soaps, etc., is quite what might be expected. Highly charged and strongly absorbed ions impart distinct charges (positive or negative) to the small mercury-drops and they, therefore, increase the stability of the emulsion; in the case of strong emulsifying agents (soaps, etc.) we get emulsions of still greater stability.

Another experimental result was more surprising and unexpected. The phenomenon was observed by Söllner and Rogowski [4] in the first place for certain other systems, but can easily be verified also for mercury and water. The new observation is that the presence of gas is of great importance in the formation of an emulsion. If the experiments are carried out in vacuo, the liquids being freed from gas as far as possible, no emulsion is produced under conditions which are otherwise most favourable; perhaps a very poor emulsion may be formed which breaks immediately. In presence of air an influence of oxygen might be assumed, but the same results are found with inert gases, for instance, hydrogen. Similar results are obtained with other pairs of liquids. There is a certain difference since emulsions are produced in both liquids, e.g., one of water-in-benzene and one of benzene-in-water. The effect of the presence of gas was confirmed; in some cases, it was shown that nitrogen and argon also have an influence. It is perhaps owing to this phenomenon that emulsification is very poor in liquids in which mercury is strongly wettable. In gasolene, for instance, mercury is not emulsified at all in the absence of gas and also not under the ordinary conditions of these experiments.

Before endeavouring to give any explanations for this behaviour, another effect of ultrasonics upon emulsions should be discussed. On making them in the way described, it does not seem possible to increase the concentration of the disperse phase beyond a certain limit, even if the treatment is extended over a much longer time. A stationary state is reached, the ultrasonics not only producing the emulsion, but also destroying it. This holds only if one phase, for instance the aqueous phase, does not contain large amounts of emulsifying agents (soaps, gelatin, etc.), which prevent the coalescence of the drops.

That ultrasonics are able to destroy an emulsion may be easily shown by using a different kind of experimental device. An emulsion of benzene-in-water, for instance, prepared by the aid of these waves, is poured into a U-shaped, thick-walled capillary tube. If the tube is dipped into the vibrating oil-bath, striations of beautiful regularity are formed after a short time, in both branches of the tube. The droplets are gathered in the nodes, the antinodes in between often being absolutely clear. The distance between two nodes is equal to half a wave-length in the liquid. If the tube is taken out of the bath, the striations persist for some time, the settling of the coarser particles, currents in the liquid, and Brownian movement destroying the orientation. If an emulsion of a sufficiently high concentration is kept sufficiently long under the influence of the ultrasonics, large drops are formed in the nodes which settle and collect in the curvature of the tube. They are most likely produced by a so-called orthokinetic coagulation; the small droplets which move parallel from the antinodes to the nodes with different velocity being driven together and then coalescing. Thus it is seen directly that the ultrasonics are also able to destroy an emulsion, and it is obvious also that under the conditions mentioned above, when, using a test-tube, there may be regions, perhaps near the walls of the tube, where the ultrasonics are destroying the emulsion, whereas in other regions they are dispersing the liquids in one another.

Satisfactory explanations for all these phenomena cannot be put forward just yet, but the main points seem to be as follows:

The ultrasonics cause locally very strong and very variable movements of the molecules of the liquids. It is believed that it is a direct dispersing action mainly due to transverse vibrations of the walls, which causes the primary dispersion of the liquids. A high viscosity of one of the liquids is as a rule disadvantageous for emulsification.[5] The same holds if the dispersion medium has strong elastic properties resisting any displacement. An example of the latter kind is the vitreous body of the eye; it is not very viscous, but has a strong elastic coherence. If attempts are made to emulsify mercury in this body by a few seconds treatment, as can be done in water, very little success will result.

The impression has been formed that the stabilising effect of gases is not due to a direct influence upon emulsification, but is caused by a change in the stability of the emulsion after formation. Thin layers of gas are most likely formed rapidly on the droplets, their coalescence being prevented or retarded by these layers.

The formation of striations observed in capillaries is most likely a phenomenon similar to that used by Kundt for determining the wave-length of acoustic waves. Experiments of this kind, using small particles in liquids and normal acoustic waves, are not readily accomplished. Thus it is rather surprising that these striations are produced so quickly and easily, if we subject, for instance, quartz particles of about 1μ in diameter in water contained in a capillary tube to ultrasonics. It can be shown that these striations are produced by longitudinal waves in the liquid.[6] The theory of Kundt's experiment does not seem to have been developed fully for liquids. Obviously the reflection of the waves by the small particles of the second phase is important. Only when such a reflection takes place may we expect a strong movement of the particles; then they may be transported into the nodes and remain at rest there. The particles must not be too small, for then, they do not reflect sufficiently. With the author's arrangement, true colloidal solutions (of gold, silver, As_2S_3, etc.) never produced any striations. Larger particles may also be oriented poorly, if they have the same acoustic density as the medium, the waves then not being reflected. So far, a case of the latter kind has not been found.

The results which have been discussed are not due to a specific property of the ultrasonic waves. These only represent a method of introducing mechanical energy in a way which is, perhaps, in some respects, better defined than ordinary shaking or stirring. Thus a mixture of two liquids, completely freed from gas, is not emulsified on shaking, whereas it is so in the presence of traces of gas. Further, it is a well-known fact that the art of making emulsions strongly depends upon the method of shaking or stirring, and that a certain type of stirring device may be disadvantageous, because it destroys the emulsion formed, instead of producing it. A device of this kind might be characterised by the fact that the droplets formed travel parallel to another with different velocity along too great a distance and that this may cause an orthokinetic coagulation.

REFERENCES

1. Wood and Loomis, *Phil. Mag.*, 1927, **4**, 418.
2. Bull and Söllner, *Kolloid-Z.*, 1932, **60**, 263.
3. Wood and Loomis, *loc. cit.*, p. 430; and some new experiments by C. Bondy.

4. Rogowski and Söllner, Z. physikal. Chem., **A**, 1933, **166**, 428.
5. But this does not hold for the emulsification of mercury and low-melting alloys in organic liquids like glycerine, etc. The cause of this behaviour is not known as yet.
6. Kundt and Lehmann, Poggend. Ann., 1874, **153**, 1; K. Dörsing, Ann. d. Physik, 1908, **25**, 227; Boyle, Science Progress, 1928, **23**, I, 75.

THE FUNDAMENTAL PRINCIPLES OF PRACTICAL EMULSION MANUFACTURE

By Miss R. M. K. Cobb

(Chemist in Charge of Research Laboratory, Lowe Paper Co.)

INTRODUCTION

A S SHOWN throughout this book, two or more liquids may be virtually insoluble in each other and yet may be formed into a stable mixture by proper dispersion. In the classification of colloidal systems, liquid-in-liquid dispersion systems are known as emulsions. By common consent, the term is extended to cover dispersions of molten materials such as wax and resin in liquids, even though, on cooling, the non-polar phase is a solid.

In nature, oil-and-water dispersions are so well and widely distributed that it may seem as if emulsion formation is a most casual performance. But in reality, the production of a satisfactory commercial emulsion calls for an exacting blend of scientific knowledge, practical skill, and intuition, commonly known as a "flair." To master emulsion manufacture, it often seems, that one must be smarter than the emulsion, get up earlier in the morning, work harder, and study more.

According to Gibbs' classical definition, an emulsion is at equilibrium only when broken. Thus, an industrial emulsion system possesses an immense amount of potential energy. Stored in a 50 gallon drum, or a 1,000 gallon tank, it has nothing else to do with that energy all day and all night but to coalesce, cream, and break into its original components. Working out formulae, for permanently usable emulsion products, presents a problem different, therefore, from that of the scientist in the laboratory. For the scientist forms his emulsion, measures, tests, and pours it down the sink with satisfaction, often within the space of a single hour or day.

It is the object of this chapter to outline the fundamental principles of practical emulsion manufacture in a very general way. The actual formulation and production of industrial emulsions is covered elsewhere in this volume by Hofmann, q.v.

The commercial bulletins, listed at the end of this chapter, also provide specific formulae utilizing the emulsifying agents produced by the individual manufacturers. The bulletins contain much valuable, although non-critical, information regarding industrial emulsifying agents.

NATURE OF EMULSIONS AND THEIR COMPONENTS

Whereas any insoluble liquids may be dispersed in one another, the commercial emulsion is usually limited to mixtures of oils, solvents, waxes, resins, or elastomers dispersed in water (oil-in-water); or water dispersed in oils, solvents, waxes, resins, or elastomers (water-in-oil). In forming such a dispersion, the maker usually desires to secure, in the end, a combination of the best features of each component; an ambition which is sometimes happily achieved.

COMPARATIVE CHARACTERISTICS OF EMULSION AND EMULSION PHASES

Oil Phase	Water Phase	Corresponding Emulsion
Non-polar solvent.	Polar solvent.	Can carry non-polar solutes in oil phase and polar solutes in water phase.

Oil Phase	*Water Phase*	*Corresponding Emulsion*
Viscosity varies from .01 poises (gasoline) to ∞ (carnauba wax).	Viscosity varies from .01 poises (water) to almost ∞ (heavy aqueous solutions of colloids).	Can be a thin emulsion of a heavy oil or a viscous emulsion of a thin oil. This adjustment of viscosity is one of the most valuable characteristics of emulsion systems.
Wets most surfaces readily; penetration is governed largely by viscosity.	Wetting power and tendency to spread and penetrate is varied by adjustment of contact angle as well as viscosity.	Can be made to wet and penetrate to any desired degree, or to a very limited amount.
Specific gravity varies from 0.66 to 4.42.	Specific gravity 0.9 up.	Specific gravity as desired.
Leaves film as residue if not volatile. Usually films are water-insoluble.	Leaves residual film, if emulsifier is not volatile. Films are more water-soluble than those from oil phase, though treatments are available to render them less sensitive to water.	Films can be laid down as desired. Usually the films from emulsions are less water-resistant than films out of organic solvents, because of solubility of the emulsifier, and the "memory" of the once-oriented-to-water oil phase.
Available surface corresponds to surface of container.	Available surface corresponds to surface of container.	Both phases have greatly extended and potentially reactive surfaces; that of the inner phase having much the greater extension and reactivity.

DESIRABLE CHARACTERISTICS OF EMULSIONS

Before formulating an emulsion, it is necessary and advisable to know the properties desired for the particular application in mind. Commercial emulsions range in stability from the coarsest mixtures of oil and water, with no pretense of permanency, to the almost water-clear, self-polishing floor waxes whose wax phase remains permanently dispersed in the water for years. In body, they vary from water-thin dispersions to stiff pastes.

If permanent stability is desired, there is no better preliminary guide to the stabilizing features of an emulsion than Stokes' law. Using Robinson's [18] modification of Stokes' equation

$$C = \frac{d^2 \ (s - s_1)g}{18\eta} \qquad (I)$$

Where

C = rate of emulsion phase separation (creaming) in cm/sec.
d = diameter of spherical particles in cm.
s = density of emulsified particles in g/cc.
s_1 = density of whole emulsion in g/cc.
g = 981 cm/sec² (gravity constant).
η = viscosity of whole emulsion in poises.

This equation indicates that to make an emulsion as stable as possible, four things must be accomplished:

1. The original particle size of the emulsified droplets must be as fine as possible.

2. The original fine droplets must be prevented from reuniting into coarser droplets.

3. The density of the oil, wax, or resin must be made as close to 1, the density of water, as possible.

4. The viscosity of the emulsion must be made as high as possible, provided it does not affect the rate of particle reunion adversely.

It is clear that if, for any reason, one of the above favorable factors must be disregarded, the other factors must be adjusted to compensate for it, if stability is to be maintained (Fig. 1). For example, there are applications where fine particle size is not desired in an emulsion, because the emulsion, when applied to a porous material, is supposed to break on the surface; and to do this, the emulsion particles must be large. Despite large particles, this emulsion must be stable enough not to break during shipment or storage. A glance at Stokes' Law will indicate that to compensate for large particle size, it is necessary to decrease density differences and/or increase emulsion viscosity, if stability is to be maintained.

On the other hand, a dilute emulsion of low viscosity, made with an oil much lighter than water, or with a heavy liquid like mercury, obviously calls for an extremely fine particle size, if it is to be stable over an appreciable period of time.

GENERAL PRINCIPLES OF EMULSIFICATION

After deciding upon the emulsion characteristics desired, that is, whether the droplets should be of oil or water, fine or coarse, the emulsion thin or viscous, and knowing the density of the oil to be emulsified, the problem of emulsification comes to the stage where conditions of formation are to be considered. Here is a kettle of oil or molten wax or resin; there is a kettle of water; what must be done to make them into an emulsion of the desired stability?

Thomas [22] states that to disperse one liquid in another, in the form of an emulsion, requires doing an amount of work upon the system equal to the product of the interfacial tension multiplied by the increase in surface

$$W = \gamma \triangle S \qquad\qquad (II)$$

Where
  W = work in ergs/cm².
  γ = interfacial tension of oil-water in ergs/cm².
  $\triangle S$ = increase in surface of dispersed phase due to formation of emulsion droplets. S is in cm².

The original surface of the dispersed phase may be considered negligible in comparison with the surface of that dispersed phase extended in the form of droplets. Thus, the increase in surface $\triangle S$ is related to the total volume of the emulsion droplets, and the diameter of each droplet, as

$$\triangle S = 6V/d \tag{III}$$

Where

V = total volume of emulsified internal phase in cc.
d = diameter of emulsified droplets in cm.

Substituting in (II)

$$W = 6 \gamma V/d \tag{IV}$$

That is, to emulsify a given amount of oil in water, a definite amount of work has to be done—a fact which the layman intuitively acknowledges when he shakes oil-in-water medicines before taking.

Equation (IV) states that the forming of an emulsion is facilitated when the interfacial tension of the water against the oil is low.

Term d in the denominator of equation (IV) indicates that the smaller the particle size of the emulsion, the more work must be done to get that fine-sized droplet.

ROLE OF EMULSIFYING AGENT IN REDUCING INTERFACIAL TENSION AND STABILIZING THE EMULSION

To reduce the amount of energy required for emulsification and yet obtain small droplets, it is evident from (IV) that the interfacial tension between water and oil must be lowered to a marked degree. This calls for the presence of a third component of the emulsion system—the emulsifying agent.

Without the presence of an emulsifying agent, emulsions of the oil-in-water type can be prepared only by intense agitation and, according to Lewis [14], only up to a maximum concentration of 2%. To prepare a more concentrated stable emulsion, the presence of an emulsifying agent is essential.

Workers in the field of emulsions have indicated that an emulsifying agent should have all or most of the following characteristics:

1. Reduce the interfacial tension of the oil against water to 10 dynes or less for emulsions which are to be made with a colloid mill or homogenizer [11].

2. Reduce the interfacial tension of oil against water to 1 dyne or less for emulsions to be made spontaneously, i.e., by mere paddling, without violent mechanical agitation [4] [11].

3. Be more soluble in the outer than the inner phase of the emulsion, so that it will be readily available for adsorption at the membrane around the emulsion droplets. If the oil is to be in droplets, and water the outer phase, the emulsifying agent should be more water-soluble. If the water is to be in dispersed droplets, and oil the outer phase, the emulsifying agent should be more oil soluble [2].

4. Adsorb quickly around the emulsified droplets in a condensed, viscous, rigid, non-adherent film which will not thin out when two droplets collide, hence will not permit coagulation or coalescence of the emulsion particles [15] [20].

5. Impart appreciable viscosity to the emulsion itself [1] [5].

6. Impart an electrokinetic potential difference between the phases of .03–.06 volts, which, it seems, is most easily obtainable in slightly alkaline solution [8] [21].

7. Be of such specifically designed molecular structure that the non-polar end of the molecule may be persuaded to fit into the molecular structure of the oily material, whereas the polar end of the emulsifying agent has strong affinity for water [9].

8. Emulsify at least four parts of material per unit of emulsifying agent [4].

9. Be relatively inexpensive; add not more than two to five cents to the cost per pound of the solids in the emulsion.

10. Impart to the dried film the desired soluble or insoluble properties.

SECURING THE PROPER EMULSIFIER

The quickest way to solve the problem of emulsifying any given oil, wax, or resin is to state the problem to the manufacturers of emulsifying agents. In this way, one may secure a material specifically designed and tailored to emulsify the oil in question. The manufacturer will also supply an exact or approximate emulsion formula, including the average particle size obtainable and the stability of the emulsion.

If an economical solution of the problem is not obtained by such inquiry, it will be necessary to make a systematic survey of the situation.

If the oil is to be dispersed in water, one of the most effective ways of reducing the interfacial tension of the oil, to the point where it is really soluble in water, is to sulphonate it, and convert the sulphonic group to the sodium salt. The addition of the SO_3Na radical to the oil provides the water-soluble hook which reduces the interfacial tension to zero, and makes the oils water-soluble. Sulphonation is commonly used to disperse glycerides such as castor, cottonseed, corn, fish, lard, linseed, neatsfoot, olive, soybean, and sperm oils. Unfortunately, sulphonation often modifies the oil, to such extent, that its desirable properties are unduly altered; an effect which cannot be minimized even by careful control of the sulphonating process.

Saturated organic materials such as waxes and some oils have no available double bond and resist sulphonation. Waxes, due to their melting points, present the further difficulty of requiring a high sulphonating temperature, at which they are apt to char, during the sulphonating process. When an oil or wax is of such nature that the water-soluble group cannot be built into the molecule itself by sulphonation or other chemical means, an external emulsifying agent must be employed.

EMULSIFYING AGENTS

Though the list of emulsifying agents is almost endless, many of those used in commercial emulsions may be found in the following list:

Agar agar
Albumen
Alginate
Aluminum oleate, resinate, stearate
Amino-methyl-propanol
Ammonium laurate, linoleate, oleate, stearate
Bentonite
Bile
Calcium oleate, stearate
Carbon black
Caseinates
Cholesterol
Clay
Copper oleate, resinate
Dextrin
Diethylene glycol oleate, palmitate, stearate
Egg yolk
Ethylene glycol laurate, oleate, ricinoleate, stearate
Fuller's earth
Gelatin
Gliadin
Glue
Glyceryl laurate, myristate, oleate, palmitate
Gum arabic
Gum tragacanth
Hemoglobin
Irish moss
Lanolin

Lecithin
Lignin
Montan wax
Morpholine oleate, stearate
Pectin
Potassium linoleate, oleate, resinate, stearate
Proteins
Quaternary ammonium compounds
Resins
Saponin
Sodium linoleate, myristate, resinate, stearate
Sodium salts of sulphonic acids
Starch
Sulphated alcohols
Sulphonated castor, corn, fish, mineral, neatsfoot, olive, soybean, and sperm oils

In general, monovalent soaps and hydrophilic colloids make oil-in-water emulsions. Polyvalent soaps and hydrophobic colloids make water-in-oil emulsions. Some materials, such as sodium stearate, yield either type, depending upon the quantity used, and the method of emulsion manufacture.

INTERFACIAL TENSION DETERMINATION

There is a very definite advantage in determining the interfacial tension of the oil to be emulsified against water in the presence of the emulsifying agents. For, not only does every oil to be emulsified require a definite amount of a specific emulsifying agent, but also, almost every emulsion system has to be formed in its own special way. *The value of an emulsifying agent depends a great deal upon the manner in which the emulsion is formed.* By measuring the interfacial tension in the presence of varying amounts of the emulsifying agent, two of the variables are eliminated. The agent, most likely to form a good emulsion, may thus be selected for thorough emulsifying tests, in the concentrations indicated, and by the emulsifying methods later described.

Interfacial tension tests may be readily made by the DeNouy surface tension apparatus, or with the Donnan pipette, both described by Holmes.[12] As stated before, spontaneous self-emulsification calls for lowering the interfacial tension of the oil against water to 1 dyne or less; by means of the colloid mill or homogenizer, satisfactory emulsions may be formed if the interfacial tension is 10 dynes or less (Table I).

REQUIRED AMOUNT OF EMULSIFIER

Although interfacial tension between the oil and water phases, in the presence of the emulsifying agent, indicates the potential ease of emulsification of the system, it is equally important to determine the *amount* of emulsifier required.

If the orientation theory of emulsification is accepted, the droplets of the dispersed phase are neatly surrounded by a film or skin of emulsifying agent. The film is oriented so that the polar or water soluble part of the emulsifying agent is dissolved or hooked in the water, and the non-polar or oil-soluble part of the molecule is dissolved or hooked in the oil. Obviously, the ratio of emulsifier to disperse phase, needed to provide a stable emulsion, will be governed by the following factors:

1. The diameter of the droplets in the emulsion, and the corollarial factor, the total surface of the disperse phase.

2. The concentration of emulsifier needed to bring the interfacial tension down to the value required for emulsification.

3. The tendency for the emulsifying agent to adsorb at the interface. Contrary to the general impression obtained from

references to Gibbs' Laws of adsorption,* this positive adsorption of surface active materials at the interface is small except at low concentrations of the emulsifier.

4. Structural compatibility of the groups in the non-polar end of the emulsifier with those in the wax or oil; and the water-solubility of the polar end of the emulsifying agent.

5. Required thickness of the interfacial layer.

Griffin [10] and others have stated that the film surrounding an emulsion droplet will contain enough emulsifier to form a tightly packed monomolecular film.

The length of an oriented soap molecule being in the order of 25×10^{-8} cm, and the specific gravity being around 0.9, in a solid vertically oriented monomolecular soap film, the weight of soap per cm² of interface is

$$25 \times 10^{-8} \times 1 \times 0.9 = 2.25 \times 10^{-7} \text{ g/cm}^2, \text{ (checking the value of Holmes).}^{[13]}$$

If 100 g of oil of specific gravity 0.9 were to be emulsified into droplets one micron in diameter, the total surface of the oil droplets would be (See III)

$$\frac{100 \times 6}{0.9 \times 1 \times 10^{-4}} \text{ cm}^2 = 6.6 \times 10^6 \text{ cm}^2$$

A monomolecular film of soap around 100 g of oil, dispersed into one micron droplets, would, therefore, weigh

$$2.25 \times 10^{-7} \times 6.6 \times 10^6 = 1.5 \text{ g}$$

Or, in other words, if the film of emulsifying agent were a monomolecular soap film 100% adsorbed in the oil-water inter-

---

*
$$D = \frac{-C}{RT} \frac{d\gamma}{dC}$$

Where

D = difference in concentration of surface active material at interface in g/cc
C = concentration in g/cc in bulk of solution.
R = gas constant = 8.31×10^7
T = absolute temperature = $273° + °C$.
γ = interfacial tension in ergs/cm²

face, only 1.5 parts of soap would be needed to form the emulsion, per 100 parts of oil to be emulsified.

In commercial practice, from 6 to 20 times that theoretical amount of emulsifying agent is frequently needed. This is not surprising. For, in the first place, not all the emulsifying agent orients at the interface, much or most of it is dissolved in the outer phase of the emulsion. In the second place, the film around the droplets may not always be monomolecular. Several observers, including Ramsden [17] and Seifriz [19], have *seen* a film around droplets in the ordinary miscroscope. Such a film would be at least 0.2 μ, or 2×10^{-5} cm thick, as that is the limit of resolution in the microscope—an average of 80 molecules thick.

The smaller the percentage of emulsifier required to perform an emulsification, the better the emulsifier is considered to be. The booklets, describing commercial emulsifiers such as triethanolamine soaps or polyhydric alcohol partial esters, recommend from 10 to 35 parts of emulsifier to 100 parts of oil.

The use of a colloid mill or homogenizer generally results in a lower consumption of emulsifying agent. From consideration of the above, this may be due to two reasons: 1. The action of the mill or homogenizer can effect fine dispersion even at the high interfacial tension values obtained with less emulsifier. 2. The action of the mill or homogenizer may drive the emulsifying agent into the adsorption zone of the interface where it lowers the interfacial tension and is effective in surrounding the droplets.

By forming a concentrated emulsion, diluting later, if desired, the emulsifier is used most efficiently.

EMULSIFYING METHODS

Having obtained a preliminary idea of the oil and water phases of the emulsion, including the likeliest emulsifying agents and the interfacial tensions to be overcome, the best of the emulsifying methods must be selected by trial and test.

Emulsions may be formed in a great many different ways, all of which are variants of the following:

A. Brute force.

B. Persuasion.

1. The emulsifying agent may be dissolved in the water, and the oil added, with considerable agitation.

Method 1. makes oil-in-water emulsions directly. If a water-in-oil emulsion is made by this method, the oil should be added to the oil-in-water emulsion until inversion occurs.

2. The emulsifying agent may be dissolved in the oil. The emulsion may then be formed in two ways: (a) By adding the mixture directly to water, in which case, an oil-in-water emulsion forms spontaneously. (b) By adding water directly to the mixture, in which case, a water-in-oil emulsion is first formed. To form an oil-in-water emulsion by method (2b), it is necessary to invert the emulsion, by addition of more water than can be held, in water-in-oil form.

3. The fatty acid part of the emulsifying agent may be dissolved in the oil, and the alkaline part in the water. In this case, the formation of nascent soap, at the moment of mixing the two phases, brings about emulsification, either oil-in-water, or water-in-oil.

4. The oil and water may be added alternately, in several steps, to the emulsifying agent, forming either water-in-oil or oil-in-water emulsions.

APPLICATION OF EMULSIFYING METHODS

1. Agent-in-Water Method

Method 1. is the least scientific of all emulsion methods. It involves the use of force to make the emulsion, except when the interfacial tensions are a fraction of a dyne. A particularly crude variant of method 1., employing only one kettle, is outlined below.

Water	457 lb
Stearic Acid	10 lb
Japan Wax	50 lb
Borax	10–12 lb

Boil the water up, with direct steam, until the wax and stearic acid are all melted. Add the dry borax and boil until the emulsion is formed.

This emulsion has "a wide range of particle size," a delicate technical expression meaning it is a coarse emulsion of irregular particle size. Like most* emulsions made by method 1., its uniformity and stability may be greatly improved by mechanical treatment in a colloid mill or homogenizer. The emulsion should be processed in those while hot, i.e., above the melting point of the wax.

2. Agent-in-Oil Method

Method 2. is the most scientific and interesting of the emulsion formation processes. It is particularly applicable to inversion emulsions, in which the emulsion starts as a water-in-oil dispersion, and then is inverted to end up as an oil-in-water emulsion of extremely fine and uniform particle size. The most desirable way to use an emulsifying agent is to get it into the interface between the oil and water, where its concentration will count. Apparently, the best way to get the emulsifying agent into the interface is to dissolve it first in the oil, by method 2. By judicious additions of water to the oil plus the emulsifier, the emulsifying agent is persuaded to leave the oil phase and start towards the water phase. Just as the emulsifier reaches the interface in goodly percentage, the emulsion can be inverted into the desired finely divided oil-in-water form.

One of the most interesting commercial emulsions illustrates many of the points in application of method 2.

A. Paraffin wax   240 lb
    Nopco Emulsifier 1765X   60 lb

    Heat together to 210°F.

B. Water at 195°F.   60 lb

Add water to base and stir until clear.

C. Water at 195°F.   60 lb

Add water and stir until smooth and opalescent, without streaks. Examination under the microscope will show the water held in the cleavage planes of the wax.

D. Water at 195°F.   180 lb

Add this water very quickly—within 10 seconds—while stirring the emulsion at moderate speed. The rapid addition of the water inverts the emulsion, whereas slow addition of the water fails to invert it because there is not sufficient energy-release. This need for fast addition of the water was first discussed by Quincke in 1868 and usually redis- covered, after painful experiences, as by the author in 1933.[4]

Stir for 2 minutes and stop stirrer. Cool to 175°F., letting it stand and "ripen." As it cools toward 175°F., the emul- sion takes on a glossy appearance which indicates it is start- ing to re-invert to become water-in-oil again. That is, the emulsifier is again moving toward the oil-in-water interface.

E. Water at 180°F.   900 lb

Add this water quickly, within 2 minutes, as soon as the emulsion cools down to 175°F. This fast addition of water, as the emulsion nears the re-inversion point, disperses the paraffin into fine particles and ends forever the idea of its becoming a water-in-oil emulsion. When properly made, the particles are no bigger than 0.5 μ, barely resolvable in the microscope. Thin films of the emulsion are intensely blue in color.

3. Nascent Soap Method

The method of making an emulsion with nascent soap is suitable for either water-in-oil or oil-in-water emulsions. Dorey has fully illustrated it in Section 7 of this volume. In a detailed study of method 3., he finds that the best results are obtained by admitting the liquids to his emulsifying equipment in two streams. One stream consists of the alkali dissolved in water, the other consists of the fatty acid dissolved in the oil. Size analysis indicates that 98.3% of his emulsion droplets are less than 1 μ in diameter.

Davis and Bartell [6] point out that the amount of fatty acid in the oil must be in excess over the amount of alkali in the aqueous phase, for stable nascent soap emulsions.

4. Alternate Addition Method

The addition of the water and oil alternately to the emulsifying agent is illustrated by Corran [5] in Section 9 of this volume, where he discusses mayonnaise manufacture. To the egg yolk and other dry ingredients is first added, the minimum amount of water needed to form a workable emulsifying nucleus. Then the oil is added. Finally, the rest of the aqueous phase is poured in. Corran points out that the formation of the nucleus is the most important operation in making mayonnaise and that the amount of water added to the egg yolk and the beating time have vital influence on the final emulsion.

Method 4. is particularly applicable to food products and to other emulsions of vegetable oils. With vegetable oils, 1/3 of the oil is usually added to the emulsifying agent before the first addition of water.

FINISHING AND TESTING THE EMULSION

The most stable emulsions consist of particles whose diameters are 0.5 μ. At this diameter, Lewis [14] proves that a round droplet is in equilibrium with a plane surface, and the tendency for the droplets to coalesce is practically nil. Most good commercial emulsions of the white variety contain particles ranging between 1 and 1.5μ in diameter (*Fig. 1*). The transparent or translucent floor wax emulsions go as low as 0.1 μ in droplet size.

After an emulsion is finished, and before it is stabilized, it is advisable to take a sample, dilute it carefully to 15–20% solids, and examine a covered drop under the microscope at 750–1000 magnifications, using the micrometer eyepiece.

If in microscopic examination, at these magnifications, the emulsion exhibits particles ranging around 1 μ, in violent Brownian motion, with few, if any, coarse particles, if the fine droplets are all independent, not touching or in clusters, and if thin films are intensely blue or transparent to the eye, the indications are that the product is well-made. As it stands, it could last indefinitely. But since, as Bhatnagar [8] observes, the properties of the emulsion change in complicated fashion on aging and aggregation, in many cases, it is better to play safe and stabilize the emulsion by adjustment of the solids content, or by addition of materials which exert the favorable influences called for in Stokes' Law.

FINAL STABILIZING ADJUSTMENTS

Whereas, in theory, 76% of the emulsion may consist of inner phase, in practice, this particular concentration is seldom used; it may even be exceeded. Emulsions are most stable when their individual particles are not in too close proximity and their viscosity is between that of thin and heavy cream. These conditions are realized, usually, when the emulsion carries 20–30% solids, if a fluid, 45–55% if a paste.

The viscosity of an emulsion can be affected in several ways, as indicated by the equations of Einstein

$$N_1 = N_0 (1 + 2.5 Q)$$

and Hatschek

$$N_1 = \frac{N_0}{1 - \sqrt[3]{Q}}$$

Where
  N_1 = Viscosity of emulsion
  N_0 = Viscosity of continuous phase
  Q = Fraction of total volume, which is the disperse phase

Thus, the viscosity can be increased [1] by maintaining high solids content (*Fig. 2*). For oil-in-water emulsion, adjustment of viscosity by the device of increasing solids is a mixed blessing. High viscosity decreases the tendency for the phases to separate. But when the emulsion particles are crowded together by high concentration, they tend to unite into coarse particles, thus destabilizing the emulsion. The viscosity of the aqueous phase can also be increased [2] by addition of 1–4% of a hydrophilic colloid such as starch, albumen, pectin, gum tragacanth, acacia, or casein. If not chemically antagonistic to the system, such addition agents always confer great stability upon the emulsion (*Fig. 1*). They increase the overall viscosity of the emulsion, reduce or stop Brownian movement, and often encase the emulsion particles in a tougher, less adhesive film than does the emulsifying agent itself. The presence of such natural, organic stabilizers, however, calls for an antiseptic to prevent bacterial decomposition. The effectiveness of a stabilizer can be tested by rubbing a film of the emulsion between the fingers and noting absence of dry "roll-up."

In adjustments of emulsion concentration, by addition of water, dilution should be made gradually with thorough, gentle stirring. Addition of water at 90–160°F, depending on the temperature of the emulsion, is preferable to addition of cold water.

After the emulsion has been brought to its final concentration, if too coarse and unstable, it may be processed in a colloid mill or homogenizer. These mechanical dispersers may be relied upon to bring the coarser particles down to 2 or 3 microns, no smaller. The processed emulsion will look very uniform and, by proper adjustment of viscosity and pH, will have satisfactory stability.

Any tendency for the emulsion to cream and separate, due to inherent flaws in physical characteristics, will usually show up overnight, in the form of a distinct layer. Failure due to chemical self-aging is not so easy to evaluate.

STABILIZING EMULSIONS TO ELECTROLYTES

The addition of electrolytes, such as inorganic acids and salts, to the aqueous phase, is called for in certain formulae. For example, aluminum acetate is frequently added to wax emulsions to increase the water-insolubility of the dried wax film laid down out of the emulsion.

The electrolytes may be dissolved in the water before the formation of the emulsion, so that they are present during emulsification; or they may be added after emulsification is complete. Adding electrolytes, after the emulsion is completed, is, in many cases, less apt to result in disaster; though it must be remembered that there is no such thing as precipitating a little bit of a colloid system. It is all or nothing.

Addition of electrolytes to an emulsion, therefore, calls for especially protective emulsifying agents, many of which are described in the commercial bulletins.

OTHER IMPORTANT CONSIDERATIONS

Other important considerations in emulsion manufacture are the hardness of the water, the temperatures at which the emulsion is made and stored, the control of agitation, and the batch size.

The softer the water, the better the emulsion, distilled water representing the optimum. Naturally soft water is preferable; addition of softening agents such as phosphates to hard water is not so effective a cure for emulsion failure as it is for other industrial difficulties due to hard water. It may even accentuate the trouble.

Most emulsions form best at temperatures near the boiling point of water. Both phases should be at approximately the same temperature. All solids, which are to be finely divided and dispersed in the emulsion, including waxes, resins, and emulsifying agents, must be processed either above their melting points or dissolved in suitable solvents.

As previously indicated, the amount of agitation needed varies with the interfacial tension between the phases, and the degree of dispersion desired. For emulsions, in which the inner phase is forcibly dispersed, to overcome high interfacial tension, intermittent agitation is frequently advocated.

Since oxidation of even fairly inert material, in finely divided form, is rapid and destructive, agitation should be carried out in a way to prevent inclusion of large quantities of air in the emulsions.

In cooling emulsions to a solid or stiff paste, slow agitation is usually continued during the cooling period, to prevent separation of the phases. This applies particularly to water-in-oil emulsions. Water-in-oil emulsions are, as a rule, heavy in consistency and suspect of being little more than mechanical mixtures, in which the water is held in place largely by the viscosity of the system.

A successful trial of an emulsion in a five gallon can, before going on to more ambitious commercial batches, is highly advisable. Problems of procedure, which cannot be suspected in a 500 cc beaker formulation, show up in the five gallon batch. For example, it may *seem* as if the addition of water, in making a beaker batch of a particular emulsion, is slow and cautious. Not until a five gallon batch is tried will the experimenter find out that for this particular formulation it is really necessary to add the water quickly, a fact which has not shown up in the beaker formulation, because there even a small stream of water takes only 10–15 seconds to add.

In changing or modifying emulsion formulae, only one ingredient should be varied at a time.

STORAGE AND SHIPPING CONDITIONS

Emulsions must be stored away from steam pipes, under favorable conditions of temperature and preferably in air-tight containers, to avoid evaporation. Few emulsion systems can stand either the freezing rigors of the Arctic, or the heat engendered by the sun blazing on an emulsion storage tank outdoors.

To the hazards of temperature extremes, during shipment, must be added the peculiarly destructive effects of vibration upon the emulsion system. Every laboratory, dealing with oil-field emulsions, has at least one story of the emulsion which was shipped to them as "unbreakable" in the field, but which arrived in completely broken condition, as a result of its travels by freight car. Emulsions, which are to be shipped any distance, must have high viscosity, or a high surface viscosity shell around each droplet.

Some emulsions made with a small amount of viscous emulsifier will cream without breaking, and can still be used after stirring or shaking. But emulsions that cream are never so trustworthy as permanently dispersed emulsions and competition is pushing them off the market.

SUMMARY

The steps in creating a satisfactory commercial emulsion may be summarized as follows:

1. Definition of the aims and desirable properties of the emulsion, covering

> Materials
> Emulsion type

Stability
Viscosity
Particle size
Density of oil phase
Final concentration
Resistance of dried film to oil, water, gas, or chemicals.

2. Selection of the emulsifying agent, considering
Interfacial tensions
Relative oil and water solubilities
Efficiency
Cost
pH
Chemical stability
Viscosity in thin films.

3. Selection of the emulsifying method
Spontaneous and/or mechanical
Mixing methods 1–4, with modifications
  1. Agent-in-water
  2. Agent-in-oil
  3. Nascent soap
  4. Alternate addition

4. Finishing, testing, and stabilizing
Mechanical treatment
Microscopic examination
Viscosity, concentration, and pH adjustment
Stabilizing agents.

5. Storage and Shipment
Maintenance of favorable temperatures
Protection from evaporation
Adjustment of viscosity to withstand vibrations of shipment.

REFERENCES

1. Bancroft, W. D., *J. Phys. Chem.* **16**, 179, 233, 746 (1912).
2. Bancroft, W. D., and Tucker, *J. Phys. Chem.* **31**, 1681 (1927).
3. Bhatnagar, *J. Phys. Chem.* **25**, 735 (1921).

4. Cobb, R. M., Chamberlin, D. S. and Dombrow, B. A., *Paper Trade J.* **97**, 35 (Sept. 7, 1933).
5. Corran, J. W., *Tech. Aspects of Emulsions* (Chemical Publishing Co., 1936) 100.
6. Davis, J. K., and Bartell, F. E., *J. Phys. Chem.*, **47**, 40 (1943).
7. Dorey, R., *Tech. Aspects of Emulsions* (Chemical Publishing Co., 1936) 51.
8. Ellis, R., *Trans. Far. Soc.* **9**, 14 (1913).
9. Finkle, Draper & Hildebrand, *J. Am. Chem. Soc.* **45**, 2780 (1923).
10. Griffin, *J. Am. Chem. Soc.* **45**, 1648 (1923).
11. Harkins, W. D. and Zollman, H., *J. Am. Chem. Soc.* **48**, 69 (1926).
12. Holmes, H. N., *Lab'y Manual of Colloid Chem.* (John Wiley & Sons, 1928) 66.
13. Holmes, H. N., *Ibid.*, p. 95.
14. Lewis, *Kolloid-Zeitschr.* **4**, 211 (1909).
15. Newman, *J. Phys. Chem.* **18**, 34, 45 (1914).
16. Quincke, *Wied. Ann.*, **35**, 562 (1888).
17. Ramsden, *Trans. Far. Soc.*, **22**, 484 (1926).
18. Robinson, C. S., *Ind. Eng. Chem.*, **18**, 869 (1926).
19. Seifriz, W., *J. Phys. Chem.* **29**, 587, 595, 600, 746, 838 (1938).
20. Serrallach, Jones & Owen, *Ind. Eng. Chem.*, **25**, 816 (1933).
21. Steik, K., *Am. Dyestuff Reptr.* **25**, 429 (1936).
22. Thomas, A. W., *J. Am. Leather Chem. Assn.* **22**, 171 (1927).

COMMERCIAL BULLETINS ON EMULSIONS

Aerosol Wetting Agents, 1941, pp. 46–48, American Cyanamid & Chemical Corp., 30 Rockefeller Plaza, New York, N. Y.
Chemicals by Glyco, 1942, Glyco Products Co., Inc., 230 King St., Brooklyn, N. Y.
Emulsifying with the Fatty Alcohol Sulfates, 2nd Edn., 1940, E. I. duPont de Nemours & Co., Inc., Fine Chemicals Div., Wilmington, Delaware.
Emulsions, 6th Edn., 1937, Carbide & Carbon Chemicals Corp., 30 E. 42nd Street, New York, N. Y.
The Nitro-Paraffins, 1941, pp. 21–27, Commercial Solvents Corp., 17 E. 42nd St., New York, N. Y.
Spans and Tweens, 1942, Atlas Powder Co., Wilmington, Delaware.
Technical Emulsion Data, 1942, National Oil Products Co., Harrison, New Jersey.

TABLE I

Characteristic Effect of γ on Diameter of Spontaneous Emulsion Droplets
Temp. 90°C.

grams Wax A	100	75	50	25	0
grams Wax B	0	25	50	75	100
grams 2% Soap Soln.	900	900	900	900	900
γ in ergs/cm^2 (De Nouy)	5.2	2.5	1.8	1.6	1.6
diameter of Droplets	18μ	5μ	3.6μ	1.6μ	1.6μ

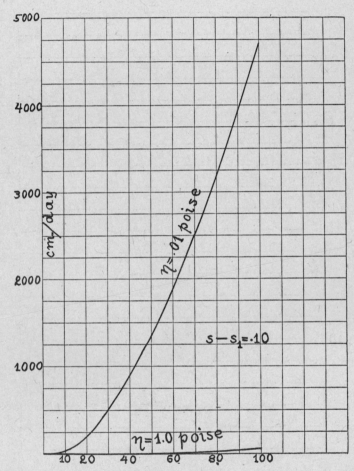

Fig. 1. STOKES' LAW. RATE OF PHASE SEPARATION VS. DIAMETER OF DROPLETS.

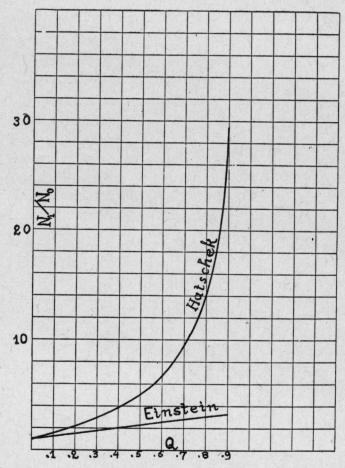

Fig. 2. EFFECT OF CONCENTRATION OF DISPERSED PHASE ON EMUL-SION VISCOSITY, ACCORDING TO EINSTEIN AND HATSCHEK.

SECTION 3

THE USE OF HIGHLY DISPERSED EMULSIONS IN THE TREATMENT OF TOXAEMIC CONDITIONS

By V. G. WALSH, M.B., B.CH., B.Sc.

and

A. C. FRAZER, M.R.C.S., L.R.C.P., M.B., B.S.

(Physiology Department, St. Mary's Hospital Medical School),
(University of London)

LETHAL doses of diphtheria and tetanus toxin are non-toxic upon subcutaneous injection provided that they are previously mixed with a finely dispersed oil-in-water emulsion. This fact was established and recently published by the present authors [1] and has since been confirmed by various workers. Mixtures of emulsion with more than the minimum lethal dose of toxin, prepared at room temperature and immediately injected intravenously, proved fatal in experiments on animals. Toxin in the same amounts added to 0.5 cc of 5 per cent olive oil-in-water emulsion and incubated at 37°C. for half an hour produced no ill effects upon intravenous injection. Toxin itself incubated in a similar manner was in no way destroyed and caused death when injected in equal doses intravenously. It appeared then that the adsorption phenomenon was more complete and more rapid at body temperature than at 20°C. Investigations are in progress to establish the relationship between these various factors.

The symptoms and fatal termination of many diseases depend upon the formation and liberation of bacterial toxins. These toxins, circulating in the blood stream, come into contact with

33

the tissue cells, producing various degrees of damage depending upon the affinity of the toxin for particular cells. Thus tetanus toxin exerts its effect especially upon the nervous system. It is not the presence of bacteria in the animal body but the toxins they elaborate which are responsible for the symptoms and death in bacterial diseases. Experiments were carried out to attempt the reproduction *in vivo* of the detoxicating action of finely divided emulsions which had been already demonstrated *in vitro*.

Various toxaemic conditions were selected and intravenous injections of different doses and percentages of emulsions were tried, in order to discover the best means of obtaining a sufficient concentration of oil particles in the blood stream to effect the adsorption of the circulating toxin. Experiment showed that the best method was to employ in adults a dose of 15 cc of 5 per cent olive oil-in-water emulsion. This emulsion is prepared with the apparatus already described by us,[2] the stabiliser used being 0.2 per cent sodium oleate made alkaline to pH 8 with sodium carbonate. Such an emulsion is extremely stable, and the oil particles average 0.5μ in diameter. It is not considered that the soap, present in this emulsion, has any influence on the adsorption of the toxins since emulsions of liquid paraffin will show the same adsorption phenomenon. Such mineral oil emulsions are not, however, suitable for injection purposes. Also the authors have found that the use of any oil, which readily oxidises, is likely to produce toxic symptoms when injected intravenously. No ill effects have been observed from the use of olive oil emulsion in doses up to 50 cc. As the size of the particles is less than one tenth that of a red blood corpuscle there is no danger of fat embolism.

The technique employed is to autoclave the emulsion in separating funnels for twenty minutes immediately as it is produced. The sterile emulsion is then allowed to stand for 56 hours. It is then run into sterile ampoules under aseptic conditions. As an additional precaution, the filled ampoules are again boiled, prior to use. Fifteen cubic centimetres of the emulsion are injected intravenously, and repeated doses are given at six-hour intervals, until four injections have been given. In certain cases, more than four injections may be administered. The toxic conditions, which have been successfully treated, are streptococcal septicaemia, erysipelas, bronchopneumonia, acute rheumatism and lobar pneumonia, particular attention having been concentrated upon these last two diseases. It is not proposed to give detailed accounts of the various cases which have been treated by this method, but it is of interest to consider the effect of intravenous injection of emulsion in a case of pneumococcal lobar pneumonia by way of illustration.

Case Report

Male. Aged 19 years. Came under treatment on second day of the disease. He was at work on May 18th, 1934. He was suddenly taken ill in the evening and came into hospital the next day. He was semi-comatose with a temperature of 102°F., rapid irregular pulse and increased respirations. He was found to be suffering from acute lobar pneumonia, which was later confirmed as being due to *Pneumococcus* Type II. He received his first injection at 1 a.m. on May 20th, further injections were given throughout the day. On May 21st his temperature, pulse and respirations were normal and the patient appeared quite well. Four days later his lung was practically free from signs of consolidation and was completely clear on the 29th. He was discharged from hospital on June 6th after being in hospital 19 days.

This case shows the value of the treatment. Cases of pneumonia treated on the usual lines suffer from acute toxaemia for about seven days, which if it does not cause death, at least results in serious damage to the body with slow recovery and lengthy convalescence. Treated with emulsion the toxaemia lasts only a few hours and recovery is rapid and complete. Apart from any question of bodily damage there is also an important economic factor both to the individual and to the institution to which he is removed. The average pneumonia is in hospital for at least four to five weeks and is unable to work for six to eight weeks. In our cases, patients leave hospital in under twenty days practically fit for work.

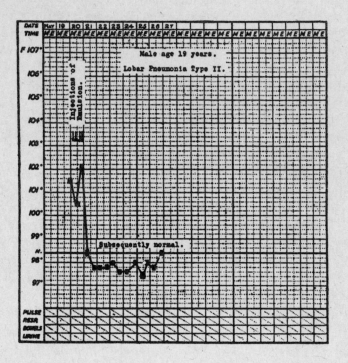

To obtain the best results, it is important that the treatment should be instituted as early as possible in the course of the disease. Cases treated late in the disease react in a similar manner, but much of the damage due to the toxin is already done and the great advantage of cutting short the toxaemia is obviously lost. Our best cases are those coming under treatment within 36 hours of the onset of the disease.

As regards the mortality, it is not possible, as yet, to make any statement on this point. Many hundreds of cases are necessary before it is possible to compile any sort of statistics comparable with standard mortality rates of the various types of lobar pneumonia.

This effect of emulsions in toxaemia is, in our opinion, due to the adsorption on to the oil particles of the toxin, preventing it from acting upon the body.cells. This is supported by the disappearance of all the symptoms attributable to free circulating toxin. The oil particles are probably removed from the blood stream into the fat depots, but the ultimate fate of the toxin is as yet unknown. It is presumably either destroyed by oxidation or very gradually liberated producing no ill effects.

It would appear from experiments that the adsorption of two or more different toxins will not be affected simultaneously. In a large number of experiments *in vitro* 20 M.L.D. of diphtheria toxin added to 0.5 cc of 5 per cent olive oil-in-water emulsion was found to be non-toxic upon subcutaneous injection. Similar results were obtained using tetanus toxin. If 5 M.L.D. of diphtheria toxin were added to 0.5 cc emulsion and then 5 M.L.D. tetanus toxin to this mixture, upon subcutaneous injection, the animal died from tetanus. On reversing this procedure, adding the 5 M.L.D. of diphtheria toxin after the tetanus toxin the animal died from diphtheria. These results have been borne out clinically. In those cases, where there was a mixed infection, a longer time and greater number of doses of emulsion were required to bring the temperature to normal.

Another application of the adsorption phenomenon is in the administration of vaccines. It is possible to give enormously increased doses of vaccines and of tuberculin combined with emulsion without causing the general reaction which would otherwise occur. Emulsions of pH 8 are too alkaline for subcutaneous use and may cause pain, so, for this purpose, an emulsion of pH 7.4 is employed. Also various drugs such as the heavy metals and certain alkaloids can be administered in combination with emulsion in doses which would otherwise cause serious effects. It is the opinion of the authors that the materials adsorbed are only slowly liberated from the site of injection and exert their action over a longer period. In this connection, investigations are in progress on the behaviour of insulin.

This application of the phenomenon of adsorption by finely dispersed oil-in-water emulsions to medicine thus opens up an entirely new field, not only in the treatment of toxaemia, but also in other branches of therapeutics.

REFERENCES

1. Walsh and Frazer, *Brit. Med. J.*, 1934, March 10th.
2. Frazer and Walsh, *J. Physiol.*, 1933, **78**, 467.

SECTION 4

EMULSIONS IN THE PATENT LITERATURE

By WILLIAM CLAYTON, D.Sc., F.I.C.

(Chief Chemist, Messrs. Crosse & Blackwell Ltd.)

WHEREAS publications dealing with the pure physical chemistry of emulsions are infrequent, the granting of patents, especially in Great Britain, Germany and the United States of America continues without interruption, hundreds of patents being listed annually. Perusal of their contents reveals firstly the many-sided interests engaged in the practical study of emulsions, and secondly, how academic research meets with technical application. Very occasionally, a patent specification will provide a striking instance of the incursion of "pure" science.

MULTIPLE USES OF EMULSIONS

It may come as a surprise to some engaged in special fields to realise the varied uses of emulsions. The following list is not exhaustive, but illustrative of the patents granted.

Emulsions enable the presentation of minimum amounts of oils, and in a more fluid condition than the normal material. Thus, emulsions have been proposed for allaying dust. As example,[1] oil is emulsified in water by the aid of a volatile agent like ammonia. About 5 per cent of oil is dispersed in 95 per cent of water. On spraying roads, the water evaporates and leaves an oil film. An emulsion wash[2] for treating foundry moulds or cores consists of silica flour, linseed oil, gum acacia and water.

39

Fuel may be treated to reduce dusting, an emulsion of water-in-oil [3] being useful, as well as oil-in-water systems stabilised by carbon black.[4] As a medium for laying coal dust in mines, bitumen emulsion is obviously indicated.[5] Thus, a bitumen and green tar oil mixture, stabilised with soap, is familiar as Bituloid.[6]

An emulsion of heavy fuel oil, montan wax, colloidal clay and aqueous zinc chloride has been proposed for the preservation of wood.[7] Fresh fruit preservation by means of an emulsion of paraffin wax, a phenolic mould retarder (xylenol with xylene), and a solvent such as light mineral oil of the kerosene type, is gained by spraying the fruit, when the emulsion spreads over in a continuous film.[8]

Some miscellaneous examples of the uses of emulsions towards unexpected ends are:

(a) The preparation of salt organosols.[9] A salt is dissolved in water or other solvent (X), which is mixed and emulsified with a liquid (Y) which is not a solvent for the salt. Then (X) is distilled off, under reduced pressure, leaving a colloidal solution of the salt in (Y). As a rule (X) is water and (Y) is oil.

(b) The purification of hydrocarbons.[10] Hydrocarbons are rendered conducting by emulsifying them with an electrolyte, and a current is then passed through to precipitate resins and render the colloidal sulphur attackable. Hydrogen peroxide may be added to oxidise the sulphur to sulphuric acid and this is neutralised by the electrolyte, e.g., NaOH.

(c) The preparation of activated carbon.[11] Hardwood charcoal is mixed in a finely divided state with an aqueous emulsion of a binder, which chars on heating, made by combining a suspension of hard pitch from a coal tar in an alkaline solution of casein with an emulsion of oil in a similar medium; the mixture is compressed and comminuted, charred and activated with steam, and then treated with acid to remove acid-soluble components.

Extraction by aqueous emulsions of solvent instead of by the solvent itself is claimed by several patents. Examples are: the de-fatting of fish meal [12] by solvent/water emulsions, employing Irish moss or agar as emulsifiers; the de-inking of paper [13] by emulsions of turpentine oil; "tetralin" or "decalin" in aqueous soap solutions (camphor oil emulsion [14] is also recommended); and the clarification of sewage. Here the sewage is mechanically agitated with about an equal amount of petroleum, and the resulting emulsion, on standing, separates into two liquid layers and a sludge of the solids. [15] An emulsion of chloroform or benzene in water is claimed for the removal of caffein from coffee beans; [16] a neutral oil emulsion also serves. [17]

A black powder having a slow combustion rate is formed by incorporating about 0.5 per cent of an oil emulsifiable with water, such as a sulphonated oil. [18] In fire-fighting, an aqueous solution of an energetic emulsifying agent (sodium alkylsulphonaphthenate) in combination with an alkali or salt of alkaline reaction is proposed for extinguishing burning oil, fats or waxes. [19] The idea seems sound.

Emulsions permit extensive subdivision of an oil (using this term in a general sense) with the consequent formation of an enormous oil-water interface, by the aid of which chemical reactions may be accelerated. This idea finds an application in preparing products suitable for paints, water-proofing, adhesives and linoleum by oxidising emulsions of drying oils or lacquers. [20] The hydrogenation of oils and fats in emulsion form may be carried out by cultures of hydrogen-producing bacteria. [21] Aquolysis, or petroleum oil conversion, is a recent application of the principle. [22] According to Dubbs and Morrell, [23] emulsified oil and water are passed through a heating coil where the oil is raised to a conversion temperature and the ratio of oil is maintained at at least 85 per cent of the mixture by introducing additional water-free oil to the charging material as necessary; the highly heated emulsion is delivered to an enlarged zone in which it is subjected to the action of Fe_2O_3, unvaporised material is withdrawn from the enlarged zone, and vapours are led off for condensation and collection. In Ditto's patent,[24] the emulsion of hydrocarbon oil and water is preheated with air to aerate the liquids to the extent of 10 to 25 per cent in volume, and the emulsion is heated to produce a fixed combustible hydrocarbon gas. Emulsion polymerisation is a further instance, there being numerous patents,[25] relating to the preparation of synthetic rubber, based on the polymerisation of dienes in emulsion. Whitby and Katz [26] have enumerated the patents in this connection. They state: "By carrying out the polymerisation of the dienes in emulsion, especially in the presence of suitable catalysts, it has been found that polymerisation can be effected more rapidly, at lower temperatures (with the consequent avoidance of oily by-products), and to better products than by heating the dienes in the massive condition. Further, the resultant emulsions of synthetic rubber have advantages as compared with solid products in the matter of convenience of manipulation and ease of preservation." Vulcanisation of linseed oil or other suitable fats or fatty oils containing a substantial proportion of unsaturated oils is carried out at temperatures above $100°C$. by the action of sulphur on the oils in emulsion condition.[27] Thus, the aqueous phase may contain casein, ammonia and ammonium oleate as stabilisers. An ingenious use of emulsions in connection with rubber concerns the use of compounding ingredients, such as $Ca(OH)_2$ or PbO, which normally coagulate latex.[28] These agents may be added to latex without impairing its stability by coating their particles with a water-impermeable material, e.g., beeswax or paraffin wax, before dispersing them in water. The wax is preferably applied to the powder as a solution in a solvent as C_6H_6.

Fine subdivision is utilised in the emulsification of heavy liquid hydrocarbons for the production of gas or for the refining of oil.[29] A liquid fuel in stable water-in-oil emulsion [30] is claimed by subjecting an intimate mixture (2 : 3) of water and crude petroleum to a pressure of more than 7,000 lb./sq. in. at 37°C. Emulsions of hydrocarbon oils and water stabilised by oleates have been proposed as fuels for internal-combustion engines.[31]

Emulsions of lard oil or mineral oil in soap solution are claimed to take up shocks in shock-absorbing devices,[32] whilst linseed and other oil emulsions are patented for the prevention or removal of fur in boilers.[33] In order to prevent aqueous liquids which come into contact with metals from causing corrosion and/or incrustation or precipitation emulsions may be employed. As example, water for cooling the cylinders of internal-combustion engines and for use in hydraulic machinery is treated with 0.5 to 5 per cent of an emulsion of a mineral oil in a sulphonated fatty oil soap.[34] A corrosion-inhibiting compound to be added to the cooling water of automobiles consists of: yellow sodium chromate (20), paraffin oil (15), sulphonated red oil (50), liquid soap (2), liquid bark extract (5), and water to 100 parts.[35]

Numerous emulsions have been proposed as lubricants for use in drawing, boring, die pressing, etc.[36] The emulsifying agents named are: oil-soluble sulphonate soaps from mineral oils,[37] saponified sulphonated sperm oil,[38] alkali metal soaps of the acid products of oxidised mineral oil,[39] alkali metal naphthenate,[40] water- or oil-soluble alginates,[41] and the saponification products of montan wax bleached by oxidation.[42] A cooling lubricant of the water-in-oil emulsion type contains rubber and asphalt.[43] Non-freezing lubricants are prepared by emulsifying fatty and mineral oils with glycol or a hydroxyl-bearing ether thereof (e.g., ethylene glycolmonoethyl ether) by the aid of a dispersing agent such as Turkey-red oil.[44]

The subject of paints is to be dealt with by another author, but attention may be drawn to a patent dealing with bronzing.[45] Bronzing and like powders are introduced into a mixture of two immiscible liquids such as ethyl oxide and water. This is an interesting application of the accumulation of solid material at the dineric interface, a phenomenon fundamental in the physical chemistry of emulsions. Another patent deals with rendering paints and varnishes microbicidal by the addition of an emulsion, *e.g.*, p-chlor-m-cresol dispersed in an emulsion of linseed oil in water, stabilised by potassium linoleate.[46] It is claimed that an emulsion of resin added to paints and varnishes increases their hardness and resistance to weather and water.[47]

Cleansing compounds are familiar in emulsion form such as emulsions of chlorinated hydrocarbons in water.[48] Solid powders are well-known as emulsifying agents and a patent has been granted relating to the use of a suspension in water of insoluble earth *colours* which act' as emulsifying agents in shoe creams composed of waxes, turpentine and water.[49] Alternatively, an oil-soluble dye may be dissolved in the internal phase of the wax-turpentine emulsion.[50] Toilet soaps may be rendered perfumed by using emulsions of aromatic odour (comprising terpenes, resins and floral wax) stabilised by ammonium sulphoricinoleate.[51] Other, closely-related emulsions, concern shaving creams,[52] skin-protective creams [53] and pomades.[54]

INSECTICIDAL EMULSIONS

Of the numerous patents granted for emulsions intended for use as insecticides the following recent specifications are typical illustrations.

Naschold [55] employs an aqueous emulsion of a mixture of borneol, terpene oil and fenchyl alcohol, using soft soap as emulsifier. As a stabilising and spreading agent, a water-soluble protein material is claimed,[56] such as dried blood-albumen in an aqueous solution containing ammonia. According to a French patent,[57] the emulsion is one of a vegetable oil in aqueous ammonia; a mineral oil and an insecticide such as nicotine or phenyl chloride may be added. Colloidal clay, especially bentonite, is mentioned [58] as emulsifying agent for organic insecticides such as anthracene oils, wood oils and chlorine compounds in water,

The familiar pyrethrum extract may be emulsified with a sulphonated mixture of aromatic compounds, e.g., the by-products of petroleum manufacture.[59] Patents for mineral oil emulsions are frequent, the claims dealing with the addition of insecticidal material or the use of an emulsifying agent. Thus:

(a) Petroleum white oil and a compound of nicotine with an oil-soluble sulphonic acid, derived from petroleum, are emulsified using aqueous soap solution.[60]

(b) From 1.5 to 8 per cent of water-soluble sulphonates, derived from acid treatment of mineral oil, are used to disperse mineral oils in water.[61]

(c) The emulsion contains mineral oil, an alkali metal compound of sulphonic acids derived from mineral oil, a colloidal emulsifying agent such as glue, and water.[62]

(d) The petroleum oil emulsion contains up to 1 per cent (by weight of the oil) of a naphthylamine; [63] or quinol or a chloro-substitution product thereof.[64]

(e) An emulsion of the extract obtained by the extraction of kerosene distillate with liquid SO_2 is combined with a small quantity of arsenic compound, soluble in one of the phases.[65]

(f) Petroleum oil is emulsified in water containing an oxidised mixture of organic acids derived from mineral oils (particularly from naphthenic hydrocarbons).[66]

(g) A light petroleum oil and an aqueous solution of a polysulphide are emulsified by the aid of gum arabic and gum ghatti.[67]

(h) The mineral oil and naphthenic soap system may contain a substantially anhydrous aliphatic alcohol such as C_4H_9OH.[68]

(i) Knight has patents granted for kerosene-water emulsions, using butyl acetyl ricinoleate; [69] again, the mineral oil may be mixed with 0.1 to 2 per cent of a poly-hydroxy alcohol partially esterified with a high molecular weight acid such as glyceryl-mono- or -di-oleate, ricinoleate or acetylricinoleate.[70] Further, the mineral oil can be mixed with 2 to 10 per cent of an oil-soluble hydroxy ester of a high molecular weight organic acid with a polyhydric alcohol, such as glyceryl naphthenate or partially esterified glyceryl oleate and aluminum naphthenate.[71]

(j) The emulsion consists of a non-toxic, substantially saturated, liquid hydrocarbon product such as a topped petroleum product and an emulsifying agent, comprising toxic hydrocarbon sulphones and sulphonic acids, in water.[72]

(k) A spray insecticide consists of a concentrated aqueous emulsion of white oil and derris extract diluted with 50 to 100 times its volume of water.[73]

(l) The aqueous emulsion is formed from a light mineral oil, oil-soluble sulphonates derived from acid-treated mineral oil, and a small amount of creosote.[74] The sulphonation products of neutral brown lubricating stock from crude petroleum has been claimed for the emulsification of nicotine or extracts of derris or pyrethrum.[75]

(m) Organic compounds containing OH, COOH or NH_2 groups and into which have been introduced polyglycoliether residues, containing at least four C_2H_4 groups, are dissolved in oil having an insecticide action. Thus, the reaction product of ethylene oxide on a mixture of alcohols containing eight to eighteen carbon atoms is dissolved in white oil to yield a solution readily emulsifiable in water.[76]

(n) Sulphur is employed in insecticidal emulsions, either as a suspension in the petroleum oil spray [77] or in solution, e.g., an emulsion of a carbon disulphide solution of sulphur, water, and fish oil soap.[78]

(o) Nicotine sulphate has been claimed as an emulsifying agent, the emulsion containing pine resin dissolved in a mixture of CCl_4 and mineral oil, saponified with aqueous NaOH and cresol.[79]

EMULSIONS FOR TREATING LEATHER

The patents in this connection mainly turn on the use of various emulsifying agents. The common colloidal materials are mentioned: glue or glue with gums or starch; [80] egg yolk substitute as sodium glycerophosphate. [81] Röhn claims [82] an emulsion of neatsfoot oil, using freshly precipitated $Al(OH)_3$. Typical patents claim:

(a) Esters of sulpho-fatty acids and organic colloids such as albumins, glue or their decomposition products, or alkylated celluloses, or polysaccharides. [83]

(b) Diethyloctylamine hydrochloride or other tertiary or quaternary amine salts of the same general type. [84]

(c) Aqueous-solution of methylcellulose. [85]

(d) Lecithin is mentioned in several specifications, [86] as also the residues from the extraction of soy-bean phosphatides. [87]

(e) Colloidal clays such as bentonite permit emulsions which are stable in the presence of ionisable metal salts. [88]

EDIBLE EMULSIONS

In the domain of food technology, numerous patents have been granted for emulsions. Many refer to artificial milks. Of marked controversial interest is the question of incorporating oil and fat emulsions in bread in order to effect modification of the gluten. [89] In bakery goods, emulsions of shortening agents are frequent, the patent claims referring to the nature of the emulsifying agent. [90]

The advantages of preparing medicinal oils as emulsions are obvious and account for the many patents in this connection. Thus, pure liquid paraffin oil is emulsified by the aid of agar-agar, [91] malt extract (or a malto-dextrin syrup) [92] alkaline casein or egg yolk proteins [93] and a jelly containing psyllium seed, agar-agar and gelatin. [94] Castor oil is emulsified with aqueous NaOH or milk of magnesia, [95] or gelatin and sugar. [96] Cod liver oil emulsions contain protalbic acid, [97] alkaline casein, [98] egg yolk and lime water, [99] and calcium saccharate. [100] As a feeding stuff emulsion, there is named an emulsion of marine oils in water containing casein and Na_2HPO_4. [101] Mention, too, may be made of the suggestion that to obtain resinous or waxy materials in milk, the fodder should contain the desired substance as oil-in-water emulsion.[102]

Recently lecithin emulsions have become prominent, especially in confectionery, e.g., toffee.[103] These emulsions are substitutes for egg yolk [104] and the emulsifying power of the lecithin is claimed to be improved by treating the emulsion with hydrogen peroxide.[105] The wide utilisation of lecithin in chocolate,[106] in order to reduce the tendency to "bloom," to enhance fluidity in the conche and to save cocoa butter, depends on wetting phenomena fundamental in the study of emulsions. That this is due to molecular groupings of polar character is emphasised by the recent patent claiming increased fluidity of chocolate by the use of a compound prepared by causing a polyhydric alcohol, a compound introducing an acid radical containing P and O, and fatty acids or oils to interact.[107] Incidentally, "blooming" is claimed to be avoided by the proper incorporation of gelatin.[108]

EMULSIFYING AGENTS

One cannot fail to be struck by the enormous number of patents granted for emulsifying agents, especially in connection with emulsions for use in the textile, leather and similar industries. The application of the physical chemistry of complex organic compounds is abundantly manifested. The conception of polar and non-polar molecular groupings is the root basis of modern technical research.

The most readily available emulsifying agents are the natural colloids. In illustration may be mentioned recent patents, such as *gelatin* [109] for bituminous emulsions, *starch* for similar emulsions [110] and for ointments,[111] *casein* for artificial milk,[112] cutting oils,[113] fish oil emulsions [114] and tar or bitumen emulsions,[115] *alginates* for bituminous emulsions,[116] aqueous emulsions of fat solvents,[117] and tar emulsions,[118] *linseed extract* for margarine [119] and bituminous emulsions,[120] *humates* for bituminous emulsions,[121] *tannic acid* [122] or *rubber latex* [123] for bituminous emulsions, *lecithin* for margarine [124] and bitumen emulsions.[125] *Pectin* [126] is used in emulsions of insecticidal oils and edible oils, whilst *egg yolk* is frequently named in patents.[127] Other colloids are *metarabic acid,*[128] *blood serum,*[129] *locust-kernel gum,*[130] and *montan wax.*[131] *Sodium gluconate* [132] is named for emulsifying cheese. Water-in-oil emulsions are claimed by the use of *lanolin* [133], *phytosterols* [134] and wax-like products [135] made. by uniting neutral waxes or hydrocarbons of high fusion point with alcohols of high molecular weight (*e.g.,* spermaceti, cetyl alcohol, and stearic acid, in the ratio 65 : 25 : 10, are fused together to give a product capable of absorbing 600 per cent of its own weight of 2 per cent aqueous NaOH).

No attempt can be made to arrange the above and other emulsifying agents in order of effective emulsifying capacity. All that can be said is that each has its own particular use conditioned by factors of economy, edibility, *etc.,* whilst emulsions are prepared by so many different types of apparatus as to introduce another factor against quantitative arrangement of emulsifying agents. The nature of the internal phase of the emulsion can also be important in this respect.

The modern conception of the disposition of an emulsifying agent, at the interface between two immiscible liquids, is that developed by Hardy, Langmuir and Harkins. They have shown that in the dineric interface the molecules are not disposed in random fashion, but are in ordered array, like groups facing like groups. The organic radical turns towards the organic liquid ("oil"), while active or "polar" groups face towards the aqueous phase. The presence of polar groups in an organic liquid enhances its attraction for water, manifested in reduction in the interfacial tension and raising the possibility of miscibility. Examples of polar groups are:—NO_2, CN, COOH, COOM, COOR, NH_2, $NHCH_3$, NCS, COR, CHO, OH, I, Br, Cl, and groups containing N, S, O and double bonds. When a compound, containing polar groups, is added to two immiscible liquids, it is adsorbed at their interface, being arranged there in oriented fashion, its presence ensuring more intimate union between the two phases.

The introduction of polar groups into organic compounds of molecular weight sufficiently great to bring the compounds into the realm of colloidality obviously offers a very wide range of possible emulsifying agents. The instances which now follow are by no means exhaustive, and must serve merely as illustrating the modern tendency in technical research. Recent patents will be named so far as possible.

1. Ethers and Esters

(*a*) Etherification or esterification of part of the OH groups in aliphatic polyhydric alcohols, or their polyhydric derivatives, or substitution products containing more than three carbon atoms in the molecule, with aliphatic substances which contain at least six (and preferably from ten to eighteen) carbon atoms in the molecule. Thus: sorbitol hexahydroxyethyl ether [186].

(*b*) Esterify or etherify water-insoluble organic compounds, excluding carbohydrates, that contain at least one OH or COOH group, or a group reacting like COOH, with polyethylene glycols containing a chain of at least four $CH_2.CH_2O$ groups. [187]

(*c*) A dihydric alcohol, such as glycol, diethylene glycol, *etc.*, is esterified with a fatty acid containing more than five carbon atoms. [138]

(*d*) Acid esters of polybasic organic acids and high molecular weight alcohols; thus: esters of adipic acid and sperm oil alcohols. [139]

(*e*) The products obtained by the polymerisation of ethylene-α, β-dicarboxylic acid with unsaturated compounds, such as styrene, indene, vinyl ether, vinyl ester and their derivatives soluble in water. [140]

(f) Alkali salts of acylated hydroxy fatty acids, e.g., acetyl- or benzoyl-ricinoleic acid.[141]

(g) Esterify di- or tri-glycerol with higher acids such as stearic, palmitic or oleic acid.[142]

(h) Mineral acid esters of glucosides.[143]

(i) Esters prepared by the reaction of a carbohydrate such as inulin or grape sugar with an alcohol such as lauric alcohol or with a phenol and with an inorganic acid such as H_3PO_4.[144]

2. Oxidation Products

(a) Liquid or solid paraffin or naphthene hydrocarbons are subjected to partial oxidation until practically no unoxidised hydrocarbon remains and the products are sulphonated.[145]

(b) The oxidation products (other than ozonides) of paraffin hydrocarbons, waxes, etc., or the acids isolated from the oxidation products are chlorinated and the chlorinated products are neutralised.[146]

(c) Treat oxidation products of hydrocarbons boiling above 180°C. with alkali to saponify the saponifiable constituents.[147]

(d) "P.E.O." or Schou oil,[148] used as an agent for the preparation of water-in-oil emulsions, particularly in the margarine trade, is prepared by oxidising soy-bean oil at 250°C. until gelatinisation sets in. Probably, the HC = CH bond changes to polar character and provides C = O and OH groupings.

3. Complex Nitrogenous Compounds

(a) Aliphatic or mixed aliphatic-hydroaromatic derivatives of NH_3 containing one or more alkylhydroxylic or cycloalkylhydroxylic groups.[149] Thus: cyclohexyldiethanolamine; cyclohexylmonoethanolamine; triethanolamine. Monoethanolamine [150] and phenylamine [151] or its homologues are also named.

(b) High molecular weight products containing OH or NH_2 or both, such as trihydroxyethylamine.[152]

(c) Amides of polyricinoleic acids.[153]

(d) Esters of aminoalcohols are claimed,[154] e.g., the di-hydroxypropylaniline ester of castor oil acids, or N-β-hydroxyethyl-piperidine ester of phthalic acid.

(e) Quaternary ammonium salts of relatively high molecular weight are made by causing esters of alkylmonosulphonic acids to react with secondary or tertiary amines.[155]

(f) Aliphatic or hydroaromatic compounds, containing at least one OH group and at least six carbon atoms in the molecule, are esterified with carboxylic acids containing NH_2 groups.[156] Examples: dodecyl ester of phenylamino acetic acid; octyl ester of anthranilic acid.

(g) Salts of partially acylated polyamines.[157] Example: oleyldiethylethylenediamine-hydrochloride.

4. Sulphonated Compounds

A familiar emulsifying agent is Turkey-red oil, the ammonium salt of ricinoleicsulphuric acid, $C_{17}H_{32}(SO_4H)COOH$. Besides the sulphonation of castor oil [158] acylated [159] (e.g., acetylated or benzoylated) if desired, the sulphonation is claimed of waxes,[160] various fats and fatty products,[161] the mixture of acids obtained from the fatty alcohol mixture of cacao and palm nut oils,[162] black or white mustard seed oil,[163] wool fat or its distillation products,[164] mixtures of cholesterol with fatty acids,[165] squalene,[166] polymerised styrene and polymerised alkyl derivatives of styrene,[167] the hydrocarbon oils obtained from brown-coal tar, [168] mineral oils,[169] the oxidation products of petroleum hydrocarbons,[170] derivatives of terpineol,[171] and derivatives of the hydrocarbon mixture corresponding to montanic acid.[172] Other sulphonation products, of which a very large number are claimed in the patent literature, are:

(a) Sulphonate the isopropylglycol ester of oleic acid.[173]

(b) Sulphonate monoalkyl ethers of glycerol in which the alkyl group contains sixteen to eighteen carbon atoms.[174]

(c) Chondroitinsulphuric acid and its salts.[175]

(*d*) Sulphonate esters and amides having the formulæ RCONR'R" and RCOOR'.

(*e*) Organic thiosulphates prepared by the reaction of salts of $H_2S_2O_3$ with esters (including thioesters) of aliphatic, hydroaromatic or aliphaticaromatic OH or SH compounds having at least six carbon atoms, with carboxylic acids containing reactive halogen atoms.[177] Thus: treat dodecylchloroacetic ester with $Na_2S_2O_3$.

Certain important patents, dealing with the conception of hydrophilelipophile balance in emulsifying agents, deserve more than passing mention because of the physico-chemical ideas involved.[178] An American specification [179] explains the matter in very detailed fashion. The principal object of the invention is to improve water-oil (magarine) emulsions and to reduce spattering of margarine during frying. The agent concentrates at the water/oil interface and "the effect of quality and quantity in the lipophile group becomes evident when the quantitative results are compared." Unless proper balance is secured, the substances with hydrophile and lipophile groups lack anti-spattering power. "In the case of triethanol amine oleate, isopropyl naphthalene sodium sulphonate and sodium triricinolein sulphate, the hydrophile character is too pronounced; the substances are rather freely soluble in water, and perceptible anti-spattering power is absent." Again, "in the case of cholesterol, palmityl alcohol and melissyl alcohol and also in hydroxystearic acid, the lipophile character predominates and is inadequately balanced by the hydroxy group to endow the molecule with anti-spattering power." An excellent example of the correctly-balanced agent is the palmityl ester of betaine hydrobromide:

$$C_{16}H_{33} - O - \overset{\overset{\textstyle O}{\|}}{C} - CH_2 - \overset{\overset{\textstyle Br}{|}}{N} \overset{\textstyle \diagup CH_3}{\underset{\textstyle \diagdown CH_3}{- CH_3}}$$

DE-EMULSIFYING OR BREAKING EMULSIONS

The great majority of patents, dealing with the separation of emulsions, concern the important crude petroleum emulsions, which are of the water-in-oil (W/O) type. The separation of O/W emulsions is much less frequently mentioned, although centrifugal *concentration* (creaming) of such systems is well known.

Dealing firstly with O/W emulsions, there are a number of patents which centre around the Ramsden phenomenon of the preferential accumulation of certain surface-active colloids at an air/liquid interface. Such accumulation may be accompanied by denaturation of the colloid, notably protein.

Clavel [180] claims that by converting milk into froth by streaming gases through it, the cream fat may be obtained by pouring through a fine sieve. A variant of the method is due to Salenius,[181] who boils cream at low temperature *in vacuo;* agitation thus causes butter separation. Cream may also be churned in thin layers which are subjected to continuous vibration of suitable amplitude and frequency.[182]

The principle of breaking O/W emulsions by creating a foam is familiar in the recovery of wool fat from wool washing liquors,[183] and Mertens [184] has a number of patents in this connection, the foam being washed and then autoclaved.

Protein-stabilised emulsions, like salad dressings, are sometimes broken with free oil separation, during transport, the degree of breaking depending on the extent of the gas head-space. Musher [185] claims the use of paraffin wax to fill the air space in bottles containing such emulsions.

Concerning W/O emulsions containing dispersed water, the numerous patents fall into several groups according to the type of treatment claimed. Methods for gravity separation [186] are only applicable to the less stable systems. Inclined baffles [187] may be used or the emulsion may be separated by passing it over plates which are rapidly oscillated in a direction at right angles to the flow.[188] Methods involving heat treatment [189] include heating under pressure [190] (followed by gravity separation).

Interesting patents relate to the use of powdered solids for breaking the emulsions. The fundamental principle is that the solid must be preferentially wetted by one of the liquids. Hatschek,[191] in 1908, employed finely divided calcium carbonate to de-oil water such as condensed water from steam engines. Aqueous (O/W) emulsions of tars, oils, *etc.*, may be treated with a finely divided mineral powder (granite dust, slate dust or powdered marble) which is more easily wetted by water than by oil.[192]

Water-in-petroleum emulsions are passed through a filter of diatomaceous earth, wetted, if desired, with oil or a liquid which is miscible with the oil of the emulsion.[193] Fine layers of graded sand, silica, pyrite, Al_2O_3 (crystallised in an electric furnace) are named,[194] or the emulsion may be passed through porous diaphragms [195] which are of progressively greater area, permitting the time of separation for water to be progressively increased. Capillary media, such as cloth, are claimed.[196] Fisher states that the emulsion may be passed between two relatively moving bodies, such as intermeshed gears, one of which is preferentially wetted by one phase of the emulsion and the other by the other phase.[197] Again, the emulsion may be agitated with a predetermined amount of zeolite minerals in the presence of iron sulphide minerals which are preferentially wetted by oil and quartz minerals which are preferentially wetted by water.[198]

Crude oil-field emulsions are frequently broken by the aid of re-agents which promote the opposite type of emulsion, the inversion point of the emulsion being reached. A few illustrations only are given below: (*a*) an oxidised product from hydrocarbon motor fuel produced by vapour-phase cracking of high boiling-point hydrocarbons; [199] (*b*) a mixture of a sulphonated fatty glyceride and an inorganic alkaline earth salt such as $CaCl_2$; [200]

(c) the product derived from chemical reaction of an abietene-nucleus hydrocarbon such as abietine, an aldehyde and a sulphonating agent; [201] (d) wood sulphite liquor material and a sulphonic material such as a propylated naphthalenesulphonic acid; [202] (e) an acetylated derivative of a hydroxylated fatty acid such as acetylsulphoricinoleic acid; [203] (f) the sodium salt of the sulphobenzyl ester of phthaloricinoleic acid; [204] (g) a complex condensation product prepared from a sulphonated aromatic amine such as sulphonated aniline and an alcohol or aldehyde of the aliphatic series; [205] (h) a sulphonic acid or sulphuric acid ester such as the sulphuric ester of cetyl alcohol [206] (or its ammonium salt) or lauryl alcohol; [207] (i) an amylated aromatic compound such as an ammonium amylated aromatic sulphonate characterised by capability of producing an insoluble precipitate with a soluble alkaline earth salt. [208] It has also been proposed to treat the emulsion first with SO_2 and then with SH_2; after heating, the system is set aside to separate. [209] The addition of ammonium sulphide followed by heating is also claimed. [210]

By far the greater number of patents relating to the breaking of crude oil-field emulsions are concerned with electrical treatment, many patents specifying particular apparatus. Several illustrative patents may now be mentioned: (a) the emulsion is subjected to mechanical vibration, both while in a pre-treatment zone and while passing between high-tension electrodes; [211] (b) the emulsion is introduced within an inner perforated rotatable electrode and passed through the perforations of this electrode into a surrounding drum which constitutes the other electrode; [212] (c) pass the emulsion in a flowing stream between a pair of electrodes between which a potential of 250–600 volts is maintained, spaced sufficiently far apart to prevent passage of any substantial amount of current. The electrodes may be of tubular form and concentrically placed; [213] (d) a continuous, substantially uniform, electric field is provided between electrodes within a conduit constituting a relatively long path, to polarise the water globules tending to chain formation and the liquid is moved through the field at such a velocity as to break up or prevent persistence of chains of polarised globules or entrapped liquid between the electrodes; [214] (e) the emulsion is subjected to the action of an electrical field of an alternating high-potential character produced by use of a non-oscillatory alternating potential of a frequency between 60 and 10,000 cycles per second; [215] (f) subject the emulsion to the coalescing action of an electric field between immersed electrodes with intermittently increased and decreased intensity; [216] (g) finely divided water-insoluble conducting material, such as iron powder, is suspended in the emulsion, and an electric current is passed (A.C. at 550–33,000 volts); [217] (h) flow the emulsion upwards between successive sets of electrodes, the spacing of the electrodes being reduced as the resistance of the emulsion increases.[218] Fisher claims [219] that for emulsions which are not susceptible to the usual electrical dehydration, sodium carbonate is to be added to invert the emulsion prior to the application of a high-potential electric field. Roberts claims [220] the combined action of magnetic and electric fields, whilst Herbsman specifies [221] treatment with violet, ultra-violet, X-rays, cathode rays, canal rays or radiation from radio-active substances.

A novel patent [222] deals with the addition to the crude oil-field emulsion of a medium adapted to sustain the life of micro-organisms which are added with the object of destroying the emulsifying agent stabilising the W/O system.

MISCELLANEOUS PATENTS

The numerous patents covering an extraordinary range of emulsion problems make it difficult to limit the discussion. For example, bituminous road emulsions are covered by hundreds of specifications, the great majority concerning the use of colloidal clay (or bentonite) and like material, or the use of alkaline solutions which make use of the free acids in natural bituminous substances. The anode deposition of rubber provides a constant flow of patents, as do also wetting and penetrating agents.

In 1924, Sakurei [223] reported the remarkable fact that small quantities of a 1 per cent hydrosol of Irish moss, added to milk or rubber latex, caused the emulsion to separate into two layers of different concentration. A patent was granted to Traube, [224] in 1924, for such concentration of latex and since then numerous patents have been granted referring to a variety of colloids as creaming agents. [225]

The physical chemistry of the phenomenon, wherein a substance normally acting as an emulsifying agent for O/W types of emulsions nevertheless accelerates creaming of certain fairly stable natural emulsions, is still a matter for investigation. Temperature plays a role, as the effect is enhanced at 50–60°C.

The colloids mentioned in different patents are: Irish moss, [226] gum tragacanth, [227] pectin, [228] gelatin, [229] ammonium alginate, [230] agar and casein. [231] Centrifugal aid may be further imposed, [231, 232] or the creaming may be facilitated by applying an electrical potential insufficient to cause current flow or deposition of rubber. [233] The addition of a substance such as alcohol, which is more volatile than water, [234] is stated to increase the creaming effect due to added organic colloids. The physical chemist will note the remarkable fact that saponin is claimed to stabilise the creamed layer of latex, i.e., saponin is an anti-creaming agent. [235]

Of scientific interest are specifications relating to the preparation of transparent emulsions [236] by adjustment of the refractive indices of the liquid phases: the stabilising of emulsions by equalising the densities of the phases; [237] the use of coconut oil stearin for promoting water-in-oil emulsions, the stearin being wetted by oils. [238] Finally, attention is drawn to several patents concerning the art of emulsification. The early patent of Blichfeldt [239] drew attention to the advantage of slow addition of the internal phase of an emulsion to the main bulk of the external phase. Four patents dealing with bituminous emulsions refer to the presence or use of a pre-formed emulsion; (1) an emulsion is permitted to stand and separate into two emulsions, the more concentrated is used direct whereas the weaker is used for making other emulsions.[240] (2) a concentrated emulsion is first formed and then this is used to emulsify larger quantities of the same material; [241] (3) a stable aqueous bitumen emulsion can be prepared in unlimited quantities by mixing the material to be emulsified with alkaline water in presence of a small quantity of emulsion of the material previously prepared by aid of an emulsifying agent such as gum arabic; [242] (4) water, already-formed emulsion and asphalt kept in circulation and agitation from, to, and in a vessel, fresh materials being continuously added and emulsion removed.[243] Very specific claim is made in this connection in a patent [244] of a process for the continuous solidification of liquid hydrocarbons. Quoting (italics by the present writer): "On the one hand, liquid hydrocarbon is brought continuously and in a relatively small amount into contact with an already emulsified mass, and it is submitted simultaneously to the action of the emulsifier and of a mixing device, and on the other hand, emulsified hydrocarbon is concurrently withdrawn from the mass in a continuous manner. *The already emulsified mass of hydrocarbon will facilitate the emulsifying of the small quantity of liquid hydrocarbon supplied thereto, in the same manner as in a chemical operations a catalyst facilitates a chemical reaction, so that the emulsion is formed in a short time and with the expenditure of a minimum amount of mechanical energy.*" The present writer is certain that this idea will provoke comment and discussion by the physical chemists present.

REFERENCES

1. Anderson, U.S. 775,909 (1904).
2. Winchester and Fragopulos, U.S. 1,856,526 (1932).
3. Odell, U.S. 1,922,391 (1933).
4. Odell, U.S. 1,902,886 (1933).
5. Hines, Brit. 239,922 (1925).

6. Briggs and Wales, *Colliery Guardian,* **128**, 673 (1924).
7. Fisher, U.S. 1,824,428 (1931).
8. Brogden and Trowbridge, U.S. 1,809,016 (1931).
9. Horiba, Otagiri and Kiyota, Japan 101,948 (1933).
10. Bruzac, Fr. 764,813 (1934).
11. Morrell, U.S. 1,968,845 (1934).
12. Wilcken, Brit. 405,906 (1933).
13. Watanabe, U.S. 1,833,804 and 1,833,805 (1931).
14. Osawa, U.S. 1,833,852 (1931).
15. Krieser, Ger. 500,347 (1928).
16. Scheele, U.S. 1,957,358 (1934).
17. Max Brunner and Co., Swiss 166,486 (1934).
18. McIntyre, U.S. 1,882,853 (1932).
19. Soc. auxiliaire de materiel d'incendie, Fr. 752,621 (1933).
20. van der Willigen, Brit. 333,690 (1928).
21. von der Heide, Ger. 482,919 (1926).
22. Ellis, U.S. 1,956,567 (1934); Haslam, U.S. 1,956,573 (1934); White, U.S. 1,956,603 (1934); Gas Fuel Corp., Brit. 410,773 (1934) and Fr. 744,602 (1933); Russell, U.S. 1,970,771 (1934).
23. Dubbs and Morrell, U.S. 1,744,109 (1930).
24. Ditto, U.S. 1,970,996 (1934).
25. Cf. E. I. du Pont de Nemours and Co., Brit. 387,340 (1933); 389,109 (1933).
26. *Ind. Eng. Chem.,* **25**, 1338 (1933).
27. I.C.I. Ltd., and Naunton, Brit. 313,252 (1928).
28. Crawford and Schoenfeld, U.S. 1,919,775 (1933).
29. Gas Fuel Corp., Fr. 744,602 (1933).
30. Vance, U.S. 1,926,071 (1933).
31. Explosions-Turbine-Studien Ges., Danish 21,974 (1917).
32. Newton, U.S. 1,791,832 (1931).
33. Filtrators Ltd. and Saks, Ger. 512,698 (1926); Kobseff, U.S. 1,950,494 (1934).
34. N.V. de Bataafsche Petroleum Maats., Brit. 408,896 (1933).
35. Oeding, U.S. 1,925,672 (1933).
36. See Hartmann, *Chem. Weekblad,* **20**, 59 (1923).
37. Adams, U.S. 1,871,939 (1932); Wilkin, U.S. 1,907,920 (1933).
38. Hoel, U.S. 1,875,001 (1932).
39. Sullivan, U.S. 1,773,123 (1930); Adams and Kittrell, U.S. 1,817,599 (1931); Adams, U.S. 1,871,940 (1932).
40. Merrill, U.S. 1,739,686 (1930).
41. Rutherford, Can. 338,571 (1934).
42. I. G. Farbenind. A.-G., Fr. 674,215 (1929).
43. Strauch, U.S. 1,909,080 (1933).
44. Johnson, Brit. 340,294 (1929).
45. Davion, Fr. 741, 174 (1931).
46. Les bactericides colloidaux (S.a.r.l.), Fr. 761,172 (1934).
47. Miaulet, Fr. 761,097 (1934).
48. Alex. Wacker Ges. f. Elektrochemische Ind. G.m.b.H., Fr. 720,152 (1931); Peel, Brit. 363,794 (1930).

49. Carl Gentner chem. Fabr.-Göppingen, Fr. 755,016 (1933).
50. Klingenstein, Ger. 576,007 (1933).
51. Villain, U.S. 1,887,743 (1932).
52. Mack and Bennett, U.S. 1,888,601 (1932); Kelly, Brit. 283,711 (1926).
53. Frederickson, Brit. 342,947 (1930).
54. Kohn, Fr. 757,146 (1933); Brown and De Hoff, U.S. 1,927,916 (1933).
55. Ger. 556,932 (1929).
56. McBeth and Allison, U.S. 1,787,585 (1931).
57. Lafarge and Chanut, Fr. 747,562 (1933).
58. Progil (Soc. Anon.), Fr. 729,930 (1931).
59. I. G. Farbenind. A.-G., Ger. 506,889 (1928).
60. Grant, U.S. 1,877,851 (1932).
61. Johansen, U.S. 1,373,661 (1921).
62. Sullivan and Adams, U.S. 1,830,969 (1931).
63. Yates, U.S. 1,778,239 (1930).
64. Yates, U.S. 1,778,240 (1930).
65. De Ong, Can. 305,500 (1930).
66. De Ong, Can. 305,502 (1930).
67. Tower, Dye and McDonough, U.S. 1,869,526 (1932).
68. Merrill, U.S. 1,695,197 (1928).
69. U.S. 1,875,466 (1932); U.S. 1,937,969 (1933).
70. U.S. 1,949,798 (1934).
71. U.S. 1,949,799 (1934).
72. Hessle, U.S. 1,921,158 (1933).
73. Grant, Can. 333,642 (1933).
74. Adams, U.S. 1,969,491 (1934).
75. Volck, U.S. 1,922,607 (1933).
76. I. G. Farbenind. A.-G., Fr. 746,258 (1933).
77. Yates, Can. 308,745 (1931).
78. Hartzell and Moore, U.S. 1,772,511 (1930).
79. Okada, Japan 101,617 (1933).
80. Röhm, Brit. 353,846 (1929); Ger. 518,920 (1929).
81. Röhm, U.S. 1,981,363 (1932).
82. Röhm, U.S. 1,751,217 (1930).
83. H. Th. Böhme A.-G., Brit. 313,966 (1928).
84. Somerville, U.S. 1,883,042 (1932).
85. I. G. Farbenind. A.-G., Ger. 524,211 (1926).
86. Bollmann and Rewald, Ger. 514,399, 516,187, 516,188 and 516,189 (1927).
87. Hanseatische Mühlenwerke A.-G. and Rewald, Ger. 522,041 (1927).
88. Progil (Soc. Anon.), Fr. 742,563 (1933).
89. Augmentine Soc. Anon., Brit. 289,060 (1927).
90. Dunham, U.S. 1,432,057 (1922); Duff and Dietrich, U.S. 1,931,892 (1933); Tranin and Irwin, U.S. 1,895,694 (1933); Baker, U.S. 1,553,294 (1925); Paessler, U.S. 1,203,905 (1916); Archibald, Brit. 330,779 (1929); Matti. U.S. 1,750,720 (1930).
91. Miller, U.S. 1,605,130 (1926); Can. 277,180 (1928); Kelp-Ol Laboratories Inc., Brit. 317,713 (1928).
92. Hamburg, Brit. 26,390 (1913).

93. Dunham, Brit. 148,587 (1919).
94. Noonan, U.S. 1,920,926 (1933).
95. Merrell and Bye, U.S. 1,862,315 (1932).
96. Valentine, U.S. 1,804,135 (1931).
97. Hattori, U.S. 1,752,176 (1930).
98. Miyake et al, Japan 35,730 (1920).
99. Holz, Ger. 503,623 (1925).
100. Deutsch Pentosin-Werke G.m.b.H. Ger. 593,395 (1934).
101. Olsén and Co. A. S., Danish 36,481 (1926).
102. Jena and Jena, Ger. 501,332 (1924).
103. Jordan, U.S. 1,859,240 (1932); Bollmann, Ger. 480,480 (1925); Bollmann and Rewald., Brit. 328,075 (1929); Riedel-E. de Haen A.-G. Ger. 474,269 and 474,543 (1923).
104. Oranienburger Chem. Fabr. A.-G., Brit. 317,730 (1928).
105. Bollmann, Ger. 511,851 (1929) and Brit. 356,384 (1929).
106. Bollmann and Rewald, Brit. 330,450 (1929); Working, U.S. 1,781,672 (1930).
107. N. V. Algemeene Beleggings Maatschappij, Fr. 759,074 (1934) and Brit. 407,248 (1934).
108. Esmond and Duecker, U.S. 1,800,985–6–7 (1931).
109. Loebel, U.S. 1,960,115 (1934); Baume, Chambige and Boutier, Ger. 594,310 (1934); Hailwood, U.S. 1,873,580 (1932); Nippon Sekiyu K.K., Japan 96,313 (1932); Elkington, Brit. 342,296 (1929); Colas Products Ltd., Brit. 322,792 (1928); Disney and Kernot, Brit. 274,142 (1927).
110. Levin, U.S. 1,881,729 (1932); Kirschbraun, U.S. 1,878,974 (1932); Union Chim. Belg. Soc. Anon., Brit. 344,490 (1929); Colas Products Ltd., 320,847 (1928); Lister et Cie, Brit. 305,742 (1927); Lutyens and Child, Brit. 238,586 (1924).
111. Kelly, Brit. 283,711 (1926).
112. Monhaupt, Brit. 154,627 (1917); Naamlooze Vennootschap Anton Jurgens Ver. Fabr., Brit. 129,165 (1918).
113. Goodwin, U.S. 1,907,789 (1933).
114. Miyake, Japan 35,730 (1920); Olsen, Danish 36,481 (1926).
115. Lacau, Brit. 400,045 (1933); Rodewald, Brit. 393,868 (1932); Kirschbraun, U.S. 1,859,517 (1932).
116. Thornley, Brit. 219,348 (1923); Thornley, Tapping and Reynard, U.S. 1,653,026 (1927); Gloess and Marini, Fr. 633,687 (1926).
117. Wilcken, Brit. 405,906 (1934) and Fr. 760,958 (1934).
118. China and White, Brit. 351,242 (1930); Gloess, Fr. 694,905 (1929).
119. Blichfeldt, Brit. 104,899 (1916).
120. Schutte, U.S. 1,950,272 (1934).
121. I. G. Farbenind. A.-G., Brit. 369,242 (1930); 334,426 (1928); 317,496 (1928); Ges. für Teerverwertung m.b.H., Ger. 591,340 (1934).
122. Levy, Brit. 246,907 (1924).
123. Colas Products Ltd., Brit. 329,965 (1929); U.S. 1,886,334 (1932).
124. Behrend, Brit. 405,116 (1933); Bollmann and Rewald, Brit. 369,990 (1930).
125. Hanseatische Mühlenwerke A.-G., Brit. 383,432 (1931).
126. Deiglmayr, Ger. 585,586 and 575,922 (1934); California Fruit Growers

Exchange, Brit. 369,518 (1930); Patteson, U.S. 1,726,364 (1929); Douglas and Loesch, Brit. 221,466 (1923).
127. Bergsvik and Hellerud, U.S. 1,941,243 (1933); Hellerud, U.S. 1,941,261 (1933) and Brit. 341,414 (1929); Heide, Brit. 357,246 (1930).
128. Seltzer, Fr. 717,837 (1931) and Brit. 361,262 (1931).
129. Firma Moskovits Mór és Fia, Holland 2,269 (1918).
130. Schwarzkopf, Brit. 378,273 (1931) and Ger. 564,046 (1930).
131. Agasote Millboard Co., Fr. 684,048 (1929); Elosequi, Fr. 752,178 (1933); Deutsche Erdöl A.-G., Ger. 556,250 (1928); Lichtenstern, Austrian, 137,894 (1934).
132. Pasternack and Burnham, U.S. 1,890,948 (1932).
133. Barnes, U.S. 1,830,502 (1931).
134. Sandqvist and Lindström, Brit. 329,305 (1929).
135. Deutsche Hydrierwerke A.-G., Fr. 671,063 (1929).
136. I. G. Farbenind. A.-G., Brit. 375,842 (1932); U.S. 1,959,930 (1934).
137. I. G. Farbenind. A.-G., Ger. 573,048 (1932); Brit. 380,431 (1932).
138. Bennett, Can. 322,765 (1932); U.S. 1,914,100 (1933).
139. Hueter, Ger. 512,979 (1928).
140. I. G. Farbenind, A.-G., Fr. 728,712 (1931); Ger. 571,665 (1933).
141. Oranienburger Chem. Fabr. A.-G., Ger. 540,065 (1928).
142. Nakayama, Japan 98,851 (1932).
143. H. Th. Böhme A.-G., Brit. 404,684 (1934).
144. Bertsch, U.S. 1,951,785 (1934).
145. I. G. Farbenind. A.-G., Ger. 588,139 (1933).
146. I. G. Farbenind. A.-G., Ger. 545,094 (1928) and Brit. 321,239 (1928); Beller and Luther, U.S. 1,882,741 (1932).
147. I. G. Farbenind. A.-G., Ger. 566,797 (1930).
148. Schou, Brit. 155,398 (1919); Brit. 178,885; Brit. 187,298–9 (1922); Danish 30,741 (1922); U.S. 1,603,155 (1926).
149. I. G. Farbenind, A.-G., Fr. 646,816 (1928).
150. Bennett, U.S. 1,807,563 (1931).
151. Melamid, Fr. 648,138 (1928).
152. F. Steinfels Soc. Anon. Fr. 717,390 (1931).
153. Deutsche Hydrierwerke A.-G., Ger. 552,251 (1930).
154. Schicht A.-G. and Ulbrich, Brit. 314,072 (1929).
155. H. Th. Böhme A.-G., Fr. 753,189 (1933).
156. Henkel et Cie. G.m.b.H., Fr. 759,821 (1934).
157. Soc. Anon. Pour L'Ind. Chim. à Bâle, Fr. 713,743 (1931).
158. Röhm and Haas A.-G., Ger. 549,031 (1929); J. Riley and Sons, Ltd., Brit. 365,904 (1931); N.V. Ver. Fabr. van Stearine Kaarsen en Chem. Prod., Dutch 27,274 (1932).
159. I.C.I. Ltd., Hailwood and McGlynn, Brit. 357,670 (1930).
160. Levinstein, U.S. 1,219,967 (1917).
161. Chemische Fabrik Milch Akt.-Ges., Brit. 275,267 (1926).
162. H. Th. Böhme A.-G., Brit. 365,938 (1930) and Ger. 593,709 (1934).
163. I.C.I. Ltd., Callan and McGlynn, Brit. 380,836 (1932).
164. Oranienburger Chem. Fabr. A.-G., Ger. 575,831 (1933).
165. Stiepel, Ger. 589,015 (1933).
166. I.C.I. Ltd., Bunbury et al., Brit. 354,417 (1930); U.S. 1,961,683 (1934).

167. I. G. Farbenind. A.-G., Brit. 367,416 (1930).
168. I. G. Farbenind. A.-G., Ger. 552,328 (1926).
169. Gelbke, Ger. 595,604 (1934).
170. I. G. Farbenind, A.-G., Brit. 303,281 (1928); James, U.S. 1,753,516 (1930).
171. Soc. Pour L'Ind. Chim. à Bâle, Brit. 398,086 (1933).
172. I. G. Farbenind, A.-G., Brit. 371,822 (1931).
173. Chem. Fabrik. vormals, Sandoz., Swiss 151,958 (1930).
174. I.C.I. Ltd., Baldwin and Bunbury, Brit. 398,818 (1933).
175. Traube, Ger. 572,544 (1933).
176. I. G. Farbenind, A.-G., Brit. 390,840 (1933).
177. Henkel et Cie G.m.b.H., Brit. 397,445 (1933).
178. The Emulsol Corporation, Brit. 366,909; 378,372-3 (1932).
179. Harris, U.S. 1,917,256 (1933).
180. Ger. 314,090 (1918).
181. Brit. 333,233 (1929).
182. Perks, Brit. 322,416 (1929); U.S. 1,791,000 (1931).
183. Broadbridge and Edser, U.S. 1,505,944 (1924); Karpinsky, Brit. 177,498 (1922); Bailey, U.S. 1,770,476 (1930).
184. Brit. 328,606 (1928); U.S. 1,853,871 (1932); Ger. 546,231 (1929).
185. U.S. 1,728,011 (1930).
186. Barber, U.S. 1,945,766 (1934); Edwards, U.S. 1,968,131 (1934); Mahone, U.S. 1,940,762 (1933); Pink, U.S. 1,698,002 and 1,698,067 (1929).
187. Fisher, U.S. 1,940,794 (1933).
188. Palmer, U.S. 1,781,076 (1930).
189. Novotney and Hunter, U.S. 1,968,614 (1934); Turner, U.S. 1,948,481 (1934); Brady, U.S. 1,754,079 (1930); Moscicki, U.S. 1,710,374 (1929).
190. Champion, U.S. 1,943,367-8 (1934); Dubbs, U.S. 1,123,502 (1915); Elliott, U.S. 1,928,282 (1933).
191. Brit. 26,228 (1908).
192. Robinson and Parkes, Brit. 268,547 (1926); Roth, U.S. 1,665,189 (1928).
193. Zoul, U.S. 1,501,877 (1924).
194. Van Loenen, U.S. 1,944,479-80 (1934) and 1,967,601 (1934); Garrison and Van Loenen, U.S. 1,947,709 (1934); Eddy, U. S. 1,807,833 (1931); Pollock, U. S. 1,847,413 (1932); Meinzer, U.S. 1,887,774-5 (1932).
195. Trumble, U.S. 1,304,124 (1919); Haseman, U.S. 1,914,665 (1933).
196. Dyer and Heise, U.S. 1,242,784 (1917).
197. U.S. 1,932,093 (1933).
198. Brown and Meinzer, U.S. 1,911,797 (1933); Meinzer, U.S. 1,911,839-40 (1933).
199. Hyman and Schlandt, U.S. 1,811,177 (1931).
200. Herbsman, U.S. 1,959,824 (1934).
201. De Groote and Wirtel, U.S. 1,961,963 (1934).
202. De Groote and Monson, U.S. 1,780,343 (1930).
203. De Groote, Monson and Keiser, U.S. 1,812,393 (1931).
204. De Groote and Keiser, U.S. 1,954,585 (1934).
205. Wayne, U.S. 1,937,259 (1933).
206. De Groote and Monson, U.S. 1,938,322 (1933).
207. De Groote and Monson, U.S. 1,938,323 (1933).
208. De Groote, Monson and Wirtel, U.S. 1,780,344 (1930).

209. Hyman and Schlandt, U.S. 1,800,887 (1931).
210. Hyman and Schlandt, U.S. 1,860,248 (1932).
211. Lawrason, U.S. 1,942,480 (1934).
212. Worthington, U.S. 1,783,595 (1930).
213. Seibert and Brady, U.S. 1,290,369 (1919).
214. McKibben, U.S. 1,299,589 (1919).
215. Roberts, U.S. 1,959,385 (1934).
216. Alden and Eddy, U.S. 1,394,462 (1921).
217. Morrell, U.S. 1,827,276 and 1,827,714 (1931); Eddy, U.S. 1,796,750 (1931).
218. Gage, U.S. 1,754,009 (1930).
219. Fisher, U.S. 1,838,379 (1931).
220. U. S. 1,949,660 (1934).
221. Herbsman, Brit. 356,926 (1930); U.S. 1,783,471 (1930); Ger. 592,877 (1934).
222. Beckman, U.S. 1,753,641 (1930).
223. *Biochem. Z.*, **149**, 525 (1924).
224. Brit. 226,440 (1924); U.S. 1,754,842 (1930).
225. Cf. Rossman, *India Rubber World*, **87** (vi), 33; **88** (iii), 31 (1933).
226. K. D. P. Ltd., Brit. 337,269 (1929); Fr. 686,821 (1929); Westcott, U. S. 1,754,535 (1930); Hauser, U.S. 1,831,492 (1931).
227. Johnson, Brit. 286,527 (1927).
228. McGavack, U.S. 1,647,805 (1927); Deutsche Pektinges. m.b.H. Ger. 560,259 (1923).
229. Banks, U.S. 1,755,379 (1930).
230. General Rubber Co., Brit. 294,002 (1927).
231. Loomis and Stump, U.S. 1,816,018 (1931).
232. Wescott, U.S. 1,754,535 (1930).
233. McGavack, Brit. 344,647 (1929); U.S. 1,921,575 (1933).
234. Stevens, Brit. 415,133 (1933).
235. Teague, U.S. 1,772,647 (1930); Nikitin, U.S. 1,880,975 (1932).
236. Rector, U. S. 1,389,161 (1921); Whatmough, U.S. 1,663,323 (1928).
237. Volck, U.S. 1,914,902 (1933); Imray, Brit. 200,036 (1923); Hartman and Kägi, U.S. 1,611,190 (1926); Mecke, Ger. 368,234 (1922).
238. Ayres, U.S. 1,467,081 (1923).
239. Brit. 4,505 (1912).
240. Firma P. Lechler, Brit. 254,701 (1925).
241. Billinghame, U.S. 1,700,581 (1929).
242. Braun and Hay, Brit. 254,012 (1925).
243. Robinson, U.S. 1,923,888 (1933).
244. Neveu, U.S. 1,525,409 (1925).

SECTION 5

INDUSTRIAL EMULSION FORMULATION

By M. P. Hofmann

(Manager, Colloid Mill Division, The C. O. Bartlett & Snow Co.)

ONLY practical applications of colloidal principles and practical working emulsion formulae will be discussed in this section. The theory, accounting for the behaviour of the various colloids, peptizers, and dispersants, will be found elsewhere in this volume, and no attempt to explain these phenomena will be made here. As the list of chemicals, compounds, by-products, and other materials, having potentialities as dispersants and protective colloids, is very long and is daily being augmented, only the best known of these materials will be discussed in this section.

The claims of various manufacturers for their products may be evaluated by substitution in the various formulae, and, undoubtedly, in many cases, improvements will result.

In the creation of an emulsion, the reason for the emulsification or dispersion, in many cases, has considerable bearing on the selection of the emulsifying agent to be used. The reasons for desiring to emulsify materials are many, *i.e.,*

1) To make possible the use of water as a diluent or extender in place of expensive solvents.
2) To prevent penetration of coatings and to permit very thin films to be coated on the surface of porous materials.
3) To increase penetration.
4) To produce lustrous films (waxes).

5) To enhance and increase tinctorial strength of colors.
6) To produce smoother consistencies.
7) To disguise taste of oils and medicinals.
8) To extend and enhance flavor values.
9) To bring about both hydrocarbon and water solvency (as in various cleaners and polishes).

All of the properties desired in the emulsion should be reviewed carefully and the emulsifying agent best suited to these requirements then selected.

The interest of manufacturers of food and pharmaceutical emulsions is limited to those protective colloids and peptizers which are classed as edible. For this reason, these will be discussed first. A few examples of food or edible pharmaceutical emulsions follow:

Cod Liver Oil .... See Formula No. 1
Mineral Oil and Agar .... "   "   " 5
Castor Oil .... "   "   " 2
Mayonnaise .... "   "   " 4
Salad Dressings .... "   "   " 3
Flavoring Emulsions (Beverage) .. "   "   " 7
Flavoring Emulsions (Baker's) .... "   "   " 8 (at the end
                                                                        of this section).

A brief list of edible emulsifiers, in the order of their efficiency, follows:

Gelatin
Gum Arabic
Casein
Neutral Soaps
Carrageen (Irish Moss)
Isinglass
Egg White
Egg Yolk
Gum Tragacanth
Gum Karaya
Locust Bean Gum

Pectin
Agar-Agar
Alginates (Sodium and Ammonium)
Lecithin
Dextrin (Wheat Starch, Potato Starch, Tapioca Flour, Flour)

Methods of formulation and formulae of the various emulsions are given at the end of this section.

GENERAL FORMULATION

Gelatin

First place in performance is equally divided between gelatin and gum arabic. It should be noted, at this time, that many of the protective colloids are incompatible with one another and cannot be used together. Gelatin is incompatible with many gums and is generally used alone. A marked disadvantage of gelatin is that it "jells" or sets when used in concentrations higher than 0.25%. One of its largest fields of usefulness is in the preparation of ice cream, sherbets, and in medicinal emulsions such as mineral oil and agar, cod liver oil and castor oil emulsions. Some very interesting emulsions of this type have been developed. For typical formulae, see formulae Nos. 13, 14 and 15 at the end of this section.

Gum Arabic

This versatile gum can be used in dispersions of almost every type. It may be used in acid or alkaline medium, and the smallest oil particles and finest disintegration can be produced with it; the efficiency of the mechanical dispersing means used is the only limiting factor. All types of food and pharmaceutical emulsions can be made with gum arabic. The percentage used varies from 2 to 10% and more. Gum arabic solutions are comparatively free-flowing. If a small amount of glycerin is added to the dry gum, water can be stirred in and a smooth mucilage or dispersion of the gum prepared quickly, without danger of lumping. One of the foremost uses for gum arabic is in the preparation of beverage concentrates of the orange type. For typical formulae, see Nos. 1, 5, 7, 8 and 11 at the end of this section. Particle sizes of as low as 1/10 micron can be produced with the formulae given. To create absolute stability in these formulae, "weighting" of the oil must be resorted to. This technique will be described under Special Emulsifying Techniques.

Casein

Casein is perhaps one of the most widely used protective colloids because of its abundance and availability, the only limiting factor to its use being the pH of the external phase. As casein is precipitated in neutral or acid solutions, and is only soluble in alkaline solutions, its use is limited to emulsions having a pH higher than 7.5. Numerous pharmaceutical emulsions employ casein as a protective colloid. Water-soluble paints, shoe coatings, paper coatings, rubber and resin emulsions, in which, it is used as both emulsifier and dispersing agent, are compounded with casein. It is prepared by dissolving in ammonia and borax, and proportions of from 1 to 5%, calculated on the entire emulsion, are used.

Mosses

Agar, carrageen and alginates are extensively used as protective colloids. Their efficiency is far less than that of gum arabic and their greatest field of usefulness is in jellies and salad dressings. Alginates such as sodium alginate are extensively used in stabilizing the dispersion of the fat globules in ice cream and can be used to replace gelatin in formulae 13 and 14 at the end of this section. For typical formulae for their use, see Nos. 1, 5, 9 and 11.

Soaps

Sodium soaps such as the oleate and stearate are extensively used in the preparation of pharmaceutical emulsions of the type which contain saponifiable animal or vegetable oils. In such formulae, a small amount of caustic soda, sodium carbonate, or bicarbonate is added to the mixture of oil and water. This saponifies a portion of the oil, making a soap, which acts as protective colloid to emulsify the balance of the oil. In some cases, soaps of castor and other oils are added to pharmaceutical emulsions; a typical illustration of this type of emulsion is No. 2 at the end of this section.

Albumen

Although, albumen is frequently used to stabilize emulsions intended for human and animal consumption, its most outstanding use is in the form of eggs in the production of mayonnaise. The conventional method for the preparation of this product is well known. For formulae and special technique, used in making mayonnaise by the continuous process, see formulae Nos. 3, 4, and 10 at the end of this section.

Gum Tragacanth, Gum Karaya

These gums are frequently used in conjunction with arabic and other gums. Their function is to aid stability by increasing viscosity rather than by aiding in attaining smaller particle sizes. Alone, they are poor dispersants. Salad dressings, compounded with and without mayonnaise, are thickened with such mixtures as starches, dextrin, tapioca, gum tragacanth, gum karaya, or locust bean meal. For formulae for many of these, see Nos. 1, 5, 9, 10 and 11 at the end of the section.

Choice of Emulsifying Agents

Although, the method of manufacture of an emulsion, to a certain extent, influences the choice of emulsifying agent to be used, the greatest limiting factor is the pH of the continuous phase. Wherever the pH is less than 7, the choice of emulsifiers will be restricted to products similar to those listed below:

Gelatin	Tapioca
Glue	Emulgor A
Gum Arabic	Diethylene Glycol Stearate
Eggs	Aerosol
Albumen	Duponol
Gums	Bentonite
Starches	Quebracho
Flour	

To illustrate this type of emulsion, formulae for water-proofing textiles are given. These are high in acetic acid and their pH is generally less than 5. See Nos. 6 and 12 at the end of this section.

Emulsions having various idiosyncrasies having been disposed of, the rest of this section will be devoted to discussion of various commercial emulsions and techniques used in their manufacture. Almost all emulsions and dispersions can be made by a combination of mechanical agitation, hydraulic shear, and the proper selection of emulsifying agents. Many emulsions can be made spontaneously, and these will be discussed later.

Mechanical Emulsifying Aids

For emulsions, requiring mechanical agitation, three types of mechanical devices are available, *i.e.*, high-speed stirrers and mixers of various types, homogenizers, and colloid mills. The simpler emulsions will be satisfactory when agitated with conventional stirrers of various types. For these emulsions, it is merely necessary to mix the various ingredients together, and then give them a more or less prolonged or intermittent agitation with stirrers. For the more difficult types, treatment by homogenizers or colloid mills is required, to produce stable emulsions. It is impossible to fix a point where the efficiency of a homogenizer or colloid mill excells one over the other. In cases of emulsions, these machines are generally equally efficient. However, because of wear on valves and valve seats, homogenizers cannot be used for any dispersion containing abrasive materials and for such emulsions and dispersions, the colloid mill is indicated. In the formulae given at the end of this section, the type of apparatus, required to produce most satisfactory emulsions, will be pointed out.

Special Techniques

Stabilizing of emulsions and dispersions becomes more difficult as the specific gravity of the dispersed phase increases. To offset this difference in specific gravity between the internal and external phase, increasing the viscosity of the external phase is resorted to, generally. However, where fluidity is desired in the emulsion, other methods must be used. Where the emulsifying agent is to be highly diluted when the emulsion is used, as in beverage concentrates, the problem becomes still more complex. In such cases, these emulsions may be stabilized by increasing the specific gravity of the internal phase as near to that of water as possible. If the specific gravity of an oil can be increased to the same as that of water, each dispersed droplet will remain suspended in the water phase, *i.e.*, will neither sink nor rise. Thus, very little, if any, protective colloid will be required.

Generally, such increase in specific gravity is produced by the addition of compounds of very high specific gravity to the oils before emulsifying. Brominated olive and cotton seed oils, haloginated naphthalene, etc., are used for this purpose.

TRANSPARENT EMULSIONS

Frequently, it is desired to create emulsions of immiscible components which will be clear and transparent and show no milkiness or cloudiness. As the milky appearance of the conventional oil-in-water emulsion is caused by the difference in refractive index between the oil phase and the water phase, the answer to the problem is obvious. To make an emulsion clear and transparent, it is necessary only to adjust the continuous phase or dispersed phase or both in such a way that they have the same refractive index. This is usually accomplished by adding various materials such as sugar, salt, levulose, glucose, sodium silicate or other chemicals to the water phase. The adjustment of the phase is usually quite delicate and must be done carefully, using a refractometer for refractive index determinations.

GELS

Bentonite, Magnesium Hydroxide, Silica Gel, Aluminum Hydroxide

Because their character, on drying, closely resembles other ingredients used in these formulae, many of the gels, bentonites, etc., are frequently used for emulsions such as agricultural sprays, auto polishes, furniture and metal polishes. In a general way, the stabilizing effect of these materials depends, to a great extent, on the viscosity of the emulsion and is greatest when the emulsion consistency is from that of a heavy cream to a paste. One of the widest uses of clay and bentonites is in the manufacture of asphalt emulsions, and it is also extensively used in rubber, oil, polish, sulfur and many other emulsions, in proportions of ½ to 3%.

The recent developments in emulsions of lacquer and resins are commercially interesting because they offer both an improvement in product and a substantial saving in materials. As these are water phase emulsions, they may be diluted with water and the use of solvents is reduced to a minimum. In many places where these emulsions are now used, *e.g.,* in lacquers, varnishes, etc., they were unusable because of their great penetrating power. In coating paper, cover stock, textiles or leather, in many instances, varnishes or lacquers would strike through rendering the reverse side unsightly. An emulsion does not have this effect as the resin or lacquer particles are in the dispersed or internal phase surrounded by the water phase. When the emulsion is applied, the paper, leather or textile is first contacted by the water phase which wets the fibers less than would lacquer solvents. The lacquer or resin particles can no longer penetrate because of viscosity and remain, to a great extent, on the surface, penetrating only sufficiently to give adherence to the film.

DISPERSIONS

Dispersions of pigments, colors, clays, oxides, and metals are most readily and cheaply made in water. Many peptizers, dispersing and deflocculating agents are commercially available and produce great improvement in dispersions of pigments, clays, etc., in water. Among the more familiar materials used for this purpose are gum arabic, casein, tannic acid, tannates, quebracho, ammonia, soap, and sodium silicate. From 1 to 15% is used, based on the entire dispersion. When pigments, colors, etc., must be dispersed (ground) in oils, as in paint, the output is quite slow and great care must be used in the selection and compounding of these oil vehicles so as to obtain the greatest "wetting out" power without sacrificing film-forming characteristics of the oils or resins; therefore, where pigments are reduced to colloidal dimensions by dispersing in water, much time is saved. An interesting process for manufacturing paint, printing ink and other pigment dispersions, using water as the vehicle, is as follows:

The pigment is mechanically dispersed on a colloidal mill, high speed mixer or otherwise, using water containing from 2 to 10% soap as protective colloid. The oil or resin is similarly emulsified in water, using soap as the protective colloid. The two emulsions, being water-phase, can be mixed together in whatever proportion is required to bring the correct ratio of pigment to oil. After they are mixed, a small amount of acid is added. This breaks the emulsions and, in almost all cases, the oil and pigment go together, leaving the water clear and free. Most of the water can be poured off and any traces of water remaining, if objectionable, can be removed by heat, vacuum, or roll mill. The finest dispersions of the pigments most difficulty dispersible in oil can be attained rapidly by this process.

EMULSIFYING METHODS AND MATERIALS

In a recent bulletin, issued by the National Formulary Committee over 288 surface-active agents are listed. These constitute only the newer materials in this classification.

In outlining the various procedures for emulsion making, emulsifying agents will be suggested and the reader may experiment and substitute others of the same class, at his discretion. Where mechanical mixing machines are available, such as colloid mills, homogenizers, or high speed stirrers, the simplest method of preparing emulsions is by making up both water and oil phase, combining the two with superficial stirring, and running the mixture through the emulsifying apparatus.

Often good emulsions can be made by mixing, without the use of colloid mills or homogenizers, but most emulsions are improved by such mechanical aids. When they are not available, other methods of emulsifying can be resorted to. The simplest of these probably is the spontaneous method. A typical formula for such an emulsion is as follows:

Kerosene	89.0
Oleic Acid	8.0
Triethanolamine	3.2
Water	100.0

The oleic acid and kerosene are mixed together. The triethanolamine and water are also mixed together in another container. The oil mixtur is then poured into the water mixture and stirred rapidly. A milky-white emulsion results. In some cases, the emulsion is improved by reversing the operation and pouring the water mixture into the oil mixture, very slowly, and with constant stirring. Similar emulsions are made by using morpholine, soda ash, potassium carbonate, caustic soda, ammonia, etc., in place of the triethanolamine.

Cod liver oil, mineral oil and agar emulsions are often made by a slight variation of this technique; i.e., the gum content of the emulsion is added to the oil instead of to the water and thoroughly incorporated therein. The water is then added, very slowly, to the gum-oil mixture, with constant stirring. This produces, in many cases, a very stable, satisfactory emulsion. This technique is also used in making the thick, livery emulsions used in some textile and other printing processes. It is also used for making bakers' flavoring emulsions and salad dressings, using gum tragacanth, gum karaya, or starch. Cold cream, ointments, and many lotions and cosmetic emulsions are prepared by the method of adding the water-phase, containing the emulsifying agent, to the oil-phase containing the fatty acid. The use for which they are intended, of course, determines which phase is to be dispersed.

PHASE

Use of proportionately small amounts of water, excess oleic acid, small amounts of emulsifying agents and the addition of the water-phase to the oil-phase, when mixing, will usually result in the oil phase being continuous and the water phase being dispersed. The stability of these emulsions is a function of the protective colloid used, viscosity of emulsion, interface materials, surface tension depressants used, etc. In almost all cases, the phase can be reversed by increasing the proportion of water and protective colloid.

The "building up" method of making emulsions is used in many cases where difficulty is experienced with phase reversals.

Many times, an emulsion, mixed by the method previously outlined, will fail to become water-phase. To add additional water is undesirable and increasing the amount of emulsifying agent does not produce any improvement. If such an emulsion is made by any of the previous methods, using all of the water and emulsifying agent and adding only 50% of the oil or dispersed phase, after the emulsion has been made, more of the oil or dispersed phase can be added. This can be continued, adding the oil by easy stages, until all of it is dispersed. In many cases, stable emulsions having as high as 90% oil or dispersed phase, and only 10% water or continuous phase, can be made. Lacquer emulsions are an example of this and although they contain, as a general rule, 75% lacquer and only 25% water, they are still quite fluid. As a variant of this technique, oils, waxes, or resins are emulsified by using soap as the emulsifying agent. An anhydrous soap is dissolved in about $\frac{1}{3}$ of the oil and to this the same amount of water as the oil, which was used, is added with agitation. After a heavy creamy emulsion has been formed, the balance of the oil is added, slowly, with constant stirring. Finally, the balance of the water is added. Sometimes, when emulsions of this type are to be shipped, the balance of the water is not added until the emulsion is ready to be used.

An illustration of this type of emulsion is found in so-called soluble cutting oils. These are generally clear and transparent and contain the oil, soap, and a very small amount of water. When more water is added, the familiar milky or white emulsion results. This method offers, perhaps, the best way to make emulsions having very small particle sizes in the dispersed phase and, when proper care is used, oil and soap carefully combined, and the water gradually and slowly added, with constant stirring, very little improvement can be produced even by the finest mechanical mixing, colloid mills, or homogenizers. Another illustration of this type of emulsion is the "Dri-Brite" type of floor waxes.

OTHER EMULSIFIERS

As previously stated, the number of emulsifying and dispersing agents available is so great as to render it an impossible task to dwell on the properties and methods of use of all of these. With the data provided by the foregoing, any emulsion can be made and stabilized.

Of the hundreds of proprietary emulsifiers, dispersants, penetrants, etc., available, a few of the best known are selected as follows:

Aerosol
2-Amino-2-Ethyl-1, 3-Propane-
    diol
Ammonium Laurate
Ammonium Stearate
Aresklene
Darvan
Daxad
Deramin
Diglycol Laurate
Diglycol Oleate
Diglycol Stearate
Dreen
Dreft
Dupanol
Emulgor A
Emulsone A
Gardinol

Igepon
Intramine
Methyl Cellulose
Morpholine
Mulsor
Nekal
Nelgin
Nopco
Proflex
Rosoap
Santomerse
Sulphonated Castor Oil
Tergitol
Triethanolamine
Trigamine
Trihydroxyethylamine Stearate
Triton

No data is given on any of these materials here as such data, formulae, etc., are readily obtainable from the manufacturers of these products.

EMULSION FAILURES

Failure to produce satisfactory or stable emulsions can be attributed to one or more of the following causes:

1) Insufficient protective colloid
2) Unsuitable protective colloid
3) Too high a concentration of protective colloid (insufficient water)
4) Incorrect ratio between external and internal phase
5) Incorrect pH
6) Wrong method of mixing
7) Wrong temperatures

EMULSION FORMULAE

1. *Cod Liver Oil Emulsion*

Cod Liver Oil	50
Gum Arabic	3
Gum Tragacanth	¾
Irish Moss	1
Calcium Glycerophosphate	1
Glycerin	6
Water	38

Procedure:

Dissolve the gum arabic in 9 parts of water while heating to 145° F. When dissolved, cool to 90° F. Disperse tragacanth in 9 parts of water while heating to 180° F. When well dispersed, cool to below 90° F., add to arabic solution. Make up a 10% Irish moss solution, boil thoroughly, then pass through homogenizer, after straining, and cool. Take aliquot equivalent to above percentage and add to gum solution. With stirring add glycerin, then glycerophosphate and, finally, the oil in a small stream. Do not add oil so that "lakes" are formed on the surface; add just sufficient for the body of the mixture to take up.

When thoroughly mixed, homogenize at a total pressure of about 2500 lb, with the greater pressure (about 2000 lb) on the first valve.

After homogenization, let set for a few hours to effect readjustment, then stir slightly and bottle.

2. *Castor Oil Emulsion*

Sodium Hydroxide	9.8 g
Water	25.0 oz
Castor Oil	6 lb, 5 oz
Sodium Benzoate	100.5 g
Triethanolamine	288.0 min

Run through colloid mill after flavoring with lemon and vanilla and sweetening with saccharine to suit.

3. *Mayonnaise*

Formula a

Egg Yolks	10.0%	400.0 g
Salt	1.5%	60.0 g
Sugar	2.5%	100.0 g
Mustard (Dry)	.6%	24.9 g
Vinegar (5% Solution)	10.0%	400.0 cc
Water	3.4%	136.0 cc
Corn Oil	72.0%	2880.0 cc

Combine ingredients and run them through a colloid mill. This makes one gallon of dressing.

Formula b

Whole Egg	8.5%	340 g
Vinegar	8.0%	320 cc
Water	2.0%	80 cc
Salt	1.1%	44 g
Sugar	1.0%	40 g
Mustard	.4%	16 g
Corn Oil	79.0%	3160 cc
Makes		4000 cc

Output of 200 gallons per hour; excellent body.

Formula c

Corn Oil	71.0%	1420 cc
Egg Yolk	10.0%	200 g
Vinegar (6% Solution)	8.7%	174 cc
Mustard	1.0%	20 g

Salt .... .75% .... 15 g
Sugar .... 2.5% .... 50 g
Water .... 6.05% .... 121 cc

Makes ½ gallon.

4. Mayonnaise

		a	b	c
Corn Oil	% by vol.	65.5	67.0	69.0
Egg Yolk (Salt)	% by wt.	15.0	10.0	8.0
Vinegar (6% Solution)	% by vol.	8.7	8.7	1.0
Mustard	% by wt.	1.0	1.0	1.0
Salt	% by wt.	.25	.35	.45
Sugar	% by wt.	2.50	2.50	2.50
Water (Soft)	% by vol.	7.05	10.45	10.35

Procedure:
For continuous operation, the egg yolk, vinegar, sugar and spices are placed in a tank and thoroughly mixed. The oil is then added to the mix and agitated with a paddle or slow-speed mixer. No attempt is made to produce a fine mixture at this point. The water is now added and, after a slight stirring, the entire mix is run through a colloid mill at a gap setting of from .002 to .010. The mix is finished as it comes from the mill. If two tanks (and a two-way valve) are used, the second tank of material can be mixed while the first tank of mixture is running through the finishing mill; in this way, continuous production is procured.

5. Mineral Oil and Agar Emulsion

Mineral Oil .... 1200 cc
Glycerin .... 320 cc
Gum Arabic .... 800 g
Gum Tragacanth .... 20 g
Sodium Benzoate .... 3 g
Benzoic Acid .... 1 g
Phenol .... 20 g
Agar .... 800 g
Water .... 1196 cc

6. *Water Repellents*

Formula a

Paraffin Wax	1¼	lb
Glue	14	oz
Aluminum Acetate	5	qt
Water	2½	gal

Procedure:

Heat the wax to approximately 150° F, hydrolyze glue in part of the water, then add the balance of the water which has been heated to 150° F. The aluminum acetate is then added to the mix and the temperature brought to about 150° F. Now add the paraffin to this mix, with rapid stirring, and run entire mixture through either an homogenizer or colloid mill.

Formula b

(Five gallon batch)

Scale Wax	28%	5320 g
Chip Glue (100 Bloom)	8%	1520 g
Aluminum Acetate (32° Basic)	45%	8550 g
Water	19%	3610 g
		19000 g

Procedure:

Dissolve glue in water with aluminum acetate, while heating to 180° F., heat wax, and add at 200° F. Homogenize at 2500 lb per sq. in. the first time, and at 4000 lb per sq. in. the second time.

7. *Orange Syrup*

Mixture A

Orange Oil	8	oz
Gum Arabic	12	oz
Water, To Make	1	gal

Homogenize or mill on colloid mill to a particle size of $\frac{1}{10}$ micron.

Syrup:

Sugar	6	lb
Water	1	gal

Add Citric Acid .... 2 oz
and Mixture A .... 2 oz

This makes a stock concentrated solution; add 1½ oz to 6 oz then bottle and carbonate.

8. *Fruit Flavoring*

Orange, Lemon, Lime, etc. .... 16 oz
Gum Arabic .... 10 oz
Gum Tragacanth .... 3 oz
Water, To Make .... 1 gal

Soak gums until they are well hydrolyzed; then add oil. Homogenize or mill on colloid mill.

9. *Mineral Oil (Non-Fattening) Salad Dressing*

Water ⎰1800 cc for Starch⎱ .... 2880.0 cc
⎱1080 cc for Agar ⎰
Agar .... 48.5 g
Starch .... 142.5 g
Pepper .... .5 g
Saccharine (10% Solution) .... 7.2 cc
Mustard .... 28.5 g
Vinegar (5% Solution) .... 513.0 cc
  (300 cc of 10% Solution would serve)
Paprika .... 5.0 g
Gum Tragacanth .... 28.0 g
Mineral Oil (Viscosity 175–185) .... 1995.0 cc
Turmeric .... 2.0 g

Combine the ingredients in the order given and homogenize.

10. *Salad Dressings with Starch*

Formula a

Corn Starch	4.87%	90 g
Tapioca Flour	1.08%	20 g
Sugar	8.29%	152 g
Vinegar	8.29%	152 g
Salt	1.68%	31 g
Mustard	.67%	12.5 g
Pepper	.16%	3.0 g

Egg Yolk	5.42%	100.0 g
Water	24.64%	455.0 cc
Cottonseed Oil	44.90%	830.0 cc

Procedure:

Add cold water to starch, heat to 184° F., mix until it cools to 120° F.; add spices, vinegar and sugar; cool to 90°; then add egg. Pour oil in slowly and homogenize the mixture.

Formula b

Corn Starch	5.37%	110.0 g
Tapioca Flour	1.22%	25.0 g
Sugar	7.42%	152.0 g
Vinegar	7.42%	152.0 g
Salt	1.52%	31.0 g
Mustard	.61%	12.5 g
Pepper	.14%	3.0 g
Egg Yolk	6.10%	125.0 g
*Water	36.07%	540.0 cc
Cottonseed Oil	34.13%	700.0 cc

11. *Emulsion of Liquid Petrolatum with Agar*

Heavy Liquid Petrolatum	500.0 cc
Agar	5.5 g
Sugar	120.0 g
Acacia (Fine Powder)	30.0 g
Tragacanth (Fine Powder)	4.0 g
Tincture of Vanilla	8.0 cc
Tincture of Lemon	2.0 cc
Oil of Cassia	0.5 cc
Water To Make	1000.0 cc

Mix the agar and the sugar with 300 cc of boiling water and, when they are dissolved, strain the resulting solution and set it aside to cool. Triturate the powdered gums with the liquid petrolatum, then add the agar solution and whip the mixture w; an egg beater. Finally add the tinctures and the oil, and lastly, enough water to make 1000 cc.

---

* 200 more cc of water is added during homogenizing; aside from this, procedure is as above.

11. *Ozomulsion*

Cod Liver Oil	76.80
Cassia Oil	0.28
Benzaldehyde	0.28
Guaiacol	0.26
Gum Tragacanth	1.84
Gum Arabic	4.24
Sodium Benzoate	0.24
Sodium Hypophosphites	0.46
Calcium Hypophosphites	0.46
Saccharin	0.02
Saponin	0.24
Glycerin	10.24
Water	142.52

12. *Colloidal Carbon Black Paste*

Carbon Black	31
Water	59
Glycerin	5
Soda Ash	1
Quebracho	4

Mill on colloid mill; this formula makes a super-colloidal black paste.

13. *Mixes containing 10% Butterfat*

1. 19.5 lb 40.0% Cream   21.0 lb 40.0% Cream
    61.0 " 3.7% Milk   (or)
       (or)   47.3 " 3.7% Milk
    25.0 lb 40.0% Cream   25.0 lb 40.0% Cream
    55.5 " Skim Milk   43.3 " Skim Milk
2. 3.8 " Powdered Skim Milk   16.0 " Condensed Skim Milk
3. 15.0 " Sugar   15.0 " Sugar
4. .3 " Powdered Egg Yolk   .3 " Powdered Egg Yolk
5. .4 " Gelatin   .4 " Gelatin

14. *Mineral Oil Emulsion (Pharmaceutical)*

Formula a

Gelatin	6 or 8 g
Tartaric acid (Sufficient to yield pH 3.2)	
Syrup	100.00 cc

Vanillin	.04 g
Alcohol	60.00 cc
Water, To Make	500.00 cc
Heavy Mineral Oil (Medicinal)	500.00 cc
To Make	1000.00 cc

The gelatin and tartaric acid are added to about 340 cc of cold water, allowed to stand several minutes, then heated until dissolved. The temperature is then raised to 95–98° C. and maintained for 15 minutes. The solution is next cooled to about 60° C., the syrup added, followed by the vanillin dissolved in the alcohol. Water is added to make 500 cc. The mineral oil is finally poured into the aqueous mixture and the whole vigorously mixed either by shaking or in an appropriate mechanical mixer. This is followed by homogenization, the emulsion being homogenized at 3,000–3,500 lb pressure and recirculated, twice, to insure uniform and fine dispersion. The resultant product is remarkably palatable, possessing none of the gummy thick taste so evident in similar emulsions made with other stabilizers.

Formula b

I. Gelatin (0.6 Porkskin, 250 Bloom)	6.000	g
*.Tartaric Acid	0.450	g
(or) Hydrochloric Acid (To Give a pH of 3.2)		
Syrup	100.0	cc
Water, To Make	440.0	cc
II. Vanillin	0.035	g
Alcohol	60.0	cc
III. Heavy Mineral Oil (Medicinal)	500.0	cc
To Make	1000.0	cc

Add the gelatin and tartaric acid to about 300 cc of cold water, allow to stand a few minutes, then heat until dissolved. Add the syrup and finally enough water to make 440 cc (I); while still quite warm add II, then III, and mix well avoiding the inclusion of air. Finally homogenize and bottle. Homogenization should be repeated, if necessary, until all the oil is completely dispersed.

Such an emulsion conforms to the USP XI monograph for Emulsion of Liquid Petrolatum.

15. Furniture Polish

I. Gelatin (0.5% Porkskin, 250 Bloom) .... 5.0 g
* Tartaric Açid .... .375 g
   (or) Hydrochloric Acid
Moldex .... 2.0 g
Water, Quantity Sufficient to Make .... 500.0 cc
II. "Lemon Oil" (Mineral) .... 250.0 cc
Light Mineral Oil .... 250.0 cc

To Make .... 1000.0 cc

Directions are similar to those for formula above. Methyl para-hydroxy-benzoate replaces the alcohol as a preservative. Such a formula provides an excellent furniture polish emulsion.

---

* The amount of tartaric acid may vary slightly, depending upon the gelatin used. If hydrochloric acid is used, the amount necessary to give a pH of 3 must be determined by experiment. If a thinner emulsion is desired, 5 g of gelatin may be used instead of 6 g.

SECTION 6

THE DESIGN OF EMULSIFYING MACHINES

By ROBERT IAN JOHNSON, B.Sc., A.I.C.

(Research Chemist, Messrs. Crosse & Blackwell Ltd.)

INTRODUCTION

ALTHOUGH emulsions are of such industrial importance, and academic interest, we are still far from a complete understanding of the hydrodynamics of emulsification, as the mechanical forces brought into play during the passage of an emulsion through a modern emulsifying machine are of an extremely complex nature. The development of emulsifying machines has, therefore, depended on qualitative rather than quantitative data, the many widely varying designs being the result of practical experience rather than of calculation. Of recent years, however, efforts have been made to base design on all the known principles involved and this is meeting with marked success as shown by the production of more uniform emulsions with reduced power consumption.

Stamm and Kraemer[1] have pointed out that the degree of dispersion finally obtained in an emulsifying machine is the result of two opposing tendencies. Firstly, the disruption of the globules due to impact disintegration and shearing forces, set up by liquid flow, tending to draw the globules into unstable laminæ or cylinders (which break up when the length exceeds three times the diameter); secondly, the tendency for the globules to coalesce on contact. Both these tendencies are influenced, though

88

to a markedly different extent depending on the circumstances, by the interfacial tension, volume ratio, viscosity, and density of the phases. Interfacial tension will, for example, only play a major part in the disintegration of globules when the mechanical stresses are low, as in a whisk, but when stresses are high, as in a high-pressure homogenising valve, it will have only slight influence on disintegration. In both cases it will have considerable influence on the subsequent coalesence of globules, especially if the volume of the disperse phase is high.

The coalesence of globules will take place both during and immediately after disintegration, so that the effect of the disintegrating forces alone is never observed unless the coalescing tendency is very small.

THE DEVELOPMENT OF EMULSIFYING MACHINES

The earliest type of emulsifying machine was probably the pestle and mortar used by the pharmacist who carried out the emulsification of oils in water by two methods. In the "American" method the oil was added to the gum solution, and in the "Continental" method the water was added to a mixture of gum and oil, both these processes being carried out with brisk agitation.

Emulsification by shaking the phases together in a closed container such as a bottle has long been practised and has been the subject of much close study from a theoretical point of view as, under standard conditions of shaking, this method gave results which were more reproducible than those obtained by other methods and has yielded much valuable data regarding the making and breaking of emulsions.[2]

The forerunners of modern emulsifying machines, excluding the agitators, were those designed by Marix [3] towards the end of the last century in which emulsification was effected by forcing the system either through a small orifice or between two moving surfaces. Later, Gaulin [4] proposed to disperse oils by forcing the coarse emulsion through capillaries at a pressure of 250 atmospheres.

The next type of machine designed by Gaulin [5] consisted of a conical valve held in its seating by a heavy spring, the emulsion being forced through this valve by a three-throw pump delivering the emulsion to the valve in a continuous flow. This type of machine was used from 1905 onwards, for the dispersion of added fat in milk and the "cream" formed could not be separated centrifugally, nor could it be whipped.

Gaulin's machine was the forerunner of the modern homogeniser, the term being derived from the apparently homogeneous nature of the product obtained.

The Plauson [6] emulsifying machine effected emulsification in a very different manner and, in its early days, received wide publicity, the fineness of the dispersions obtained earning for it the name "colloid mill" in America, a term which has been carried through to the modern machines containing a high speed rotor and a stator, although dispersions of colloidal magnitude are not, of course, obtained.

The Plauson mill consisted essentially of toothed wheels running on an axis placed eccentrically in a cylinder chamber, the teeth of the wheel passing between "resisting surfaces" in the form of adjustable toothed plates, but the mill is now seldom seen as the power consumption was high and it was not continuous in action.

TYPES OF EMULSIFYING MACHINES

Emulsifying machines fall into three main groups:

(1) Agitators, which include whisks and churns.

(2) Colloid Mills, which consist of a high speed rotor and a stator, emulsification being effected between the opposing faces.

(3) Homogenisers, consisting of an homogenising valve which is fed by emulsion at high pressure from a pump.

The term "homogeniser" is now being frequently applied to machines in both groups (2) and (3), but for the purposes of the descriptions which follow, the terminology given above will be adopted as it obviates ambiguity.

The colloid mills are being rapidly extended to deal with emulsions which were formerly only treated in homogenisers and the final products are frequently indistinguishable, both in appearance and degree of dispersion, while colloid mills offer added advantages in that they are suitable for the dispersion of both liquid/liquid and solid/liquid systems and can effect dispersions in system of very high viscosity.

WHISKS

The whisk is the modern development of the most simple means of effecting emulsification, namely, agitation, and although this method may, in certain cases, have its objections on account of aeration and denaturation of protein stabilising agents at the large air/liquid or vapour/liquid interface set up, yet it offers the advantage of rendering possible the addition of the phase to be dispersed to the whole of the continuous phase. Whisking, resulting in the formation of a comparatively coarse emulsion, is usually a necessary preliminary to treatment of an emulsion in a colloid mill or homogeniser, although, in a few cases, the phases can be fed into these simultaneously at controlled rates.

There are two main types of whisk, the former, which finds extensive use in the mayonnaise and salad cream industry, being in the form of the frustrum of a cone with a hemispherical base, the agitator spindle entering horizontally at a point slightly above the union of the base and body of the whisk, and rotating at a speed of 150–500 r.p.m., depending on the viscosity of the emulsion, some whisks being provided with a two-speed drive.

A Pfaudler whisk of this type, rated at 50 gallons, has a working capacity of 35 gallons, and employs a two-speed 5 h.p. electric motor gear driven to the agitator spindle which has a speed of 180 or 245 r.p.m.

It has to be remembered that whisking is not simply a question of mixing, as if the maximum possible degree of dispersion is to be obtained the shearing forces set up in the liquid by the agitator are of necessity much greater than those required in a simple mixer.

Whisks may also be fitted with special lids to permit the mixing to be carried out under vacuum, which considerably reduces aeration.

The beaters or agitators employed vary very considerably in form, two common designs being the multipronged blade and the basket type, but here again, the design will depend on the viscosity and nature of the emulsion and is arrived at quite empirically.

There is a wide field for research into the best form for the beaters and the optimum beater speed; the introduction of suitably placed baffle plates in the whisk may be expected not only to increase the rate of emulsification, but to decrease aeration.

The second type of whisk usually takes the form of a cylindrical tank with, in many cases, provision for heating or cooling by means of a jacket or internal coils. The agitator shaft, which is vertical in this type of machine, may enter either through the top or base of the tank and rotational speeds of 200 r.p.m. to over 3,000 r.p.m. are employed, depending on the design of the agitator.

The most simple agitator has a two or three blade propeller or, preferably, two propellers, the lower one giving an up-thrust and the other a down-thrust to the liquid.

Grashof [7] uses a stream-lined propeller rotating in a horizontal plane at the bottom of the tank; this propeller consists of a long horizontal blade which is fitted, along its length, with a series of short blades set at 45° to the radius of the circle described by the rotating propeller and vertical to it, these having the effect of throwing the liquid violently against the whisk wall, where it must pass upwards.

Another type of whisk has a high speed propeller or centrifugal pump working in a separate section at the bottom of the tank. A typical example of this machine is that designed by Garthe [8] in which the propeller draws the liquid from the body of the tank into the top of a small chamber and forces it out at the side through a series of small perforations back into the tank, a rapid circulation being thus obtained. In a somewhat similar machine, the propeller shaft enters the chamber through a gland in the base and provision is made for the introduction of the phase to be dispersed directly into the propeller chamber.

There are several modifications of this principle [9] and a further development is the portable emulsifying unit which can be lowered into any tank containing the system to be emulsified. The unit consists of a high-speed propeller, usually directly motor-driven, which is surrounded by a hood containing a series of orifices, the emulsion being forced out through these, after being drawn in from below. This method gives good emulsions if the viscosity is low.

CHURNS

The churns used in the manufacture of margarine emulsions form a very important class of agitation emulsifiers, two types being recognised, the batch churn and the continuous churn, both of which are jacketed to allow efficient heating or cooling.

The batch churn, which still competes with the continuous type, has a capacity of 250 to 500 gallons and is provided with agitators carried on two vertical shafts revolving in opposite directions. The "ripened" milk, with or without added water, is run into the churn and the melted mixture of fats run in with constant agitation, the margarine being rapidly cooled to 25–35°C., when emulsification is complete.

The continuous churn has been the subject of many patents,[10] but that patented by Silkeborg Maskinfabrik Zeuthen and Larsen [11] is a typical example and has been extensively used in margarine manufacture. The machine consists of a horizontal cylindrical chamber through which runs a shaft carrying a series of perforated discs, which alternate with baffle plates fixed to the chamber wall. The shaft is driven at 1,500 r.p.m. directly from an electric motor, a machine giving an out-turn of up to 3 tons per hour requiring a 16 h.p. motor.

The two phases are fed into the machine separately by two pumps which, being coupled together, give a constant volume ratio.

After churning, the margarine may be further treated in a colloid mill or homogeniser to improve the texture, and patents have been granted to Baumgartner [12] who effects simultaneous pasteurisation and improved dispersion, the necessary heat being generated in the mass by friction.

COLLOID MILLS

Colloid mills form a very sharply defined class of emulsifying machines and they are finding an ever increasing range of usefulness in industrial emulsification, owing to their simplicity, ease of cleaning and maintenance, high capacity per unit of power consumption, and, coupled with this, their high efficiency for the preparation of very fine dispersions of solids or liquids in liquid systems.

Many of these mills were designed primarily for the preparation of special types of emulsions, such as the tar and bitumen emulsions used in road work, but they have, frequently without alteration, been used for the treatment of many other systems.

Before giving details of some typical individual machines, it is desirable to give a brief general description of the form of these mills, as they possess certain similarities.

The two essential sections are a rotor, the speed of which may vary from 1,000 to 20,000 revolutions per minute, and a stator, the emulsion passing between the opposing faces of these two. The clearance between the rotor and stator may be constant over the faces or may vary in a variety of ways, but means are generally provided for the adjustment of the clearance to any desired value, which can be checked with feeler gauges at certain points and may be as low as 0.001 inch.

There are two types of mills, the first in which the milling surfaces are machined smooth, and the second type in which these surfaces are rough, due to a series of concentric or radial corrugations.

The emulsion may flow through the mill by centrifugal force or the surfaces between which emulsification takes place may be so designed that there is no force tending to make the material leave the surfaces by its own inertia and there may even be a force tending to hold it back. In these two latter cases the time of treatment of the emulsion, between the emulsifying surfaces, depends only on the rate of feed.

Two forms of feed are available; the two phases of the emulsion may be fed into the machine simultaneously, or a coarse emulsion, such as that prepared in a whisk, may be treated to give a finer dispersion. The former method, though giving a good emulsion in one stage is, unless special precautions are taken, occasionally open to objection where there is some uncertainty as to the type of emulsion which will be produced; special means will be required for feeding the phases at a fixed ratio, especially if there is a considerable difference in viscosity.

It may be noted here that when small quantities of material are treated in colloid mills, especially where no elaborate feed and delivery systems are available, aeration is usually pronounced and colloid mills are occasionally condemned on account of aeration during small scale tests, whereas under works conditions such difficulties are not usually encountered.

The form of power drive employed will depend on the speed

of the machine, but for rotor speeds up to 12,000 r.p.m., a belt drive from a motor running at 3,000 r.p.m. is very reliable if a jointless belt, such as a rubber impregnated canvas or the multiple "Texrope," is used. An alternative to this system is the worm gear drive running in an oil bath, or, for slower speeds, the mill may be direct coupled to the motor.

Mills are further provided with jackets for water cooling, or steam heating as the circumstances require.

It is not possible to give a complete account of the purposes for which colloid mills can be used, as new uses are continually being found. They are capable of dealing with almost any system and with materials of viscosities varying from that of milk to that of a very thick paste; Travis [13] gives an account of a wide range of uses found for colloid mills in America.

The following descriptions give a brief account of the main features of the colloid mills in use in England and each mill may be considered as representative of its type.

THE PREMIER MILL

This mill, Fig. 1, is one of the most simple of the colloid mills, the parallel faces of the rotor and stator being in the form of the frustrum of a cone with an apex angle of 90°, the side length (over which emulsification takes place) being ¾" in the case of the 5" mill.

The clearance between the rotor and stator, which can be checked at three points round the circumference, is varied by turning a micrometer ring which has the effect of advancing or withdrawing the rotor with respect to the stator.

The stator forms part of the front cover of the mill and can readily be removed for cleaning purposes. The emulsion is fed into the machine through an inlet in the cover at a point opposite the axis of the rotor and the emulsion, after passing between the emulsifying faces, collects in an annular space behind the rotor from which it is drawn off.

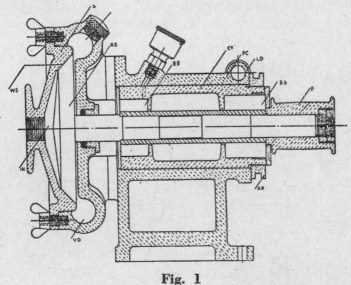

Fig. 1

THE PREMIER HIGH SPEED COLLOID MILL

The following table gives an indication of the sizes, speeds and power consumption of the standard Premier colloid mills.

TABLE 1.

Rotor Diameter	Normal Running Speed	Usual method of Drive	Usual Motor supplied	Approximate hourly output
3½ in.	15,000 r.p.m.	Flat Belt	2 H.P. at 3000 r.p.m.	15/20 gal.
5 in.	9,000 r.p.m.	Flat Belt	3 H.P. at 3000 r.p.m.	40/60 gal.
10 in.	4,500 r.p.m.	Texrope	10/15 H.P. at 1500 r.p.m.	350/450 gal.
15 in.	3,000 r.p.m.	Texrope or Direct-Coupled to Motor	25/30 H.P. at 1500 r.p.m. or 25/30 H.P. at 3000 r.p.m.	1200/1500 gal.

A modification of the Premier Mill has now been developed, the rotor and stator being corrugated as shown in Fig. 2, with the result that a combination of impact and shearing disintegration is obtained, and the time of treatment of material in the mill is increased.

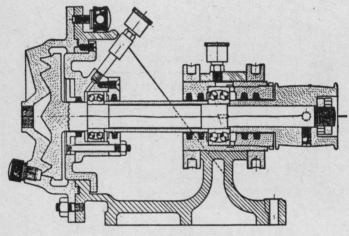

Fig. 2

THE CORRUGATED PREMIER HIGH SPEED MILL.

This mill has been designed to reduce the possibility of aeration to a minimum and the material passes through the machine in an unbroken film, being delivered, if necessary, at a definite hydrostatic pressure. The milling surfaces take the form of a series of concentric inclined planes, the angle these planes make with the rotor axis decreasing with the distance from the axis; since the rotor and stator are identical in shape when the clearance is zero, at the normal range of working clearances, *i.e.*, 0.001-inch to 0.025-inch, the clearance decreases on passing out radially from the rotor axis. The clearance is checked at a point near the periphery of the rotor where it is a minimum. The angles of the planes are so designed that when the clearance is 0.006-inch at the periphery, the volume of a body of material passing out radially would tend not to change.

THE PREMIER PASTE MILL

The Premier Paste Mill, Fig. 3, should be mentioned here as it is a direct development of the colloid mill, being designed to effect dispersions in very viscous systems.

The mill axis is vertical and directly motor driven, the material being fed in through a wide hopper from above; for very thick pastes, a force-feed hopper can be fitted.

A jacket surrounds the stator to permit heating or cooling water to be circulated and the emulsifying faces of the rotor and stator are longer than those of the colloid mill.

The following table gives details of the standard Paste Mills.

TABLE 2

Rotor Diameter	Normal Running Speed	Usual method of Drive	Usual Motor supplied (Horse Power)	Approximate hourly output
2½ in.	3,000 r.p.m.	Direct	½	40/60 lb.
5 in.	3,000 r.p.m.	Direct or Belt	6	4/6 cwt.
10 in.	3,000 r.p.m.	Direct or Belt	15/20	12/20 cwt.

THE HURRELL MILL

There are two types of Hurrell Mill, the standard model, Fig. 4, and the more recent "C" type. The former will be described first.

The short cylindrical body, jacketed for steam heating or water cooling, has a smooth, slightly tapered inner surface which forms the stator. The heavy circular end plates, which are bolted on to the body, carry glands through which the rotor shaft passes. Two circular discs, fixed together with a small clearance between them, form the rotor which thus resembles a hollow pulley, the periphery of which has a slight taper to correspond with the taper of the stator. Lateral movement of the rotor within the stator will, therefore, result in variations of the clearance between them and

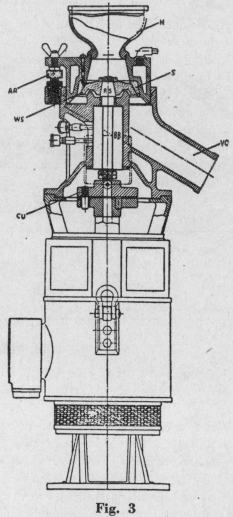

Fig. 3

THE PREMIER PASTE MILL

this movement is controlled by a handwheel, through a micrometer screw to a sleeve on one of the bearings, each half turn of the handwheel altering the clearance by 0.001-inch.

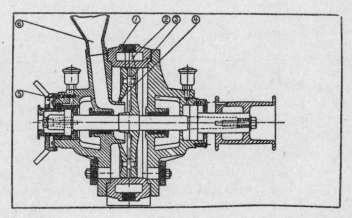

Fig. 4

THE HURRELL "HOMOGENISER"

(1) Tapered Cylindrical Body; (2) Heating or Cooling Jacket; (3 and 4) Discs Forming Rotor; (5) Clearance Adjustment; (6) Feed Funnel.

The emulsion is fed in between the discs forming the rotor and flows out between the periphery of each disc and the stator. Since the emulsifying space is practically parallel to the axis of the rotor, there is no centrifugal force tending to make the emulsion leave the emulsifying surfaces and, consequently, the time, during which emulsification is effected, depends only on the rate of feed; the No. 1 machine will give a wide range of intensity of treatment, varying from 10 to 1,000 gallons per hour.

There are four sizes, including the laboratory Model L mill, details of these being given in Table 3.

The "C" type mill is very suitable for the preparation of small amounts of pharmaceutical emulsions, and care has been taken to minimise aeration. The rotor runs within a special stator ring

TABLE 3

Type	Approximate Output Gallons per hour	Rotor Speed r.p.m.	Horse Power Consumed
Model L	20	10,000	2
00	80	5,500	6
0	400	3,500	15
No. 1	1,000	3,000	30

which gives a clearance of 0.01-inch, but other rings, giving clearances of 0.005 and 0.020-inch respectively, may be substituted. The emulsion flows up each side of the rotor, which is provided with holes to equalise the hydrostatic pressure on each side, and passes between the periphery of the rotor and the stator to a series of holes in the stator ring, through which it flows into an annular space from which it is delivered at a fairly high pressure.

There are two sizes of the "C" type machine, the following table (4) giving details of output and power consumption.

TABLE 4

Type	Approximate Output Gallons per hour	Rotor Speed r.p.m.	Horse Power Consumed
C. 4	10–20	8,000–10,000	2–3
C. 6	40–80	4,500– 6,000	5–10

THE HATT-DUSSEK "HOMOGENISER"

This machine, Fig. 5, is termed an homogeniser by the makers, but for reasons already given it will be described under the heading of Colloid Mills.

The Hatt-Dussek machine represents a distinct type of smooth-surface colloid mill, owing to the fact that the surfaces of the rotor and stator, instead of being parallel, are parabolic in section and make such an angle with one another that the cross sectional

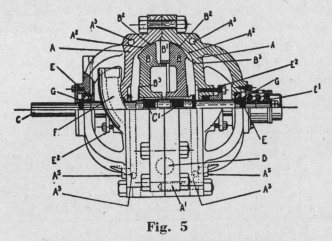

Fig. 5

THE HATT-DUSSEK "HOMOGENISER"

(B) Rotors; (B1) Annular clearance for collection of
emulsion; (B2) Emulsifying faces; (B3) Vanes on rotor;
(A3) Heating or cooling conduits; (F) Inlet; (D) Outlet.

area of a stream of liquid, passing out radially, would remain
constant.

The inner surface of the body of the machine, which is made
in two halves, forms two stators and two solid rotors, which are
screwed and keyed to a common shaft and face in opposite direction, run in conjunction with the stator faces. Variations in clearance, which can only be made when the machine is partially dis-
mantled, are effected by removing the keys between the rotors
and the shaft and turning the rotors through an angle of 90°
or a multiple thereof.

The emulsion is fed into both sides of the machine and, after
passing over-vanes on the rotor faces, which effect a preliminary
mix, it is forced centrifugally between the emulsifying faces to
be collected in an annular space between the two rotors, from
which it passes to the outlet.

A further feature of this machine is the low horse-power required for the high output, this being attained by reducing, as far as possible, the resistance offered to the emulsion on its passage through the machine.

The following table gives the essential details of the Hatt-Dussek homogeniser.

TABLE 5

Size	Output in Galls. per Hour Up to:	Rotor Speed r.p.m.	Horse Power Consumed	Horse Power of Motor
1	5,000	1,300–2,000	5–7	10–12
2	1,500	2,000–3,000	1–1½	2–2½
3	500	3,000–4,000	¼–½	½–1

ROUGH SURFACE COLLOID MILLS

Further mention must be made of the rough-surface colloid mills, of which the new type of Premier Mill, already described, is an example.

The Charlotte Mill, an American machine, is an example of a mill having radial corrugations. The emulsion is fed into the mill by gravity, emulsification being effected between a rotor and a stator which is in the form of a slightly tapered cylinder. Since the emulsion is fed in at the end of greater diameter, the centrifugal force tends to hold the material back, with a result that the time of treatment of the emulsion between the faces depends only on the rate of feed.

There are radial grooves on the rotor and stator, and the eddy currents, set up in these grooves, give rise to an intense beating and chopping action, the resulting emulsification, therefore, being brought about by a combination of hydraulic shearing and impact disintegration.

The stator has provision for water cooling, as these mills have a marked tendency to heat up on continuous running.

The Kek grinding mill may also be regarded as a rough-surface mill, using either the pin discs or the emulsifying discs. In the former case two circular plates are used, one above the other, these being fitted with concentric circles of short thick pins, the pins of each plate overlapping in such a manner that material, passing out radially, strikes the pins in both plates. The top plate is fixed to form the stator, while the bottom plate rotates at 5,000–7,000 r.p.m., the emulsion being fed in through a hopper in the centre of the top plate and collecting at the circumference.

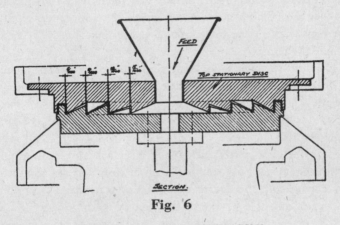

Fig. 6

THE KEK MILL EMULSIFYING DISCS

The emulsifying discs, Fig. 6, convert the mill into a far more efficient emulsifying machine than when pin discs are used. The emulsion passes out radially through gradually decreasing clearances of 0.015, 0.010, 0.005 and 0.005 inch respectively between steps in the plates.

EMULSIFYING BOWLS

Reference must be made to the emulsifying bowls, although they now find very little application. The coarse emulsion is fed into the centre of a very rapidly revolving bowl, dispersion being effected as the material is thrown out centrifugally through a small clearance between the lip of the bowl and its cover.

HOMOGENISERS

Although the term "homogenisation" is applied broadly to imply a decrease of globule size in an emulsion by any mechanical method, the machines described under this heading will include only those in which dispersion is effected by forcing the emulsion through a small orifice under high pressure. As in the case of colloid mills, a preliminary statement regarding the general design of homogenisers will suffice since, with few exceptions, the major difference, between the various machines, lies in the design of the orifice.

The original conception of increasing the dispersion of globules in an emulsion by forcing it through a small orifice, leading to the use of a valve held to its seating by a heavy spring as a means of producing the orifice, is the basis of the present design of homogenisers.

Since the first successful homogeniser was built by Gaulin, improvement has only resulted from a close study of the factors influencing both the degree of dispersion and the uniformity of dispersion and it is to the application of a knowledge of these factors, especially in the latter case, to the present types of homogeniser, that research is being directed.

The homogenising valve, which will be dealt with in greater detail later, is usually fed with the pre-formed emulsion at a uniform, high pressure, this uniformity being attained by the use of a three throw pump system, the three pistons of the pump working from a common crankshaft into three cylinders bored in one block. Each cylinder is fitted with an inlet and outlet valve, the lift of these being controlled by a light spring. Each piston, therefore, draws the emulsion into the cylinder through the inlet valve, from a duct which is kept filled by a hopper or supply tank, and on the return stroke, the inlet-valve closes and the emulsion is forced under high pressure through the outlet valve into a duct through which it passes to the homogenising valve. The three cylinders maintain an almost constant pressure in this duct and the emulsion flows through the homogenising valve at a uniform rate under a pressure which is governed by the valve loading.

The pressure of the emulsion delivered to the homogenising valve is not always absolutely constant and the uniformity of the dispersion obtained will depend on the rate at which the valve responds to slight pressure fluctuations; that is, the inertia of the valve, and its loading should be as low as possible.

It is now common practice to mount the driving motor for the homogeniser on the same base and to employ some form of reduction gear in the drive to the crankshaft. Care has to be taken to avoid the transmission of motor or gear vibrations to the valve, as this may constitute a further cause of non-uniformity in the emulsion produced.

There is a tendency at present to favour a fairly high rate of compression in the cylinder as conducive to a "breakdown of the molecular aggregation of the phases," but, unless a corresponding increase is made in the size of the inlet valves, limitations are set with regard to the viscosity of the emulsion that can be treated. When the piston is receding rapidly in the cylinder on the intake stroke, a viscous emulsion will not be drawn into the cylinder sufficiently rapidly through a small inlet valve to prevent the formation of a vacuum pocket, and when this occurs, not only will the capacity of the machine be reduced, but excessive fluctuations will take place in the pressure of the emulsion fed to the homogenising valve.

Colloid mills possess the advantage of being able to effect the dispersion of very viscous systems and it seems probable that homogenisers could only be rendered suitable for treatment of more viscous systems by increasing the size of the inlet valves and providing for their mechanical operation. A pressure feed and modifications in homogenising valve design would probably also be required.

A further difficulty, to be guarded against in homogenisers, is the accumulation of air in pockets, as, unless adequate means are provided for venting this air, usually by means of suitably cut channels, its presence may cause not only a decrease in output, but also undesirable pressure fluctuations.

PRESSURE MEASUREMENT

The working pressure of homogenisers usually lies between 1,000 and 5,000 pounds per square inch, variations in the pressure on the homogenising valve being obtained by altering the compression of an elastic spring, tube, or bar, the former being the more usual method.

A gauge, giving pressure readings up to 7,000 or 10,000 pounds per square inch, is usually employed, being so fitted as to be in direct communication with the pressure duct leading to the homogenising valve. A needle valve is usually interposed between the gauge and the pressure channel, thus rendering possible the removal of the gauge for any reason while the machine is running. The use of this valve to damp violent pressure fluctuations and thus prevent damage to the gauge is occasionally recommended, but since such fluctuations would indicate that the machine was not working correctly, due possibly to an inlet or outlet valve of one of the cylinders failing to close, such a practice would seem to be undesirable. Were pressure fluctuations such that the gauge was likely to be damaged, a uniform emulsion could hardly be expected.

It will be realised, therefore, that the gauge not only gives the homogenising pressure but also indicates any machine defects.

In conjunction with, but preferably not in place of, the gauge, the power consumption of the machine can be taken as a measure of the homogenising pressure. A measurement of the current, taken by an electric motor driving the machine, gives an accurate indication of the power consumption and the accompanying graphs, Figs. 7 and 8, give results of tests carried out on two homogenisers, a 200 gallons per hour Viscoliser and a 44 gallons per hour De Laval, under works conditions. The pressure is

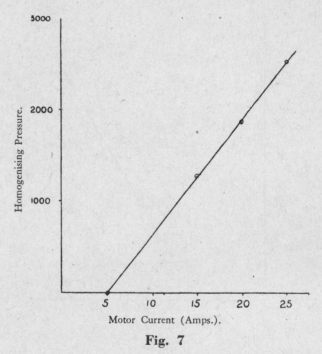

Fig. 7

found to be directly proportional to the current taken by the motor over the normal range of working pressures.

TWO STAGE HOMOGENISATION

It is found that when milk, for example, is homogenised, although the fat globules are more finely dispersed, there is a clustering of globules which gives rise to accelerated creaming and an abnormally high viscosity. A second stage of homogenisation, at lower pressure, has been found to break down these clusters.

Most standard homogenisers are provided with a single homogenising valve, but frequently provision is made for the addition of a second valve, which is a replica of the first, to follow imme-

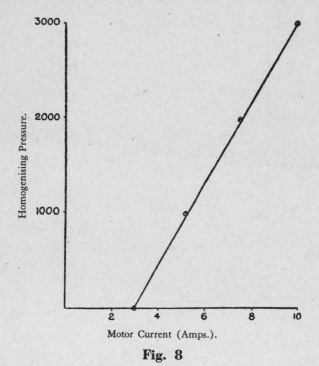

Fig. 8

diately after it. A separate gauge is provided for the second homogenising valve, a pressure of 5,000 pounds per square inch, at the first stage, being followed by about 1,000 pounds per square inch, at the second stage.

An alternative to the two-stage system is the Duo-Visco Valve, in which the homogenising valve is surrounded by a stationary grooved ring (the "breaker ring"), which serves to break down

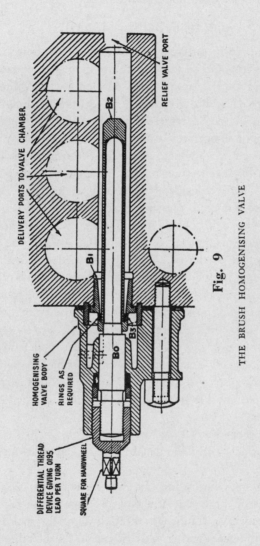

Fig. 9

THE BRUSH HOMOGENISING VALVE

the globule clusters leaving the valve, thus giving in one stage the effect of two-stage homogenisation.

HOMOGENISING MACHINES

There are many different makes of homogenisers now available and, as it would be very difficult to give an adequate description of them all, descriptions will only be given to illustrate the foregoing remarks and give a general idea of the design of these machines with special reference to the homogenising valve.

The Brush homogeniser is noteworthy on account of its special homogenising valve which, depending on the elasticity of a metal tube for its pressure loading, forms a system of very low inertia and tends considerably to reduce the time lag of the valve in responding to pressure fluctuations.

The valve, Fig. 9, consists of a tube B2 of special metal, carrying an homogenising face and a ring B3, at each side of which homogenisation is effected. The tube is fitted over a spindle B0, which extends its whole length and which is capable of lateral adjustment by means of a handwheel working through a differential thread; as the spindle is screwed into the chamber, pressure is increased. A further feature of the machine is a system of air-venting throughout the cylinder block which renders an accumulation of air at any point practically impossible.

The importance of keeping down gear vibrations is recognised, and in those machines employing a direct motor drive, belt transmission is used.

Brush homogenisers vary in capacity from 25 to 1,000 gallons per hour, which forms the usual range of capacities for this type of machine.

The drawings illustrating the Weir homogeniser, Fig. 10, give a good idea of the layout of a typical direct driven machine, the motor driving the crankshaft through a totally enclosed reduction gear; the gears and crankshaft run in an oilbath.

The Weir homogeniser has been specially designed to meet

the demands of the Food Industry, the absence of any piston packing in the three-cylinder pump system being noteworthy; provision is made for the return of any leakage past the pistons to the suction line. The cylinder block is constructed to simplify the examination and cleaning of the valves.

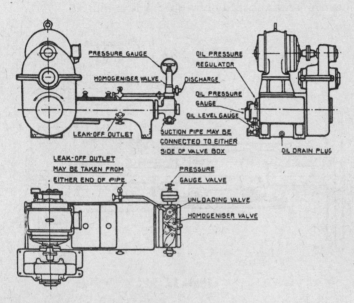

ARRANGEMENT OF THREE-THROW HOMOGENISER PUMP MOTOR DRIVEN THROUGH DOUBLE REDUCTION GEARS.

Discharge pressure up to 3,000 lb./□"

Fig. 10

LAYOUT OF THE WEIR HOMOGENISER

The single stage homogenising valve, Fig. 11, is of the conventional spring loaded type and this can be replaced by a two stage valve system unit which comprises two valves, with separate loading adjustment, set at right angles and working in series. An "unloading valve," which, when open, returns the product from the machine to the supply tank, is used to relieve the pressure when the machine is started up and is turned off when working speed has been reached.

In the Rannie homogeniser, the homogenising valve and gauge are built in one unit and the loading pressure on the valve is maintained by the elasticity of a special steel rod.

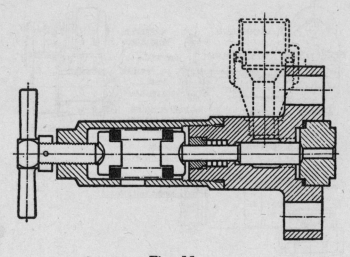

Fig. 11

THE WEIR HOMOGENISING VALVE

The Viscoliser, an American machine, is designed on very robust lines for heavy duty, the inlet and outlet valves of the three cylinders being comparatively large, thus rendering possible the effective treatment of very coarse or viscous systems. The Viscoliser homogenising valve is designed with an automatic pressure regulator, which will lift at certain pressures to permit any abnormal obstruction to pass. This machine is found to give very uniform results when fitted with the Duo-Visco valve.

The pressure gauge is set in a special head which is also fitted with pressure damping and air release valves.

A feature of the De Laval homogeniser is the special homogenising valve, Fig. 12, which consists of a series of smoothly ground metal surfaces; the whole valve system can be slowly rotated with respect to the seating by a chain drive from the crankshaft, pressure being maintained by a short but heavy spring which is controlled by a handwheel. The rotating valve minimises the possibility of any obstruction preventing the valve closing.

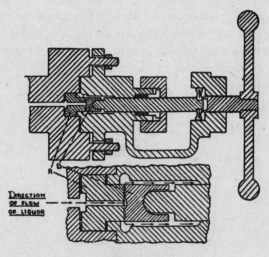

DIRECTION
OF FLOW
OF LIQUOR

Fig. 12

SECTION THROUGH DE LAVAL HOMOGENISING
VALVE & CONTROL GEAR

A very smooth control of pressure is obtained, but a safety device, which consists of a thin metal disc which bursts when the pressure becomes excessive, eliminates the possibility of the machine overloading.

The Impulsor homogeniser, Fig. 13, differs considerably from its contemporaries in several important respects, the chief of these being the use of a single-cylinder pump system and provision for feeding the two phases of the emulsion into the machine separately.

Two inlet ports are provided, one for each of the phases, and the flow through these inlets is controlled by two cocks, material from these passing through a single non-return valve to the cylinder. A piston, making 275 strokes per minute, works in the cylinder through a gland, but since the diameter of the piston is less than that of the cylinder, it has the appearance of a piston rod, with the piston removed, and the whole of the cylinder is not, therefore, cleared at one stroke. The actual volume of emulsion, forced out of the cylinder during the delivery stroke, is 1/9-th of the total volume present in the case of the 100 gallons per hour machine, and 1/7-th in the case of the 10 to 15 gallons per hour model.

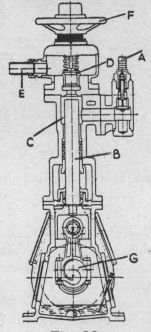

Fig. 13

THE IMPULSOR HOMOGENISER

It is apparent that the emulsion is subjected, on an average, to seven or nine cycles of compression from the time it is drawn into the cylinder to the time it is forced out through the homogenising valve, and this effects efficient mixing prior to homogenisation.

A spring-loaded homogenising valve is provided at the head of the cylinder, pressure-control being obtained through a large handwheel, working through a finely threaded screw.

It is noteworthy that the miniature laboratory machine gives emulsions which are comparable with those obtained on larger works machines.

HAND MACHINES

In concluding the discussion of homogenisers, a short statement must be made regarding the hand operated emulsifying machines which are now sold for the home manufacture of cream from milk and unsalted butter. These little machines are very useful for the small scale preparation of emulsions in the laboratory, and investigation has shown [14] that some of these machines give emulsions which are comparable with those prepared in works-scale plant.

The emulsion is usually pumped through a small fixed orifice and the mechanical advantage of the pump handle is so high as to give, in some cases, pressures up to 1,000 pounds per square inch for 25 pounds on the handle.

Finally, appreciation is expressed of the assistance afforded by the manufacturers of the machines described, both as regards willingness to supply drawings and information, and to arrange tests. It is felt that impartial acknowledgment can best be given by the compilation of the list of names of the various machines, together with the makers, which follows. Best thanks are due also to Dr. W. Clayton for his valuable help and advice during the preparation and completion of this paper.

EMULSIFYING MACHINES AND THEIR MANUFACTURERS

Brush Homogeniser	The Brush Electrical Engineering Co., Ltd.
Charlotte Mill	Chemicolloid Laboratories, Inc., New York.
De Laval Homogeniser ..	Alfa Laval Co., Ltd.,
Emulsifying Bowl	Alfa Laval Co., Ltd.,
Hatt-Dussek Homogeniser	Dussek Bitumen and Taroleum, Ltd.
Hurrell Colloid Mills	G. C. Hurrell & Co., Ltd.,
Impulsor Homogeniser ..	The Improved Emulsification Process Co., Ltd.,
Kek Mill	The Buffoline Noiseless Gear Co.,
Pfaudler Whisks	Enamelled Metal Products Corp. (1933), Ltd.,
Premier Colloid Mills	Premier Colloid Mills, Ltd.,
Rannie Homogeniser	Hiron & Rempler,
Viscoliser	Union Steam Pump Co., U.S.A.
Weir Homogeniser	G. & J. Weir, Ltd.

REFERENCES

1. Stamm and Kraemer, *J. Phys. Chem.* **30**, 996 (1930).
2. Clayton, *"The Theory of Emulsions and Their Technical Treatment"* (1928).
3. Marix, French Patents 218,946 and 218,947 (1892).
4. Gaulin, French Patent 295,597 (1899).
5. Gaulin, British Patent 22,875 (1904).
6. Plauson, British Patent 176,002 (1920); 185,878 (1922).
7. Grashof, British Patent 405,002 (1933).
8. Garthe, British Patent 405,503 (1933).
9. e.g. Hawes, British Patent 360,171 (1931); Ellinghouse, British Patent 321,130 (1929).
10. Clayton, *"Margarine"* (1920).
11. British Patent 4657 (1914).
12. Baumgartner, British Patents 378,374–5–6 (1931).
13. Travis, *"Mechanochemistry and the Colloid Mill"* (1928).
14. Johnson & Morse, *"Food,"* **3**, 173 (1934).

SECTION 7

EFFECT OF THE MODE OF PREPARATION ON THE DISPERSION OF SOAP-STABILISED EMULSIONS

By R. DOREY, B.Sc.

(Research Department, Improved Emulsification Process Co., Ltd.)

IT is well known that there is a best way of preparing an emulsion and that each type of emulsion must be treated as an individual problem. A method, which works well in one case, will not necessarily apply in another. In other words, the manufacture of emulsified products, on a large scale, nearly always involves a considerable amount of rule-of-thumb procedure before the most efficient and economical process is found. This state of affairs is, no doubt, partly due to the shortage of fundamental knowledge regarding the mechanism of emulsification and the absence of quantitative data on the relation between the way an emulsion is made and its degree of dispersion.

There is much information in the literature on methods of emulsification both mechanical and chemical, but it is of such a nature that it affords very little assistance to the manufacturer who has to formulate a new emulsion or improve an old product. So far as the writer is aware, no definite quantitative observations have been published which show the kind of dispersion that can be expected from certain methods of emulsification commonly employed in technical practice. Below are recorded some advance

119

results dealing with emulsions stabilised by simple soaps. The popularity of this type of emulsions for technical products and their comparative simplicity mark them out for primary attention. It is hoped that further results will be published later, when more complex emulsions will be given attention.

EXPERIMENTAL PROCEDURE

The first emulsions to be studied, the dispersions of which are tabulated below, had the simple formula:—oil 10 per cent, soap 0.5 per cent, water 89.5 per cent. This type of emulsion is not an easy one to make stable. It very quickly reveals poor quality by creaming owing to its low viscosity, and in badly emulsified samples, oil rapidly separates on the surface. Such obvious signs of instability and poor emulsification cannot easily be described with precision, and it is only by making a size-frequency analysis of the dispersion that an accurate picture of an emulsion can be obtained. The physical behaviour of an emulsion, on standing, can be closely predicted if the size distribution of the globules be known and the quality of an emulsion may be very precisely described by this means.

A size-frequency analysis was, therefore, made on each of the emulsions studied. The method consisted in preparing a slide of the emulsion diluted with an approximately equal proportion of strong gelatin solution. In this way, the globules were fixed and Brownian motion stopped. The slide was examined directly through a microscope, under a magnification of about 1,100 diameters. A squared eyepiece, calibrated with a stage micrometer, was used to estimate the approximate size of the globules. The large particles could be measured accurately, but this was not possible with the very small globules. It was, however, easy enough to determine whether a globule came within or outside certain size-limits, and the globules were, therefore, arranged into groups, 0-1μ, 1-2μ, 2-3μ, etc. As the analyses of the different emulsions were to be compared relatively, there was no need for an absolute determination of the size of each globule.

After a little practice, it is possible to make a comprehensive analysis of an emulsion quite quickly by this method, although, of course, it entails measuring and tabulating at least 1,000 globules. In these experiments, this number or more was selected from at least two slides and several fields taken quite at random on each slide. The focus was also varied so that the depth of the film was fully explored.

As regards mechanical apparatus to be used in this investigation, the choice, though at first somewhat bewildering, resolved itself, after consideration into the selection of two representative types of machine. There are a great variety of methods employed to-day for the mechanical preparation of emulsions, but the general principles of emulsification processes remain the same whatever the particular type of apparatus. The two phases have to be brought into intimate contact, in the presence of an emulsifying agent, and this is generally accomplished by some form of stirring gear. Nowadays, this process is rarely considered sufficient, and the emulsion so prepared is passed through an homogenising machine, which reduces the globules to a more uniformly small size, thereby increasing the stability.

As this paper is directed primarily to the technical reader and manufacturer, methods of emulsification which are not found in common factory usage have not been investigated. It was decided that the following methods should be studied: (a) simple stirring or agitation, (b) agitation followed by homogenisation; and the apparatus used for the experiments consisted of a small Beach high-speed mixer, which provided the agitation, and a small model of the Impulsor Emulsifier for homogenisation. The Impulsor is a machine of the high-pressure pump type wherein the material is ejected through a small orifice against a valve pressure of 3,000 lbs/in^2, thus giving very fine subdivision of particles. Perhaps the most attractive feature of this machine is its capacity for producing an homogenised emulsion, directly from the two separate phases, without the intervention of a pre-mixing process. This method of preparing an emulsion was compared in the present investigation with the more familiar processes mentioned above and, as the results indicate, such an emulsion was superior in quality though made in a single operation. The fact that this can be accomplished on a works-scale machine entitles it to be included in this study.

Having described the mechanical apparatus used, attention must be turned to the formula of the emulsion itself. It is more or less common knowledge that the manner in which the ingredients, and especially the emulsifying agent, are mixed, has an influence upon the quality of an emulsion. For emulsions of oil-in-water, it is generally accepted that the stabiliser goes into the water phase. There are exceptions, of course, but for the particular emulsions under consideration failure results if the soap is put into the oil. But it is still possible to add the soap in two different ways (a) by dissolving the soap as such in the water to make a soap solution of the required concentration, and (b) by adding the alkali to the water and fatty acid to the oil phases respectively, and allowing the soap to form during the emulsifying process.

The results tabulated below show the dispersions obtained with:—

(1) Olive oil and sodium oleate solution.

(2) Arachis oil and potassium oleate solution.

The following experiments were made with each pair of constituents:—

(I) The requisite amount of soap was dissolved in water to form 900 grams of solution. 100 grams of oil was then added slowly while the mixture was stirred with the Beach mixer. The oil was all added in one minute and the emulsion was stirred for another five minutes. Half this emulsion was then put through the homogeniser at 3,000 lbs/in² pressure, while the remainder was stirred for a further five minutes. In this way, two samples were obtained, representing typical factory conditions of preparation: (*a*) an emulsion by simple stirring, (*b*) an emulsion first pre-mixed and then homogenised.

(II) The mechanical procedure was the same as in (I), resulting in emulsions: (*a*) by stirring, (*b*) by stirring and homogenisation; but the soap was allowed to form during the emulsification process, by having the alkali present in the water and oleic acid in the oil, in correct proportions.

(III) With the soap again as in (I), that is in the water, the two phases were fed separately into the Impulsor Emulsifier. A portion of this emulsion was passed a second time through the Impulsor in order to see what improvement was made.

(IV) The treatment was exactly as in (III), but again the soap constituents were added separately with the oil/water phases.

The same batch of each oil and fresh soap solution was used for all the experiments so that variations in acidity of the oil and staleness of the soap were eliminated. Temperature and other working conditions were maintained constant during the preparation of all emulsions.

RESULTS

The following tables set out the size-frequency distribution of the oil globules in the various emulsions, shown as a percentage lying between size limits of 1μ.

It is obvious from a glance at these tables that there is a considerable difference in the degree of dispersion obtained by these different methods of emulsification. Both tables resemble one another as would be expected from the similarity of the materials. On the whole there is a better degree of emulsification in the case of arachis oil and potassium oleate. As far as the present study is concerned, this is by the way, and the improvement in dispersion can be attributed to the better emulsifying capacity of the potassium compound.

OLIVE OIL WITH SODIUM OLEATE EMULSION

Size of Globules	Experiment I % Globules		Experiment II % Globules		Experiment III % Globules		Experiment IV % Globules	
	(a)	(b)	(a)	(b)	(1)	(2)	(1)	(2)
0– 1µ	47.5	71.8	68.5	80.7	80.8	87.7	88.6	97.3
1– 2µ	41.1	26.4	28.4	17.1	18.1	11.6	10.7	2.5
2– 3µ	7.4	1.4	2.0	2.0	0.8	0.7	0.5	0.2
3– 4µ	2.1	0.3	0.5	0.2	0.2	..	0.1	..
4– 5µ	0.1	..	0.1	..	0.1	..	..	..
5– 6µ	0.7	0.1	0.3	..	..	..	..	..
6– 7µ	0.1	..	..	..	..	..	..	..
7– 8µ	0.6	..	0.1	..	..	..	..	..
8– 9µ	0.1	..	..	..	..	..	..	..
9–10µ	0.2	..	..	..	..	..	..	..
10–11µ	..	..	..	..	..	..	..	..
11–12µ	0.1	..	..	..	..	..	..	..

ARACHIS OIL WITH POTASSIUM OLEATE EMULSION

Size of Globules	Experiment I % Globules		Experiment II % Globules		Experiment III % Globules		Experiment IV % Globules	
	(a)	(b)	(a)	(b)	(1)	(2)	(1)	(2)
0–1µ	75.1	88.1	90.3	92.0	89.4	90.4	94.7	98.3
1–2µ	19.3	10.4	7.8	6.9	9.7	8.7	5.0	1.6
2–3µ	3.4	1.5	1.4	0.8	0.7	0.8	0.2	0.1
3–4µ	0.9	..	0.3	..	0.1	0.1	0.1	..
4–5µ	0.5	..	..	..	0.1	..	..	..
5–6µ	0.5	..	0.1	..	..	..	..	..
6–7µ	0.1	..	0.1	..	..	..	..	..
7–8µ	0.1	..	..	..	..	..	..	..
8–9µ	0.1	..	..	..	..	..	..	..

One of the main points, which these results illustrate, is the improvement obtained when the soap is allowed to form during the emulsifying process. This is shown clearly by comparing Expt. I(a) with II(a) and to a lesser degree in Expt. III(1) and IV(1). When the soap is employed in this manner, the emulsion tends to form spontaneously, immediately, when the two phases are brought together. Far less work has to be done in the initial stages of agitation and the energy expended is profitably employed in the formation of small globules. This improvement extends even to the homogenised emulsions (b), although as one would expect, the difference is not so marked.

It is interesting to note here a paper by A. Rayner,[1] in which experiments have shown that when soap is allowed to form in situ, in laundering operations, very much more effective detergent properties are the result. Rayner applies the term "nascent" to the soap formed under these conditions.

Turning to the emulsions prepared by the special Impulsor method, III and IV, we find a considerable improvement in dispersion over and above that effected by using "nascent" soap. This points to a more efficient emulsification process than the familiar agitation-homogenisation method. The reason would appear to lie in the fact that comparatively small portions of oil and water phase are treated by the machine at each stroke and thus, the full effect of the enormous amount of energy developed is expended in emulsifying this small quantity of mixture, giving a uniformly dispersed product. The whole of the emulsion is made in this way and consequently, the dispersion is very uniform throughout the bulk.

A further treatment through the Impulsor has the effect of breaking down the larger particles and still further homogenising the emulsion.

The advantages of a process such as this, on a works-scale, are obvious, as while the cost of production is low, owing to the elimination of the pre-mixing process, the emulsion is at the same time made in the most efficient manner.

SUMMARY

Two sets of experiments, on emulsions of vegetable oils in simple soap solutions, show that apart from mechanical homogenisation, the dispersion is improved by:—

(1) Allowing the soap to form during the emulsification process. This is accomplished by adding the alkali to the water and the fatty acid to the oil phase.

(2) Effecting the emulsification in such a manner that energy is expended on successive small portions of the materials rather than upon a large bulk. A machine is described which enables this to be done easily and effectively.

Size frequency analyses of emulsion dispersions provide quantitative evidence in support of the above conclusions.

The writer wishes to thank Messrs. Improved Emulsification Process Co. Ltd., for placing facilities at his disposal for carrying out the experimental work and also Dr. E. Lester Smith of the Glaxo Research Laboratory for his helpful interest.

REFERENCE

1. Rayner, *J.S.C.I.*, 1934, 53, 589.

SECTION 8

PROBLEMS CONNECTED WITH THE PREPARA-
TION AND APPLICATION OF EMULSIONS USED
IN AGRICULTURAL SPRAYING

By R. M. Woodman, M.Sc., Ph.D., F.I.C., A.Inst.P.

(Cambridge University Horticultural Research Station)

INTRODUCTION

THE word "spraying" conjures up in the layman's mind visions of the application of a fluid as a jet or droplets, and, though the student of modern spraying might insist on a much broader interpretation, emulsions are usually applied in this manner.

The chief use of spray emulsions is to kill insects and insect eggs on plants and animals. Emulsions, used in the extermination of insects, are said to be insecticidal; those used to kill insect eggs are ovicidal.

Insects may be divided into two broad classes: *sucking* insects which, when attacking plants, pierce the epidermis of the leaf by a proboscis and suck the sap, examples of this class being capsid bugs, aphides, psylla, *etc.*; and *biting* insects, which actually bite and eat the plant tissues, examples being caterpillars, beetles, and certain weevils.

To kill biting insects, it is necessary to cover the plant surfaces with a thin, even layer of toxic, but non-phytocidal chemical, such as lead arsenate, so that the insect's first bite represents a

127

poisonous dose. This would be a futile procedure with sucking insects, however, as those do not eat the plant tissues; here the spray must make actual contact with the insect by a direct hit, wet and spread over the insect surface, and then kill by inducing paralysis, by suffocation, by caustic or corrosive action, etc.

It is thus evident that there are two general types of insecticides: *stomach poisons* or *internal poison insecticides* for biting insects, usually insoluble substances such as lead arsenate; and *contact poisons* for sucking insects, usually soluble substances such as nicotine and nicotine sulphate, or emulsifiable ones such as mineral oils. Insecticidal emulsions are thus contact poisons; ovicidal emulsions are also contact poisons, the ovicide acting by direct contact with the egg.

HISTORICAL

Oils used in spraying include the so-called mineral and coal-tar oils, sometimes the fixed or true oils, and, occasionally, essential oils and other organic liquids.

These oils were originally used in the "free" or "naked" state. Thus plant-lice were destroyed by "petroleum, turpentine and other oils . . . but care must be taken in their use, since they also act upon the plant, making them sick or even killing them." [1]

The first definite recommendation for the application of kerosene or paraffin oil to plants seems to have been made in 1865, the object being the destruction of scale insects on orange and other trees; [2] the paraffin was poured into a saucer and applied by a feather. In 1866, paraffin was recommended for destroying all insect life, [3] but this recommendation was very soon modified because of injury to the foilage caused by the naked oil, and vegetable oils were advocated as being safer. [3]

Paraffin oil was next applied as a mixture with water, 1 part of oil to 25 parts of water, a fairly uniform mixture being obtained by violent syringeing by a hand syringe, the price of a good mixture obviously being rapid work. [4] Sometimes the mixture was actually made on the tree, the oil and water being sprayed simultaneously at the tree, through separate jets.[5]

Most plants, however, are easily injured by paraffin oil, and these mixtures with water are too evanescent to be safe; the use of naked oils was, moreover, too wasteful and dear. Hence, the problem of the application of oils to plants became the problem of diluting them by a commonly-occurring, inexpensive, and non-phytocidal medium such as water.[6] Such dilution by water is possible only if the oil is emulsified in an aqueous medium containing an emulsifying agent. The emulsion must necessarily be of the oil-in-water (OW) type; otherwise the objects of making the emulsion (to dilute the oil by water to a system which can be still further diluted by water in the field, and to provide a non-phytocidal external phase) are defeated at the outset.[6]

Soap was invariably the emulsifier in these first emulsions. "T.A." used soapy water and cresylic acid, mixed thoroughly; [7] Cruickshank of Whitinsville, Mass., successfully controlled currant worm in 1870 by "using kerosene with whale-oil soap, increasing the kerosene until it would kill the worm and not injure the foliage . . . 5 pounds of whale-oil soap, and 1 wine quart of kerosene to 25 galls. of soft water to mix." [8]

Undoubtedly the above mixtures were emulsions, but Cook [9] was the first to recommend definitely, in 1887 and 1888, kerosene-soap emulsions, as kerosene "would mix permanently with soap solution . . . and kill haustellate (sucking) insects like bugs and lice . . . one-fifteenth of the liquid applied would be kerosene." He gave instructions for preparation, with the quanitities of ingredients necessary, and recommended soft (K) and hard (Na) soaps, and "Cook's Soft Soap Emulsion" and "Cook's Hard Soap Emulsion" are still sometimes referred to by name. Later, kerosene-condensed milk emulsion and kerosene-sour milk emulsion were introduced for districts where the natural water supply was hard.[10]

The introduction of coal-tar oils ("tar distillate" group of spraying oils) followed a somewhat similar course. Tar oils were early known as wood preservatives, but tar was not employed as an ovicide until Robbes [11] in 1889 used it against moth eggs. Then Sajó in 1890 found anthracene oil to be an efficient ovicide for mussel scale eggs; [11] the oil was painted on the trunk when the tree was "dormant," as later applications caused injury. In 1892, heavy tar oils were emulsified and used as dormant sprays against Woolly Aphis by Del Guercio. [12]

Combinations of coal-tar fractions and emulsifying agents were first marketed as "water-soluble" carbolineums. By "carbolineum" was understood at that time a wood preservative consisting of a heavy coal-tar oil such as filtered anthracene oil plus other preservative substances; the description "water-soluble" implied that the product "mixed" with water to give an emulsion (not a solution), the essential differences between emulsions and solutions not being then recognised. The products are now called "tar distillate washes," and are extensively used as ovicides in the winter spraying of dormant trees; they really belong, for the most part, to the class of compounds termed "miscible oils," products which will be discussed later.

MINERAL OIL EMULSIONS

Possibly, because of the wide differences in the chemical and physico-chemical properties of the kerosenes used, early results with kerosene dormant emulsions were apt to be variable. Recognition of this possible explanation of the varying results obtained led to investigations into the insecticidal and ovicidal values of the heavier and more viscous fractions ranging from heavy kerosenes to oils of the lubricating type. A fillip to these investigations was given by the discovery that for some years past unsatisfactory results had been obtained in fumigating with hydrogen cyanide gas against Chrysomphalus aurantii, Mask. (citrus red scale) in Corona, California, and Orange County; [18] the unsatisfactory results were attributed to the acquirement of resistance to fumigation at the customary toxic concentration of gas used, and, as greater concentrations would have injured 'the trees, recourse was had to the alternative method of using oil emulsions.

Mineral oils, for use in spray emulsions, should be very insecticidal or ovicidal at concentrations safe for plants, should be abundant and cheap enough for the purpose intended, and should be relatively stable chemically and capable of being produced to a standard specification.

The method of refining the crude oil as pumped from the earth is by fractional distillation, gases and light benzines passing over first, these being succeeded by heavier benzines, then by light kerosenes, then by light lubricating oils, and finally by oils of greater viscosities, vaseline, etc., being left as a residue. By heating, filtering, and specially treating the various distillates, oils of differing physico-chemical properties can be produced.

Oils of widely-varying physico-chemical properties are, at present, used in insecticidal and ovicidal emulsions. Thus, viscosity may range from 335 seconds Saybolt for crude winter emulsions to 100 seconds Saybolt for a high grade, non-soap, white, winter paste emulsion.[14] For summer or foliage emulsions, the viscosity of the oils contained in certain samples analysed ranged from 39 to 105 seconds Saybolt, a narrower range.

The viscosity and rate of evaporation of the oil in the emulsion are considered very important, as they give some notion of how long the oil will remain on the plant surfaces. Oils which remain longest on the tree (or insect, or insect egg) are thought to possess the greatest toxicity; and, as lighter oils replace heavier ones, so the toxic dose is found to increase.[14]

The Toxicity of Mineral Oils to the Insect

Shafer[15] was of the opinion that the volatile oils were more insecticidal, the vapour being effective by preventing, in some manner, oxygen absorption by the tissues, and Moore[16] found that volatility and toxicity, towards the common house fly, were correlated, the more volatile oils being most toxic. Later Moore and Graham,[17] however, showed the heavier fractions to be the more toxic when the oils were emulsified.

Bedford and Pickering [18] demonstrated that, to be effective against mussel scale eggs, at least 40 per cent of a paraffin oil should boil above 250°, English lighting (paraffin) oils thus being useless as ovicides; [19] they therefore recommended "Solar Distillate," a paraffin oil distilling at 240°–350°. Lubricating oils are now widely used with great success.

Moore and Graham,[20] and de Ong, Knight and Chamberlain [21] have shown that oil may penetrate the tracheæ via the spiracles either as emulsion or as free oil obtained by the cracking of emulsion, the rate of penetration thus depending on the viscosity of the spray emulsion or free oil. The insect possesses the power of expelling the lighter fractions from the tracheæ,[21] but heavier oils are retained and possibly cause death from suffocation by deprivation of oxygen. Death by deprivation of oxygen is, in general, a lengthy process, and hence, the advantage of having heavy fractions which will leave non-volatile films of oil over the insect when the emulsion cracks. Thus the spray emulsion and/or free oil obtained by cracking should not be too viscous to prevent ready penetration into the tracheæ, but the free oil should be sufficiently non-volatile to cause a persistent film on the insect.

Bedford and Pickering have attempted to find some explanation of the ovicidal action of oil emulsions.[22]

The Action of Mineral Oil Emulsions on Plants

The former paraffin and kerosene emulsions were so dangerous to foliage and fruit that their use was limited to winter, when they were applied to kill insects and their eggs and to cleanse the trees. Even then these dormant sprays were apt to be dangerous to the trees, especially in cold weather.

Bedford and Pickering,[23] and Gray and de Ong,[24] have

described the injury to foliage resulting from the application of different fractions of petroleum, and Volck [25] and Burroughs [26] have discussed the retardation of leaf growth and the premature dropping of leaves and fruit following spraying by emulsions of mineral oil fractions. In 1916, Gray (cf. ref. 14) stated that if lubricating oils were treated with sulphuric acid, the resultant clear material was markedly insecticidal but less harmful to foliage than the original lubricating oil; Gray and de Ong showed that the constituents of lubricating oils, most destructive to foliage, were the unsaturated compounds which could be removed by refining with sulphuric acid, and highly refined lubricating oils are now found to be safe to foliage when emulsified and applied as spring or summer sprays.

The usually-accepted index of safety for the oil in the emulsion is afforded by the sulphonation test. The unsulphonatable residue, present in the oil of a dormant emulsion, may be as low as 30–70 per cent; but a purer (more refined) oil is necessary in a summer or foliage emulsion with an unsulphonatable residue of 85 per cent or above if "scorch" of the foliage is to be avoided. [14]

The Sale of Mineral Oil Emulsions

Emulsions may be put up for sale as "soapy" ("boiled," or "soap-oil") emulsions, with about 80 per cent of oil emulsified by soap, or as "cold-mix" ("non-soapy," "mayonnaise," or "paste") emulsions with non-soap emulsifiers. The cold-mix emulsions include most of the modern foliage and dormant emulsions; they are not so troublesome to make as the boiled soap ones, and they have the added advantage that the emulsifier may be quite compatible with hard waters.

A third common method of sale is as "miscible oils" containing 85–90 per cent of oil (see later), these being very effective for the control of hiding insects in winter.

Browne [14] gives interesting photomicrographs of typical emulsions from these three sources.

Emulsifiers Used in Preparing Mineral Oil Emulsions

Widespread knowledge of emulsions, if it exists, is of very recent growth. Less than ten years ago, the present author was urged by certain people, to seek the universal spray emulsifier for all spraying oils! It was of no use to point out that every emulsion system presented a different problem. From a review of the literature, one man only appears to have approached this universal emulsifier,[27] and his emulsifying medium is a mixture of calcium caseinate, dextrin, bentonite, lignin liquor, and maize oil soap in water; he has evidently proceeded on the assumption, by no means uncommon in spraying practice with some growers and biologists, that a variety of "spreaders" or emulsifiers must ensure final success.

Soaps and resinates are common emulsifiers, hard whale oil soap being used in America and soft here; herring oil and other fish oil soft soaps, sodium and potassium oleates, castor oil soaps, sulphonated soaps, and mixtures of phenols and soaps, known as "cresoaps" or "cresol-soaps," are also in general use.

Soaps, however, are "incompatible"[28] with the salts causing hardness of natural waters, being decomposed to give curdy calcium and magnesium soaps which are useless as (OW) emulsifiers, or for causing the emulsion to wet, and spread over plant, insect, and insect egg surfaces; the formation of these insoluble soaps may also lead to the liberation of masses of free oil which would be phytocidal. The serious nature of this incompatibility will be evident when it is stated that certain natural waters in the Wisbech fruit area require as much as 20 lbs. of commercial fish oil soft soap per 100 galls. (*i.e.,* 2 per cent soap present), before the waters are softened.[29] On diluting an emulsion concentrate in the field with these waters, therefore, the weight of soap finally used would have to be 2½-3 per cent of the diluted spray, the wasted soap being 2 per cent, leaving ½-1 per cent as the actual emulsifier. Taking soap at 3d. per lb., and assuming that 100 galls. of diluted emulsion will spray 30 trees, the waste in soap is $(3 \times 20)/30 = 2d.$ per tree every time a soap emulsion is applied.

In addition, the water-insoluble soaps formed are oil-soluble, and, therefore, tend to form the undesirable water-in-oil (WO) type of emulsion.[80] This tendency is often seen when diluting concentrated emulsions and miscible oils with natural waters in practice, free oil being liberated and some WO emulsion being produced as a "sticky mess."

Besides the type of incompatibility mentioned above, sprayers have often to contend with pseudo-hardness due to brackish or briny natural waters, especially in the Wisbech area, soaps in general tending to be insoluble in these.[80]

It is impracticable and much too costly to soften water in the field in the immense quantities needed for spraying; and, because of this, and also because the sprayer objects when making home-made emulsions (a rare occurrence with English growers) to the trouble of boiling to dissolve soap, cold-mix emulsions with emulsifiers uninfluenced by hard waters are used. Such emulsifiers are also used in various modern, proprietary, concentrated emulsions, and field trials or laboratory tests have been made with the following: the so-called "colloidal" clays (kaolin, bentonite, etc.);[81] lignin pitch or sulphite lye;[82] the lipin from *Hevea* latex;[83] the caseinates (ammonium, sodium, potassium, calcium, barium);[84] gelatin (or glue or glue size),[85] the inclusion of which does not, contrary to what might be expected, clog the stomata or interfere with cuticular water losses;[86] basic precipitates, etc.;[87] saponin;[88] blood albumin;[89] flour; starch; dextrins; gums; casein; dried milk; bile salts; peptones; proteins; diatomaceous earth; sulphonated products; molasses; *etc.*

With gelatin, glue, the proteins, *etc.,* the increase of viscosity conferred on the spray emulsion should lead to less dripping from the tree surfaces and hence to a greater retention of emulsion and, therefore, of dispersed oil.[40]

Compatibility of Mineral Oil Emulsions with Other Spray Substances

For purposes of economy in labour and time, and sometimes because of the simultaneous presence on the plant of a fungus and/or a biting insect with the sucking insect killed by the oil emulsion, it may be advisable to mix a fungicide or a stomach poison with the emulsion and to apply as a mixed spray.

The emulsion and the other spray must be compatible; that is, the components of one should not interact with those of the other in such a way as to unsettle the physico-chemical properties of either spray, or to form phytocidal substances.

It is usual to draw up compatibility charts showing which combinations can be recommended and which are dangerous or uncertain because of some reaction.[41]

Examples of mixtures, investigated from this standpoint, are Bordeaux-oil (or cresylic acid-oil) emulsion as a fungicide-contact insecticide;[42] free nicotine (or cresylic acid) -oil emulsion for destroying the over-wintering eggs of the European red mite and of apple aphides at the delayed dormant period of the apple tree;[43] nicotine sulphate-lubricating oil emulsion for codling-moth control;[44] lead arsenate suspension-oil emulsion for spraying during the early stages of infestation by the European maize borer;[45] lead arsenate suspension-lubricating oil emulsion for codling-moth control;[44] and polysulphide-light petroleum lubricating oil emulsion as a combined fungicide insecticide.[46] Robinson[47] has shown that the use of alkaline caseinates as emulsifiers, in preparing oil emulsions, leads to the production of a dangerous amount of soluble arsenic when such emulsions are combined with lead arsenate; similar reactions take place when alkaline caseinates are used as protective colloids for lead arsenate suspensions.[48]

Use of Mineral Oil Emulsions as Dormant Sprays

Mineral oil emulsions have been used in winter as dormant washes as follows: Pennsylvania crude oil with cresol-soap as emulsifier against the Fruit Tree Leafroller; [49] crude oil emulsion with the addition of solignum (sodium resinate being the emulsifier) for the control of the Mango Hopper; [50] dormant and delayed dormant miscible oil sprays against the Grape Mealybug; [51] lubricating oil emulsions and miscible oils as dormant and delayed dormant washes against San José Scale (*Aspidiotus perniciosus*, Comst.); [52] for controlling Cherry Case-bearer,[53] aphides and associated insects,[54] Obscure Scale (*Chrysomphalus obscurus,* Comst.) on the Pecan,[55] and pear blister mite; [56] and also for spraying empty glasshouses before planting to free them from red spider.[57]

Use of Mineral Oil Emulsions as Summer or Foliage Sprays

Oil emulsions have been used on foliage as follows: against red spider of carnations, cucumbers, and tomatoes; [58] against coconut whitefly,[59] and sucking insects such as tobacco capsid [60] and woolly aphis; [61] against citrus scales [62] and citrus red spider,[63] box leaf miner,[64] and cabbage moth; [65] as ovicidal washes for leaves; [66] and for locust extermination when sodium resinate was the emulsifier.[67] Highly refined "white oils" have been used, in emulsion form, for pineleaf scale control [68] and for European elm scale.[69] Oil emulsions have also been used in summer for codling-moth control,[70] for insects of pineapples,[71] for the Oriental fruit-moth,[72] for San José and Scurfy Scales,[73] and against second-brood white apple leafhoppers.[74]

Mineral Oil Emulsions as Sprays for Insects Attacking Animals and Man

(A few references to other oils are also included here for convenience.) A soap emulsion of engine red oil has been used against the puss caterpillar which stings man and which infests shade trees in American cities.[75] A heavy mineral oil emulsion, containing 20 per cent of oil in the actual spray, was found efficient against the chicken mite, *Dermanyssus gallinæ* De G.[76]

Spraying poultry houses with kerosene emulsion is recommended when they are infected with the poultry tick, *Argas persicus,* Oken, which attacks fowls in Queensland.[77] A 3 per cent emulsion (mixture ?) of pine tar creosote in water, containing 1 lb. of caustic soda per 97 gall. is said to repel mosquitoes attacking cattle,[78] and an emulsion of red pine oil is both a control and a repellent for the horn fly (*Lyperosia irritans,* L.) of cattle.[79] Cousins describes a paraffin-naphthalene emulsion of use for spraying cattle for ticks brought into Jamaica as a result of the introduction of cheap beef cattle.[80]

A carbon tetrachloride emulsion, with cresol-soap as emulsifier, is reported to be the best agent for the extermination of mosquitoes and flies on night-soil, though the immediate value of the night-soil, as a manure, is decreased owing to the effects of cresol on certain plants.[81]

Searching trials into the use of the well-known "Volck" proprietary mineral oil emulsions, for the control of insects infesting domestic animals, are now in progress.[82]

Precautions to be Observed when Applying Mineral Oil Emulsions to Plants

The possibility of damage to plants, caused by the wrong type of emulsion, by incomplete emulsions containing free oil, by emulsifiers incompatible with the constituents of hard waters or insoluble in brackish waters, by admixture with other sprays, and by a too-great sulphonatable proportion of oil, has been discussed previously. A list of additional references to damage, caused in these ways, and to the precautions necessary when applying mineral oil sprays is appended.[83]

TAR DISTILLATE EMULSIONS

Tar distillate washes or "water-soluble" carbolineums are invariably dormant sprays, even dilute emulsions "scorching" foliage badly.[84] A list of additional references to the properties, use, and precautions of application of tar distillates is appended; [85] Tutin, of Long Ashton, besides indicating a rather novel mode of preparation, also states that tar distillate concentrates contain about 10 per cent by weight of the 80–90 per cent tar distillate present as tar acids (cresols, *etc.*); resin soaps and water are also present. [85]

Winter spraying, with tar distillate emulsions, has been practiced widely because of two reasons: the emulsions are effective ovicides, and the spraying occurs when labor can best be spared. The tar distillate concentrate should be well-mixed before dilution and should not be stored outside in frosty weather. An efficient spray machine, working at a high pump pressure, should be used, and the whole of the tree should be sprayed, so that insect eggs on the branch tips receive the ovicidal wash. For plums, which have been regularly winter-sprayed in this manner, a 5 per cent emulsion is sufficiently concentrated; but for apples, 7½ per cent is more satisfactory. The heavy infestations of aphis, which used to occur on plums previous to the introduction of winter spraying by tar distillates, makes the regular winter spraying of plums almost a necessity. [86]

MIXED MINERAL AND TAR OILS

The main use of tar distillate emulsions is against aphis and other eggs; but they seem to encourage red spider, and to be inefficient ovicides for the eggs of apple capsid (*Plesiocoris rugicollis*). It has been claimed that the Long Ashton "Two-solution" tar oil wash [85] and the Long Ashton "Modified" tar oil emulsion [85] are capable, at 10 and 12½ per cent respectively, of reducing apple capsid markedly; [87] but this experience is far from general, and, because tar oils are so efficient against aphis eggs, and mineral oil emulsions control apple capsid and red spider (*Oligonychus ulmi*) so well, mixtures of the two have been tried with the notion of providing the "all-round" winter wash. The washes have been combined in various manners: by making actual mixtures of mineral oil emulsion and tar distillate, diluting by water, and applying as a delayed dormant spray; by mixing tar and mineral oils, and applying the emulsified mixture, at about 10 per cent concentration, as a "tar-petroleum" wash; or, better, by applying the mineral oil emulsion, at 7½ per cent, before the buds begin to swell, following a 6–10 per cent tar distillate emulsion applied some time previously.[87] The application of these mixed washes may cause serious injury to trees and bushes.[87]

EMULSIONS OF TRUE OILS AND OTHER LIQUIDS

In 1842, Haggerston [88] employed soap solutions against aphis and red spider. Siegler and Popenoe [89] demonstrated that the toxicity of the soap did not depend on causticity, but on the monocarboxylic acids present, these possessing a definite insecticidal value towards certain aphides, which increased, as the series was ascended, until a maximum toxicity was reached at capric acid (Tattersfield and Gimingham [90] obtained similar results against *Aphis rumicis*). Siegler and Popenoe, therefore, recommended "doubly distilled coconut fatty acids," containing a high proportion of the toxic capric and lauric acids, as a substitute for nicotine: the fatty acids (m.p. 27°) were dissolved in oil and the resulting solution was emulsified by powdered glue and water.

True oils are injurious to the leaves and trunks of trees, when applied naked, because they interfere with respiration; it is necessary, therefore, to apply them to plants as emulsions. Emulsions of poppy oil have been used against the beet carrion beetle; a rape oil emulsion has been reported as being equal to a nicotine soft soap wash when sprayed on foliage as a control for aphides, capsids, and other sucking insects; [91] sperm oil emulsion has been shown to be less injurious to apple and peach foliage than other oil emulsions; [92] arachis oil emulsions are said to control aphides, [93] and to be useful against scale insects of forest trees.[94]

By spraying geraniol emulsions on to unimportant foliage, the Japanese Beetle may be attracted and concentrated there (an example of positive chemotropism), ready for destruction by pyrethrum-soap contact sprays.[95]

Carbon disulphide emulsions have been used against the grass grub (*Odontria Zealandica,* White)[96] and the root-knot nematode.[97] Satisfactory control of the garden centipede, *Scutigerella immaculata,* Newport, under certain greenhouse conditions, has also been obtained by means of these emulsions.[98]

EMULSIONS OF INSECTICIDAL SOLUTIONS

It has been mentioned already that a solution of coconut oil fatty acids, in petroleum oil, has been used in emulsion form.[89] It is common practice to use an oil, afterwards emulsified, as a solvent or carrier for the insecticide. Thus a decoction of pyrethrum used to be made by filtering one gallon of kerosene through 2½ lb. of pyrethrum powder, the oil solution of pyrethrum thus obtained then being emulsified.[99] Much work on the emulsification of pyrethrum solutions has followed.[100]

Emulsions of oil solutions of naphthalene were first made and applied by Cousins as "Paranaph"[101] and were criticised on physico-chemical grounds by Pickering;[102] many investigators have followed Cousins's lead.[103]

A solution of sulphur, in carbon disulphide, has been patented as an insecticide.[104]

THE STIMULATION TO THE PLANT FOLLOWING THE APPLICATION OF EMULSIONS

Ginsburg[105] reported that the leaves of apple trees, sprayed during July and August with an emulsion of a refined lubricating oil, contained more chlorophyll than the leaves of unsprayed control trees; Volck[106] claimed that spraying citrus fruit trees with an emulsion of a mixture of a purified, viscous, non-volatile oil such as "nujol" and a highly penetrating mineral oil such as kerosene, an alkaline soap being the emulsifier, stimulated or rejuvenated the plants; Molz,[85] and later Petherbridge and Dillon Weston,[85] demonstrated that one result of using tar distillate washes, on dormant apple and plum trees, was a more luxuriant growth of foliage the next season, Jones [107] noticing more vigorous growth also; Markley and Sando [108] claimed that oil emulsions stimulated the production of the waxy substance on apples; whilst Herbert [109] noted stimulation to deciduous fruit trees from spraying, especially when miscible oils containing heavy mineral oil, were applied in late December or January, the bloom and the set of the fruit being earlier, large green leaves forming early, and larger crops and individual fruits resulting finally.

THE OIL RETAINED BY THE FOLIAGE

Methods are detailed in the literature for the determination of the amount of oil left on the foliage, after spraying oil emulsions, especially on citrus foliage.[110] Smith stated that more oil is retained by surfaces sprayed at a distance from the nozzle than close to it, and that the quantity of oil deposited is largely determined by the nature and quantity of the emulsifier used, soap causing much smaller deposits than other commonly-used emulsifiers; [111] this is in harmony with Woodman's results, where a soap spreader was found to cause less retention of spray fluid on a surface than spreaders such as gelatin and calcium caseinate, which confer greater viscosity on the spray fluid.[40] Smith recommended blood-albumin as the emulsifier, and pointed out that the amount of oil deposited on sprayed leaves, as judged by the magnitude of the leaf-fall resulting, decreased with increasing proportions of the blood-albumin.[39]

THE REMOVAL OF OILY RESIDUES FROM FRUIT

The appearance, sometimes, in the U.S. of a second series of brood moths of the codling-moth necessitates spraying with lead arsenate suspensions 12–14 weeks after the flowering stage. The amount of arsenate, then retained by apples at the marketing stage, is rarely enough to prove serious, as was shown by the Government Analyst here; [112] but, because of public scares and of the fact that these spray deposits are often clearly visible and, hence, affect market prices, it has become a routine practice, in American apple-growing districts, to remove the spray residues.

Mechanical means, such as wiping and brushing, have been found to be ineffective and to impair the keeping quality of the fruit. Of the solvents tried, hydrochloric acid solution, used at a concentration depending on the temperature of washing, is found the best. Sodium hydroxide solution is also efficient, but affects keeping quality, and hence, the acid is usually employed.

The effect of including spraying by oil emulsions along with the lead arsenate spraying in the programme is to retard somewhat the action of solvents; but not to make cleaning, in this manner, an impossibility providing a sufficient period of time has elapsed between the date of application of the oil and the treatment by solvents (shown to be 30 days minimum, at most, at the time of experiment). [113] The improper use of oil sprays is stated to cause serious complications in the removal of arsenical residues. [114]

Robinson showed [115] that oil-covered fruit is cleaned more effectively by mixed solvents than by the acid alone, though the use of solvents might be limited, as fruit, heavily coated with lead arsenate and oil, cannot be cleaned below the limit of tolerance of arsenic by organic solvent-acid combinations; in such cases, heating the acid still remains the most efficacious method of procedure.

Kerosene up to 2 per cent was the most efficient organic solvent for the organic solvent-acid mixtures; [115] the kerosene may be mixed "straight" with the acid, where admixture by violent agitation is maintained in the "flood-type" of machine, or must be added as an emulsion, when the "jet-type" of machine is used.

Robinson also pointed out that this extra trouble could be avoided by spraying only emulsions of suitable grades of oils on maturer fruit.[116]

In later experiments, Pentzer [117] has shown that warming the acid to 75–100°F. helps in the removal of the spray residue left after applications of late mineral oil emulsion-lead arsenate sprays, but that by far the most effective means is the addition of a wetting agent such as "Lethalate" to aid in the removal, in addition to this warming.

THE MECHANICS OF APPLICATION OF OIL EMULSIONS

No special work has been done on the type of machine necessary for the actual application of emulsions to plants, the machines and pumps used being the same as those for insecticides and fungicides, in general. Even here, published work is very scanty: a formula has been deduced for calculating the volume of a spray fluid necessary to "cover" trees with heads of varying sizes and shapes,[118] and the connection between size of nozzle aperture, depth of swirl (or eddy) chamber, pump pressure, volume of spray delivered per unit of time, etc., worked out to some extent.[119]

THE WETTING POWER AND FUNGICIDAL ACTION OF EMULSIONS

The capacity of paraffin soft soap emulsions to wet the fine waxy threads secreted by the woolly aphis (*Schizoneura lanigera*) suggested their use as fungicides for fungi such as *Sphærotheca mors-uvæ* which causes American Gooseberry Mildew ("A.G.M."), where soap solutions were found deficient in wetting power. Although a 2 per cent paraffin soft soap emulsion was safe to gooseberry foliage, the emulsion was not sufficiently fungicidal.[120]

The introduction of emulsions of highly-refined lubricating oils which are insecticidal without being phytocidal resulted in tests of their fungicidal value. "Volck," a proprietary mineral oil emulsion for summer use on foliage, was found to be fungicidal to powdery mildew of the rose, *Sphærotheca pannosa* (Wal.) Lev., the relative non-volatility of the highly-refined oil it contains possibly endowing it with a protective fungicidal action, though the direct toxic action should possibly not be ignored.[121]

As a result of numerous trials, Martin and Salmon [122] concluded that the margin, between the fungicidal concentration of emulsified mineral oils to powdery mildews and the concentration causing severe foliage injury, was too small for safety; no relation existed between stability of emulsions and fungicidal effect, and it was thought doubtful whether the use of the most highly-refined oils would obviate scorch of foliage, or if such oils would ever satisfactorily replace sulphur and its compounds as fungicides. Tar oils, even when freed from phenols, were also found to scorch badly when emulsified and applied at fungicidal concentrations.

These authors further observed [123] that true (glyceride) oils exerted a fungicidal action on the conidial stage of the hop powdery mildew, *Sphærotheca Humuli* (DC.), Burr. Four per cent aqueous glycerol was not completely fungicidal and caused leaf injury; one per cent oleic acid (emulsified) was also phytocidal; but 0.5 per cent triolein (emulsified) was fungicidal and did not scorch the foliage. The emulsifiers, used for emulsification, were found to exert some effect, but evidently the fungicidal action depends on the glyceride structure of the true oils. In this connection it would probably be of theoretical interest to observe the fungicidal values of substances of similar structure, such as the lipins.

Emulsions have also been used in virtue of their wetting powers to aid the contact-insecticidal effect of nicotine.[124]

THE USE OF EMULSIONS AS WEED KILLERS

A spraying emulsion must usually be a perfect OW type to be non-phytocidal.[6] A weed killer, however, should be as phytocidal as possible, and hence the presence of masses of free (unemulsified) oil in an imperfect OW emulsion is no detriment when using for weed killing purposes (e.g., creosote emulsions on garden paths), but is rather an advantage because of the phytocidal nature of the oil.[30]

It has long been known that paraffin oil is a moderately efficient weed killer [125] and it was shown in a series of tests carried out on weed killers that paraffin oil emulsions, containing 5 and 10 per cent by volume of a paraffin-containing miscible oil, were good general weed killers.[126] In the same series of experiments, a coal-tar creosote emulsion containing 10 per cent of a creosote-containing miscible oil, and 5 and 10 per cent Carbokrimp emulsions were found to be fairly effective for controlling the difficultly-eradicable wild onion arising from bulbules, but not from bulbs.

Woodman and Wiley [127] demonstrated that the fluid system, found to be of the greatest use in the eradication of prickly-pear is a WO type of emulsion, being an aqueous arsenic acid-in-cresylic acid emulsion made by shaking together one part of 25 per cent aqueous arsenic pentoxide solution, at the same time, 10 per cent as regards the emulsifier, glue, with an equal volume of cresylic acid. The pentoxide determines the type as WO, any tendency to formation of the opposite type, possessed in the absence of this acid, being suppressed by its presence. This WO type is advantageous, as the cresylic acid continuous phase easily wets foliage and is more rapidly corrosive to the plant tissues than aqueous arsenic acid solution, thus allowing the arsenic to exert its direct toxic effect more quickly; as cattle which might lick or eat the sprayed weed are warned off by the smell; and as the spray machine and nozzle are thereby protected from quick corrosion by arsenic acid solution.[127]

Diesel oils, containing 2½ per cent of asphalt, were found to emulsify water readily to form WO emulsions which easily penetrated the seed-burrs of the puncture-vine in California, and thus killed both the seeds and plants.[128]

THE ANALYSIS OF SPRAY EMULSIONS

A method for the determination of the oil content of mineral and tar oil insecticides by ether extraction of the emulsions after treatment by caustic soda solution has been described.[129] Analyses of the Jugoslavian fruit-tree products "arborin" and "karbokrimp" showed them to consist essentially of tar oils and similar products in resin soaps.[85, 130] The Koppeschaar method of determining phenols *via* the Br-derivatives in coal-tar disinfectants, used in agriculture and animal husbandry, is stated to give satisfactory and concordant results, and the same authors supply details of the methods used in the estimation of water, pyridine bases, soda, and resin.[131] A recent publication gives the official method for the analysis of soft soaps used in spraying.[132] A typical analysis of "Volck" is:[133] paraffin (sp. gr. 0.86), 80 per cent by vol.; water, 16 per cent by vol.; caseinate (casein ?), 0.5 per cent by wt.; preservative ammonia, 1.5 per cent by wt.; soap 1.7 per cent by wt. (The soap and caseinate are evidently ammonium compounds, and the ammonia tends to preserve the casein; thus, on leaving open to the air, ammonia escapes and the top layer goes black and putrid, free oil separating.)

The most searching and frequent analyses of insecticidal mineral oil emulsions are carried out by the Division of Chemistry of the Californian Department of Agriculture, in the administration of the California Economic Poison Act of 1921 for the regulation of the sale of chemical substances used for the control of crop-destroying pests and pests detrimental to the public welfare.[134] Five methods of cracking emulsions and of determining the oil are used, according to the emulsifier present; methods for soap and water are given; the viscosity of the oil is determined with a Saybolt Viscosimeter, and is the number of seconds required for the discharge of 60 cc of oil through a standard orifice; and distillation ranges are determined to afford some indication of the volatility of the oil in the spray, and evaporation tests of thin films of the oil as a more practical guide. A simple standard method of determining the now all-important unsulphonatable residue is also described, and this may be compared with the iodine value method of Tutin,[135] who states that the oil, in a summer emulsion, should have an iodine value < 1.0.

For all practical purposes, the viscosity of the oil, in seconds Saybolt, will indicate the fraction (light, medium or heavy) used in the emulsion, and the sulphonation test the degree of purification of the oil.[136] Oils, used in the preparation of dormant emulsions, may be comparatively low-grade, an unsulphonatable residue of only 50–70 per cent being satisfactory; the viscosity may vary widely between 100 and 150 seconds Saybolt. For summer use, where scorch of foliage must be avoided, the unsulphonatable residue should be high, 85 per cent or more; most have a value above 90 per cent, whereas, the oil in "Garden Volck" appears to have 98 per cent unsulphonatable value, *i.e.*, to be practically free from unsaturated compounds.[134] The range of viscosity of the oils, employed in summer emulsions, should be narrow to avoid scorch, about 65–75 seconds Saybolt; and, if used very late in the season, the viscosity of the oil should not be above 55 seconds Saybolt, to avoid complications in the removal of spray residues.[116]

THE EASE OF FORMATION OF SPRAYING EMULSIONS

The best general review, on the ease of formation of emulsions, is given by Clayton,[137] and will not be repeated in detail here.

Observations by authors, interested in spraying emulsions, on this subject, are generally quite casual references, few workers having made investigations with the set purpose of applying the results to spraying practice.

Woodman has demonstrated, independently of Briggs,[138] that intermittent agitation contributes to ease of emulsification, and has standardized intermittent hand-shaking, to some extent, in order to enable quantitative comparisons of emulsifiers to be made.[139] Thus gelatin was shown to be a better emulsifier than the soaps for toluene; and rise of temperature from 20–60° was shown to facilitate, greatly, emulsification by soaps, but not by gelatin, the viscosity of the gelatin solution due to ageing being more important.[19, 139] Increasing the concentration of emulsifier in the system aids in emulsification; [139] and addition of the oil in small quantities at a time, with emulsification between each addition (the "mayonnaise" system of addition) is very advantageous when making concentrated emulsions,[37, 138, 139] which, at certain phase volume ratios well in favour of the future disperse phase, could not be made by mixing the phases in bulk, however violent the hand-shaking given subsequently. Violent mechanical treatment, however, has been shown to be desirable in the preparation of stable, fine-grained emulsions of heavy lubricating oils,[140] even when employing mayonnaise addition and intermittent agitation.[141]

The preparation of concentrated emulsions, employing soaps as emulsifiers, is often troublesome because of the boiling necessary, and hence "cold-mix" emulsions, with other emulsifiers, are often prepared by violent agitation, which is found to be less arduous than heating the system. Miscible oils are also very easy to prepare, even if the time taken is longer; certainly the "dilution" of a miscible oil in the field to the correct spraying concentration is a much easier proposition than the dilution of a pasty stock emulsion of any type.[142]

In common with many American experimenters, Smith [39] has prepared spraying emulsions by mixing the materials in the spray tank, and emulsifying there; this is often found to be an easier and cheaper method than diluting down proprietary emulsions. The modern American method of using lignin pitch (gulac or sulphite lye) as an emulsifier seems to be the easy one of placing the requisite quantities of water, oil and lignin pitch in the spray tank, and violently agitating, during spraying, in order to ensure the stability of the home-made emulsion at least until it has reached the plant surfaces.

THE CREAMING OF SPRAY EMULSIONS

An emulsion cream should theoretically contain about 74 per cent by volume of disperse phase according to the law governing the closest packing of small spheres of the same diameter.[87] Stock concentrated spraying emulsions, however, may be semi-solid and contain more than 74 per cent of oil; this is due to the fact that the liquid disperse particles have been subjected to great distortion, and subsequent dilution to the spraying concentration results in an emulsion which will cream to yield a cream containing approximately 74 per cent, by volume, of oil.[143] The tendency of an emulsion to cream depends on the relative densities of the oil and of the aqueous emulsifying medium; for an OW type, should the oil be less dense, normal upward creaming takes place; if not, as with anthracene oil, creaming downwards to an undercream results.[35] The rapidity of creaming is important as it may modify the distribution of the toxic oil; it is found to depend on several factors, such as density of oil, viscosity of the liquid phases, size of dispersed oil particles, completeness of emulsification, degree of stability of the emulsion, emulsifier used, shape of vessel, etc.

The application to spraying is very apparent: a spraying emulsion should have a low capacity for creaming, i.e., creaming should be very slow; otherwise it is quite conceivable that the major portion of the trees might receive the bulk of the emulsion as an aqueous solution of the emulsifier, innocuous to insects and insect eggs, whereas a smaller number would then receive a phytocidal emulsion tending to contain up to the limit of 74 per cent of oil.[143]

This tendency to cream can be averted by violent agitation, in the spray tank, during spraying; or by the addition to the emulsion of a dense substance miscible or very soluble in the oil disperse phase (presumed less dense than the aqueous phase) but being insoluble or showing limited miscibility only with the continuous phase, so that a retardation of creaming takes place.[143] Thus the addition of cresol to paraffin oil-soft soap emulsions tended to equalise the densities of the phases and to retard creaming for months when added in the optimum quantity,[143] excess of cresol giving miscible oils. Volck has since been granted a patent for the addition of carbon tetrachloride to the oil of OW emulsions for the purpose of equalising the densities of the phases.[144]

For a WO type of emulsion the direction of creaming will be the reverse of the OW type.[35, 145] Thus, if the oil is the less dense phase, a WO type will cream downwards; if the more dense, upwards.

THE STABILITY OF SPRAY EMULSIONS

Besides being stable to creaming, a spray emulsion should be stable in the sense that it should not "crack" or "break" to liberate free oil or disperse phase, in mass, in the spray tank.[143] If liberation of free oil takes place in mass before application of the emulsion, then certain trees will receive a dose of naked oil which might prove phytocidal, or at least might seriously scorch the foliage in summer spraying.

But, though, a spray emulsion should be stable in the spray tank with the agitation possible there, some authors have claimed that there is a distinct gain in efficiency if the emulsion is "quick-breaking," i.e., if it will break rapidly to give free oil, once it has reached the plant, insect, or egg surfaces. Quick-breaking emulsions are, of course, somewhat unstable, and this unstability is supposed to result from large disperse globules of oil got by limitation in the amount of emulsifier used,[21] though it may be stated here that coarse-grained emulsions are not necessarily unstable (cf. emulsions of oleic acid in bentonite suspensions).[146]

One report claims that the toxicity of oil emulsions to aphides (*Aphis rumicis*) increases with the size of the oil droplets in the emulsion, and depends, to a far greater extent, on this than on the nature of the oil or emulsifier used.[147] Another, that quick-breaking emulsions of 2 per cent or less of arachis or colza oil, prepared with ammonium oleate as emulsifier, gave a high control of scale insects on forest trees, when used as late dormant sprays, injury to buds being much less than with carbolineum washes.[94]

When considering petroleum emulsions as scalecides, it is necessary to bear in mind not only the "unarmoured" scale, but the "armoured" scale with its protective waxy scale covering. Thus, de Ong and his co-workers (loc. cit.) have demonstrated that whereas the stable miscible oils are effective against the unarmoured black scale, *Saissetia oleæ Bernard,* they are not very effective against the armoured red scale, a less stable (quick-breaking) emulsion from which oil rapidly separates to act as a wetter of, spreader over, and solvent of the wax covering, being much more toxic to this insect. The size of the dispersed oil droplets and the stability of a spray emulsion are also said to govern the amount of oil retained by foliage, the emulsifier used not having any very marked effect (cf. Smith;[89] thus, quick-breaking emulsions deposit more oil and cause correspondingly greater injury to plants (Spuler, Overley, and Green[88]). On the other hand, miscible oils are more stable (or "tight"[14]) products with much smaller oil droplets,[14, 186, 147] and emulsions made from these containing up to 4 per cent of mineral oil may usually be applied without injury to trees right up to the critical period of bud development.[88]

It would thus appear that if quick-breaking emulsions, with large oil globules, are more efficient insecticides and ovicides than the more stable and closer-grained emulsions, then (providing the risk of damage to the tree can be reduced to negligible proportions) the most efficient method of applying the oil should be as a mixture obtained by violent agitation with water, in the absence of an emulsifier. A logical train of reasoning thus leads back to methods such as were first used; [4, 5] and it would be strange indeed were the cycle of research to box the compass and to lead back finally to the starting point.

Stability has so far been dealt with here under the ordinary meaning of the word, "breaking" or "cracking," on ageing, to give free oil denoting lack of stability. But another conception of stability must now be introduced: that of the stability of an emulsion to mechanical treatment subsequent to preparation (Woodman *et alia,* loc. cit.), introduced by the fact that it is possible to prepare both types of emulsion in certain dual emulsion systems. The phase volume ratio, at which both types of emulsion can exist, according to the mechanism of preparation, is often near that concentration of oil which a spray manufacturer would select as economically suitable for stock or concentrated emulsions. But, at this common ratio, ageing of one of the types, followed by shaking or mechanical treatment such as might be received during transit or "handling," might cause inversion. A curious example may make this meaning clearer: [152] 10 cc of 0.4 per cent aq. gelatin and 10 cc of cresylic acid can be made to give, at will, by different mechanical treatments, the two types OW (imperfect, and unstable on keeping), and WO (perfect and stable). On ageing, the OW cracks entirely and the WO creams upwards, to give a stable cream; subsequent reshaking in any manner of either aged type, however, always gives the unstable OW, which hence, in a restricted sense, can be labelled the "stable" type. Apparently, in dual systems, at the common phase volume ratio, therefore, two kinds of stability must be noted: (a) stability in the ordinary sense that the emulsion does not crack on standing, and (b) stability to subsequent mechanical treatment.

If, then, a manufacturer sends out an OW stock emulsion in a dual system (and this, of course, is the type he must send out, as described previously), he runs the risk that inversion, in part or in whole, to the undesirable WO emulsion might take place; and if he reduces his concentration of oil, so as to avoid the neighbourhood of the common phase volume ratio, where both types are possible, according to the mechanism of preparation or to the handling subsequent to emulsification and ageing of the system, he is probably entering the zone of uneconomic propositions.

Thus, it will be noted that this second kind of stability, which occurs in dual emulsion systems, is of great importance to the spray manufacturer, and he would be well-advised to shun these systems as definitely as he avoids single type WO systems for reasons previously given.

It is also important to distinguish this inversion, arising from instability to subsequent mechanical treatment, from inversion occurring during the field dilution of concentrated emulsions or miscible oils by hard water, when definite WO emulsifiers such as insoluble soap may be formed; this inversion, due to incompatibility of soap emulsifier and hard waters, is an entirely different problem, and has been referred to previously.[28, 30]

DUAL EMULSIONS

It is the generally accepted belief that an emulsifier is capable of promoting one type of emulsion only, with any two given liquids to be emulsified.[148] Many exceptions—apparent at least —to this have been discovered in practice, Robertson,[149] Weston,[150] Seifriz,[151] Woodman et alia,[152] Mead and Mc-Coy,[153] and Tartar, Duncan, Shea and Ferrier,[154] having demonstrated that in various systems, the dual types can be obtained with certain pairs of liquids and a given emulsifier, without the addition of substances such as electrolytes to the system.

In most cases, dual emulsions have been obtained by altering the phase-volume ratio; but the formation of two types of emulsion, in a system, by manipulation of the phase-volume ratio, postulates the existence of a ratio common to both types and, for some systems at this common phase-volume ratio, emulsions have been inverted by re-shaking on ageing,[151, 152] or the dual types have been prepared by differing mechanical treatments.[152] The exceptions, referred to, try the validity of the opinion quoted; many factors, however, might operate to cause these peculiar results, without any invalidation of this ruling.

Probably, the main factor is the possibility of chemical action between emulsifier and one or both liquid phases, resulting in the presence of alternative emulsifiers in the system. Such an interaction, between the emulsifier and the liquids, implies a certain specificity of the liquid phases used, not only for the non-aqueous phase, but, may be, for the (usual) aqueous phase of an emulsion system.

In the past, the specific action of the emulsifier itself has been the chief consideration, one emulsifier being quoted as giving one type only with any two given liquids, a different emulsifier apparently being necessary, according to simple thermodynamic reasonings, to yield the opposite type with the same two liquids. It is being recognised now, however, that the chemical and physical natures of the liquid phases are quite as important as the nature of the emulsifier.

Thus, taking the system oil-emulsifier-water, and varying the oil only, two simple possibilities may be distinguished: (a) The employment of different oils may result in emulsions all of the same type but of widely-varying degrees of completeness and stability; this must have been implicitly accepted by most experimenters on emulsion formation, and has been clearly stated by Kernot and Knaggs [155] and by Woodman and Taylor.[31]

(*b*) The employment of different oils or a mixture of oils may result in opposite types of emulsions. Specificity of this kind has been clearly recognised by Woodman,[152] Woodman and Taylor,[31, 146] and Tartar, Duncan, Shea and Ferrier.[154] A good illustration of this is given by Woodman and Taylor:[146] a 1 per cent aqueous suspension of a lignitic clay from Czecho-Slovakia gave, so far as could be ascertained, OW types only with petroleum ether (boiling range 100–120°C.), and WO types only when the oil was oleic acid, linseed or olive oil. Subconsciously, possibility (*b*) must also have been recognised by Seifriz [151] when he attributed the inversion of an aged emulsion on re-shaking to the heterogeneity of composition of the petroleum oil used.

These two possibilities need, in no way, conflict with the generally accepted opinion on emulsification, for the two liquids to be emulsified are a different pair in each system, exhibiting, therefore, different relative degrees of wetting for the emulsifier. (Unless, of course, the belief is also held that an aqueous suspension or a pseudo-solution of a given emulsifier can promote one type of emulsion only with *any* immiscible liquid, and this extended belief in the specific nature of an emulsifier must be prevalent, until possibility (*b*) is accepted.) Thus possibility (*a*) could, most probably, be explained by varying degrees of wetting (or solubility) of the emulsifier by the different oils, and possibility (*b*) in the same manner, or by interaction of oil and emulsifier, in certain cases, to yield, either wholly or in large excess, an alternative emulsifier favouring the opposite type of emulsion.

Examples of the simple possibility (*b*) are rare; [146] it usually happens, when a given aqueous medium such as gelatin solution,[152] generally taken to be an OW emulsifying medium, is found to yield with an exceptional oil such as the cresols [152] the opposite type for some reason, that this exceptional system then yields *both* types.

Possible Explanations of Dual Type Systems

An obvious explanation of these, in accord with the present theory of emulsification, is that the oil and the emulsifier interact chemically to provide a new emulsifier yielding the opposite type. If this interaction is complete (it must be remembered that the liquid phases usually exceed greatly in amount the emulsifier) then none of the original emulsifier will be left, and the system would yield only that type opposite to the one usually given by the original emulsifier. If, however, the interaction is incomplete, then at least two emulsifiers—one the original—will be simultaneously present in the system, resulting in dual types, an excess of the oil phase naturally favouring the WO emulsifier and *vice versa*. At the phase-volume ratio common to both types, where a kind of critical equilibrium of emulsifiers would thus exist, mechanical treatment, by aiding or impeding the use of one emulsifier, would govern the type of emulsion formed, though this emulsion might invert on subsequent re-shaking.[152] Alternatively, in either of these cases, such an interaction might mean the conversion of all or part of the original emulsifier into a new emulsifier, yielding the same type as the original, an opposite type or dual types not occurring then, of course; this would afford an additional explanation of possibility (*a*), for new emulsifiers so formed may be poorer or better than the original one, but giving the same type.

The emulsifiers present in a system may thus be the original (solid) emulsifier, original solid emulsifier as modified by the presence of water, emulsifier compound or compounds got by interaction with the non-aqueous phase, new emulsifiers yielded by chemical interaction of one or both phases with hydrolytic or breakdown products of the emulsifier,[146] and the residues remaining from such hydrolyses or breakdowns.[146] These are all possible complications in an emulsion system; and it would seem, possibly contrary to the general notion, that by far the simplest systems to explain are those in which the emulsifier consists of finely-divided (inert) particles (*e.g.*, carbon, silica, *etc.*), grain size and wettability, physical characteristics providing sufficient explanation for the type and character of emulsions formed.

Another explanation of the formation of dual types in a system by an emulsifier may be summarised under a usual but very vague phrase, "alteration in colloidal properties or state." Thus a gelatin solution is known to "age," and ageing has some effect on the type of emulsion formed with cresylic acid [152] and on ease of emulsification; [19, 139] again, an oil may alter the pH (and, presumably, "colloidal properties") of the aqueous emulsifying medium; or a colloid may be present in the aqueous medium in different states of aggregation (simple molecules with a substance of high molecular weight such as gelatin, molecules in varying degrees of association, and clusters of these), and ignorance must be confessed as to whether or not these different "colloidal states" have essentially different identities, what their relation is to the colloid in the dry state, and, in particular, what the variations in emulsifying action are.

A third explanation may be given to account for the behaviour of such a dual system. It is difficult to imagine definite chemical action between certain oils and emulsifiers (thus Cooper *et alia,* in a long exhaustive series of researches, [156] have failed to prove definite chemical action between phenols and proteins). In these circumstances, a tentative hypothesis has been formulated that the formation of the two types, in such systems, might be due to the differing degrees of solubility of the emulsifier in the two liquid phases. [152] This necessarily introduces the conception of a partition of emulsifier between the two phases, and the partition has been determined for one system. [157] The existence of two partition coefficients—one presumably of a temporary and unstable nature [152]—due to the mechanics of preparation at the common phase-volume ratio was not demonstrated experimentally; it has been shown, however, that such a difference might be negligible when measured by ordinary chemical methods.[152]

Differences in Partition

Differences in partition of emulsifier could also easily account for possibilities (a) and (b) relating to the "specificity" of oils; thus an emulsifier B would be differently distributed between the pairs A_1 and C, and A_2 and C, where C is water, and A_1 and A_2 are different oils (Woodman and Taylor [31]).

It is worthy of note that Bancroft,[158] in attempting to explain Robertson's result,[149] where sodium oleate solution yielded two types with olive oil, stated that the solubility of soap, in olive oil, at high concentrations of oil, might prove a more important factor than the water solubility. This is essentially the same hypothesis as the author's; and it will be found that in many apparently inexplicable systems, the emulsifier is soluble to some type of solution, true or colloidal, in both phases; the emulsifier is then wetted by both liquid phases.[152, 157]

Confirmation of the author's hypothesis has also recently been obtained by Wellman and Tartar.[159] These writers, who have apparently inadvertently passed over a series of papers by the present author on this subject, state in their summary that "the distribution of soap emulsifiers between the immiscible phases of emulsions is a type-determining factor of such systems" and that "distribution of soap is controlled by factors influencing solubility and wettability, such as temperature, phase-volume relationships, mechanical treatment," etc. This is valuable evidence for a particular instance of the present author's hypothesis.

The assumption of solubility of emulsifier in both phases—wetting being regarded as a limiting case—as the cause of the formation of dual types in a given system, might, at first sight, appear to contradict the accepted notion which is itself derived from the fact that that liquid which preferentially wets the emulsifier is the continuous phase of an emulsion system. However, the *relative masses* of an emulsifier dissolved in, and there-fore wetted by, the two liquid phases (depending on the phase-volume ratio employed), must surely play a large part (which can be labelled "perferential wetting") in determining type without any departure from the above notion. Thus if, in a sys-tem containing liquids A and B and emulsifier C, the usually accepted condition for AB-type formation, *i.e.*, that B wets C to the exclusion of A, be replaced by the condition that an AB type will result if the *relative mass* of C wetted by B is greater than that wetted by A (reverse rules holding in both instances), then the conventional hypothesis would embrace these dual emulsion systems.

At the phase-volume ratio common to both types, *one* type has always been found of a temporary nature (though not necessarily unstable if left untouched), inverting on ageing and re-shaking to the permanent (though not necessarily stable) type; this in-dicates that a false partition obtains for the temporary type, *i.e.*, that by certain mechanical treatment, the masses of emulsifier, wetted by the two phases, have been temporarily altered.

Alternatively or additionally, as already pointed out,[152, 157] solution of a colloid emulsifier, in either phase, might result in the formation of those ill-defined complexes, which are usually ignored in partition experiments; if this be the case, then the solubility and chemical interaction hypotheses would be practi-cally identical and in accord with present notions of emulsification provided these obscure complexes could act as specific, independ-ent emulsifiers. This step, however, cannot be bridged until more knowledge of solute-solvent complexes is obtained, and hence, the solubility hypothesis must rank, temporarily at least, as an independent formulation.

Consideration of Special Systems

Aqueous dispersions of lecithin form dual emulsions with tol-uene, benzene, carbon tetrachloride, chloroform, linseed oil, cresylic acid, phenol, hexalin and, possibly, light petroleum, so far as can be told by drop tests on newly-formed and aged emulsions.[160] Dual emulsions are probably also formed when the oil phase consists of olive oil or methylhexalin, though strict proof is here impossible, owing to the non-stability of, at least, some portion of the WO type. With oleic acid, the WO type, and with the bases used, OW types, are alone possible.

Possible explanations of these two effects, arising from the specificity of oils, have been given; lecithin is interesting in that it appears to be an emulsifier which might decide between the complex and solubility hypotheses offered as alternative explanations for dual emulsion formation in a system.

In the case of phenols, combination with lecithin, to produce alternative emulsifiers, might explain the formation of dual emulsions; but with such oils—"oil solvents"—as toluene, benzene, chloroform, and carbon tetrachloride, such solute-solvent complexes are improbable, the solvent action exerted on lecithin being more analogous with dissolution of true oils by these solvents. The formation of dual emulsions with these oil solvents, therefore, seems to point definitely to the solubility (or partition) hypothesis as being the true explanation.

The drawback, to the acceptance of this, is that the purity of the lecithin used is open to question; cephalin, most certainly, would be present,[161] though this has been reported, so far, only as an OW emulsifier;[151] and it is possible that other substances, capable of acting as WO emulsifiers, are present in sufficient proportion to cause dual types. Assuming that the presence of these possible impurities has no effect, then it seems certain that the solubilities of the lecithin in the two liquid phases—and hence, partition phenomena—play a decided part.

With *Hevea* lipin as emulsifier, it has been noted that opposite-type emulsions can apparently both be present in the same system at one and the same time.[88] The simultaneous presence of both types, when certain oils are hand-shaken, in certain ways, with dispersions of lipoid substances from various sources, has been found to occur very frequently,[162] and explanations are now being sought.

Proteins and allied substances (*e.g.,* Witte's peptone, albumin (egg powder), casein, gelatin, Cook's "dried farm eggs," cow's colostrum pseudoglobulin, cow serum albumin, gliadin from "strong" flour from Manitoba wheat) generally yield the dual types of emulsions with liquid phenols and organic bases; [163] an aqueous medium of dried egg is a part exception, giving only oil-in-water types with organic bases, possibly because of its lecithin content. Instability and gel formation sometimes make verification of type difficult or impossible. The preponderance of the evidence in these systems appears to point to the fact that the mechanism of dual emulsion formation, with protein-like emulsifiers (at least), is due to the formation of protein complexes with one or both liquid phases, these complexes being able to act as alternative or opposite-type emulsifiers to other emulsifiers present (*e.g.,* protein itself).

The formation of the gels mentioned above has also been discussed,[163] and the notion put forward that some measure of swelling in water is necessary before emulsoid colloids can emulsify; the presence of water may, therefore, be essential to emulsification in these instances.

DETERMINATION OF EMULSION TYPE

In view of the fact that a WO type of emulsion is undesirable to the sprayer, and that inversion may take place in certain systems to this undesirable type, because of the possibility of dual emulsion formation, or from incompatibility of soap emulsifiers with the salts causing the hardness of natural waters, it is important to have some definite tests of emulsion type.

Three main methods of determination of emulsion type are in general use: the indicator method, where indicators [149] such as Sudan III or potassium permanganate,[154] insoluble in one phase, are used; the drop test (the most usual test), first suggested by an observation of Pickering [87] and worked out by Briggs,[164] the criterion being mixing or non-mixing of a drop of emulsion when stirred with water; and the electrical conductance method suggested by Clayton,[165] based on the fact that an oil external phase will not conduct electricity.

These methods are useful for quick determination of type; but other tests and observations are often surer where the emulsion, in whole or part, is stable for some time. The present author has had occasion to use the following methods which he has noticed during his work (Cf. references 19, 30, 31, 33, 35, 103, 127, 141, 142, 145, 146, 152, 157, 160, 163).

(1) The direction of creaming of an emulsion; for oils less dense than the aqueous phase this should be upwards for OW, and downwards for WO, types, and *vice versa*.

(2) (*a*) The volume of cream so formed on standing (in a wholly stable emulsion) immediately defines the type if the initial phase volume ratio differs greatly from unity (in which latter case either type would give the same volume of cream).
(*b*) The volume of the clear underlayer or supernatant layer of a fully-creamed emulsion.

(3) Drop tests in water and in oil.

(4) Drop tests on the cream or on the stable portion of an aged emulsion in water and/or in oil (assume the stability of at least a portion of the emulsion).

(5) The viscosity of the emulsion or of the cream as judged by eye, and by the "feel" and "swish" on shaking (this depends to a large extent on the relative viscosities of the oil and aqueous phases).

(6) The "mayonnaise" method, *i.e.,* additions of one liquid phase to an emulsion with re-shaking; increasing viscosity proves that the added phase is the disperse phase, and *vice versa*. This

test is very sure when complete emulsification obtains; the presence of free disperse phase (owing to incomplete emulsification) tends, usually, to make the system very fluid.

(7) The relative volumes of the liquids obtained by cracking the cream from a fully creamed emulsion will define the type.

(8) The character of the clear or nearly-clear liquid underlayer or supernatant layer of an emulsion cream as ascertained by drop tests—whether oily or aqueous—defines the type, for this is the excess continuous phase of a perfect emulsion. (With some emulsions, where a little oil only is stably emulsified, test 8, like tests 1, 2(*a*) and 2(*b*), may lead to an erroneous conclusion, as immediate drop tests in water (test 3) may tend to do.)

(9) The arrangement, on ageing, of the three portions of a cracking emulsion when the two clear (or nearly clear) phases and some emulsion are all present; the continuous phase as a rule is clearly demarked, whereas the cracked disperse phase is often small in quantity and definitely appears to be separating out from the emulsion portion.

(10) The tendency of the emulsion portion of an incomplete or cracking emulsion to cream (this shown often by a thin rim of cream at the top or bottom of the emulsion portion, depending on type and correlated with the density of the non-aqueous phase; or, alternatively, by the gradation in the turbidity of the emulsion portion).

(11) The appearance (*e.g.*, colour, oiliness, smoothness, etc.; in the case of two transparent phases, such as water and phenol, little can be told by this method).

(12) When an emulsion is, or becomes very coarse-grained, separate minute globules of the disperse phase are often noticed in the other phase; in this case, and often when an emulsion breaks very rapidly, the dispersed phase masses itself together

(N.B.—Thus an abrupt change of viscosity to a more fluid system, after one of the additions, might signify breaking, which can easily be perceived; in a system yielding dual types, it might, of course, signify inversion.)

in large part as separate globules of varying sizes which are reluctant to coalesce for he . . . days, the mass of free disperse phase globules occupying the position which a cracking cream would occupy.

(13) When a cracked emulsion leaves a kind of "skeleton work" of turbid films, often where the cream would have been.

(14) During the preparation of an emulsion by previous gentle partial rotation [152] or feeble shaking, the tendency for one phase to be the dispersed phase is shown by that phase forming small globules in the future continuous phase.

Some of these indications are sure, others appear very slight; but even the slightest indication of type must be accepted in some difficult cases, and cumulative verifications of type are, at all times, desirable.

It has been demonstrated [145, 160, 163] that drop tests, *etc.,* made on emulsions immediately following preparation, may be misleading. The surest tests seem to be drop and other tests and observations carried out on the cream, apparent cream, or uncracked portion of emulsion. Fortunately, most emulsion systems last sufficiently long, in part at least, to allow of these being made; in other cases, the cracking is so rapid that immediate drop tests only are possible, and the determination of type must rest solely on the judgment of the experimenter concerned, and can never, probably, be put to conclusive tests. Neither would the electrical conductance test be of use with incomplete or unstable emulsions, for the simultaneous presence in mass of both liquid phases would affect the conductance. Nor would dusting the surface of such an emulsion, with an indicator, be of any use—the usual test for type with a solid indicator is to see if the colour from the indicator dust spreads through the continuous phase or not—because (*a*) such an emulsion would present both liquid phases in mass, and (*b*) if some incomplete emulsions, such as were obtained [160] with aqueous lecithin dispersion and toluene, were tested by dusting, the conclusion—erroneous as with immediate tests—

would be that the supernatant free oil (coloured red with Sudan III) was excess continuous phase.

With simple one-type systems, a portion of the emulsion, at least, is usually stable long enough to allow some of these observations to be made; in a system where dual types occur, however, sometimes one type is imperfect and very unstable, and hence immediate tests and the limited observations which can be made may be liable to yield wrong interpretations.[160, 163]

MISCIBLE OILS

Oil-containing materials are offered by the manufacturer to the sprayer in two forms: first, as "stock" or "free" emulsions, these being merely proprietary OW emulsions of the "boiled" or "cold-mix" kind containing so great a concentration of oil (usually about 80 per cent) as to be of a semi-paste consistency; secondly, as miscible oils.

The term miscible oil was probably first used in 1904 to describe certain products in which the emulsifier was dissolved in the oil.[166] The present author has defined them as clear solutions of the emulsifier in the spraying oil, the actual emulsion being obtained by stirring these solutions into water,[30] but some discrepancy seems to exist about the interpretation of the name by various authors. Thus, references in many papers and books [167] seem to incline to the notion that miscible oils contain only mineral oils, but the present author's definition includes preparations containing coal-tar, true and essential oils, organic liquids, etc., and does not, of course, exclude certain coal tar disinfectant fluids familiar to the housewife.

It will be seen that the term is a misnomer, for by "miscible" is simply meant that the miscible oil mixes or is "mixable" with water, an emulsion being the final product, not a solution, as "miscible" would imply. When it is considered that the layman often uses the term "melt" in the sense of "dissolve" (e.g., in expressions such as "the sugar 'melts' in the water"), the difficulty of clearly differentiating between "miscible" and "mixable" will be apparent, especially when it is borne in mind that the layman must think the mixing of oil and water to form an emulsion a rather wonderful occurrence: the gulf between non-mixing and mixing must be thought enormous, but that between mixing and actual solubility, negligible. That this explanation of the derivation of the name is probably correct, seems to gain weight from the fact that clear preparations containing tar oils which mix with water to give emulsions (*i.e.,* coal-tar miscible oils, or tar distillate washes) are often termed "'water-soluble' carbolineums;" here again miscibility is confused with "mixability." The cresol disinfectants known as "black fluids," which give white emulsions with water, are thus included under miscible oils, in contradistinction to the "white fluid" disinfectants, which are concentrated ("stock") emulsions made usually with glue as the emulsifier, and which are merely thinned down by the addition of water.[168]

In the preparation of miscible oils, in addition to the toxic oil and emulsifier, a third substance, known as an "aid to dissolution" [169] or "auxiliary solvent," [170] is necessary. As the emulsifiers used are invariably soaps (for a mineral oil-containing miscible oil) and/or resinates (for a coal-tar miscible oil), phenols are commonly used as aids to dissolution.[19, 171] The presence of phenols renders emulsions, made from miscible oils, to some extent, unsafe as foliage sprays, and, consequently, other aids to dissolution, such as amyl alcohol (*e.g.,* fusel oil), ethyl alcohol, *etc.,* have been used,[169, 172] the soap or resinate itself often actually being manufactured during the preparation of the miscible oil.[172]

Formulæ for the preparation of miscible oils are given by the authors cited. The present author has stressed the desirability of replacing the complex petroleum fractions of mineral oil miscible oils and mineral oil stock emulsions (fractions which can never really be standardised from year to year) by definite toxic chemicals, such as tetralin and dekalin, whose purity can always be checked by simple tests; [169] the price of these chemicals, however, might be the limiting factor, as in the suggested use of hexalin and methylhexalin to replace the more phytocidal phenol and cresols. [171]

One or two only of the earlier authors have definitely noted that, in addition to the toxic oil, emulsifier, and aid to dissolution, water is also necessary in the preparation of a miscible oil. It is quite possible that the use of soft (potash) soaps containing, as they usually do, 30 per cent or more of water, masked this necessity.

Thus the common belief was that a miscible oil was a three-component homogeneous fluid system, becoming four-component only on addition of water to prepare the emulsions. But, in practice, a miscible oil is usually a four-component homogeneous fluid system in which excess of water creates heterogeneity (*i.e.*, emulsion formation).

Working with pure substances in the system phenol-water-sodium oleate-toluene, the present author determined the equilibrium boundaries existing between liquid homogeneity and heterogeneity of some kind for the four ternary systems possible; [173] this method of investigation will be seen to have a practical bearing when it is remembered that a miscible oil should be a solution, isotropic solution appearing to be the important phase.

The results were plotted as weight percentages (g per 100 g of the total equilibrium) and are thus presented in the accompanying Figure, a consideration of the four ternary systems taken together on a regular tetrahedron opened out in the plane of the base demonstrating that quite a large surface represents homogeneous ternary solutions (shaded portion of Figure). The phenol-oleate-toluene diagram demonstrates clearly that a miscible oil of such a description (*i.e.*, without water being present), though possible, is only so at concentrations represented by the narrow strip near the toluene-phenol base of the diagram, and the soap, capable of incorporation here to give a clear solution, is far too small in amount to act efficiently in subsequent emulsification by addition of large quantities of water. The presence of a certain quantity of water is necessary to give miscible oils containing more than a very small percentage of soap, and, therefore, to be of practical utility, a miscible oil must be a four- and not a three-component system.

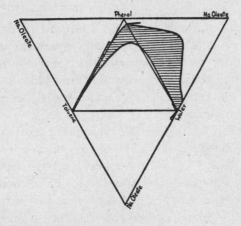

A miscible oil should, therefore, obey the following rules: it should be a clear (one-phase) solution (evidently containing isotropic soap) so that breaking or separation into layers does not occur during storage, and to avoid having to shake previous to actual emulsification. It should give a perfect, stable, non-creaming, oil-in-water type of emulsion, on stirring into comparatively large volumes of water, or by stirring large volumes of water into it.[173] Then it should contain a minimum quantity of aid to dissolution (especially if phytocidal as the phenols are) and a maximum quantity of toxic oil, the emulsifier being incorporated in a sufficient but economic amount. These factors, of course, may sometimes act against each other, optimum mixtures being desirable in arriving at the quantities of each constituent necessary in a miscible oil of practical utility; thus with fish oil soft soap and spindle oil, with a fusel oil aid to dissolution, it was shown [169] that, though excess of soap or of fusel oil within certain limits both tended to a maximum in the miscible oil-forming capacity, the soap maximum was preferable because soap is cheaper than fusel oil, because better emulsions resulted, and because a large proportion of soap entails less difficulty with hard waters. Facts such as these must be borne in mind when investigating miscible oil problems.

Finally, to be of practical utility, a miscible oil should contain a certain amount of water. The ternary system aid to dissolution-water-emulsifier seems, therefore, to be much the most fruitful system to explore when investigating miscible oils. The incorporation of any toxic oil is then a matter for trial once this system has been investigated. [173]

The influence on the miscible oil-forming capacity, exerted by varying the amount of aid to dissolution, may be enormous. [173]

Further work, on the same miscible oil system, has demonstrated that it is possible to select a ternary solution in the isotropic soap phase of optimum composition for incorporating any toxic oil. [174] Addition of excess of water, up to a certain amount, before incorporation of the toxic oil, does not seem to influence markedly the stable and non-creaming characteristics of the oil-in-water emulsions subsequently formed by addition of water in bulk; similar additions of the aid to dissolution (phenol) before incorporation of the toxic oil, cause undesirable instability and rapidity of creaming in the emulsions so obtained.

Though a miscible oil conventionally—and because of practical difficulties—is defined as a clear solution, there is no reason why a turbid miscible oil should not form good spraying emulsions. [174]

Weichherz [175] has described the stages produced by the gradual addition of water to "water-soluble" fruit-tree carbolic (carbolineum) sprays; the production of water-in-oil emulsions, then homogeneous solutions, and, finally, stable oil-in-water emulsions, seems to be very similar to results obtained with all miscible oils and cresol-soap (or cresoap) solutions.[152, 169, 171]

REFERENCES

1. Goeze, *"Geschichte einiger schädlichen Insecten,"* Leipzig, 1787, 166.
2. *"Gardener's Monthly,"* 1865, Dec., 364.
3. *Ibid.,* 1866, June, 176; July, 208.
4. Lodeman, *"The Spraying of Plants,"* 1902, 79.
5. Bedford (Duke of) & Pickering, *"Science and Fruit Growing,"* 1919, 152.
6. Woodman, *J. Physical Chem.,* 1929, **33**, 88.
7. "T.A.," *Gardener's Monthly,* 1868, Jan., 11.
8. Cruickshank, *ibid.,* 1875, Feb. 45.
9. Cook, *Mich. Agric. Exp. Sta. Bull.* No. 58 (1890).
10. Lodeman, *op. cit.,* 153.
11. Sajó, *Zeitschr. f. Pflanzenkrankh.,* 1894, **4**, 4.
12. Del Guercio, *ibid.,* 1894, **4**, 160.
13. Quayle, *J. Econ. Entom.,* 1922, **15**, 400.
14. Browne, *Calif. Dept. Agric. Mo. Bull.,* 1930, **19**, 389.
15. Shafer, *Mich. Agric. Exp. Sta. Tech. Bull.* No. 11 (1911).
16. Moore, *J. Agric. Res.,* 1917, **10**, 365.
17. Moore & Graham, *J. Econ. Entom.,* 1918, **11**, 70.
18. Bedford (Duke of) & Pickering, *op. cit.,* 153.
19. Woodman, *J. Agric. Sci.,* 1927, **17**, 44.
20. Moore & Graham, *J. Agric. Res.,* 1918, **13**, 523.
21. de Ong, Knight, & Chamberlain, *Hilgardia,* 1927, **2**, 351.
22. Bedford (Duke of) & Pickering, *6th Ann. Rep. Woburn Exp. Fruit Farm,* 1906, p. 129.
23. Bedford (Duke of) & Pickering, *10th ibid.,* 1909, p. 13.
24. Gray & de Ong, *Ind. Eng. Chem.,* 1926, **18**, 175.
25. Volck, *Calif. Agric. Exp. Sta. Bull.* No. 153 (1903).
26. Burroughs, cf. *Exp. Sta. Rec.,* 1924, **51**, 442.
27. Jones, U.S.P. 1,646,149, 18/10/27.
28. de Ong, *J. Econ. Entom.,* 1922, **15**, 339; Woodman, *"N.F.U. Year Book,"* 1931, 401; 1932, 339.
29. Codling, private communication.
30. Woodman, *J. Pomol. Hort. Sci.,* 1928, **6**, 313; *J. Soc. Chem. Ind.,* 1930, **49**, 193T.
31. Yorthers & Winston, *J. Agric. Res.,* 1925, **31**, 59; English, *J. Econ. Entom.,* 1925, **18**, 513; Woodman & Taylor, *J. Soc. Chem. Ind.,* 1929, **48**, 121T; *Chem. News,* 1931, **143**, 145; 161.
32. Hurt, *Virginia Agric. Exp. Sta. Bull.* No. 277 (1931).
33. Woodman & Rhodes, *J. Rubber Res. Inst. Malaya,* 1932, **4**, 153.
34. Parker, *Bull. Bur. Bio-Tech.,* 1923, **2**, 27; Woodman, *loc. cit.; J. Soc. Chem. Ind.,* 1930, **49**, 93T; Newcomer & Carter, *J. Econ. Entom.,* 1933, **26**, 880.
35. Cf. Woodman, *J. Physical Chem.,* 1926, **30**, 658.
36. Woodman & Barnell, *J. Soc. Chem. Ind.,* 1933, **52**, 352T.
37. Pickering, *J. Chem. Soc.,* 1907, **91**, 2001.

38. Burroughs & Grube, *J. Econ. Entom.*, 1923, **16**, 534; Woodman, *loc. cit.*
39. Smith, *Calif. Agric. Exp. Sta. Bull.* No. 527 (1932); *J. Econ. Entom.*, 1931, **24**, 985.
40. Woodman, *J. Pomol. Hort. Sci.*, 1924, **4**, 38; *J. Soc. Leather Trades' Chem.*, 1924, **8**, 517.
41. Cf. Robinson, *Oregon Agric. Exp. Sta. Bull.* No. 259 (1930); Woodman, *loc. cit.*
42. O'Byrne, *Qtrly. Bull. State Plant Bd. Florida*, 1922, **6**, 46; Winston, Bowman, & Yothers, *U.S. Dept. Agric. Bull.* No. 1178 (1923); Ginsburg, *J. Econ. Entom.*, 1933, **26**, 566.
43. Headlee & Ginsburg, *New Jersey Agric. Exp. Sta. Bull.* No. 469 (1929).
44. Newcomer & Yothers, *U.S. Dept. Agric. Tech. Bull.* No. 281 (1932).
45. Batchelder & Questel, *J. Econ. Entom.*, 1931, **24**, 1152.
46. Tower, Dye, & McDonough, U.S.P. 1,869,526, 2/8/32.
47. Robinson, *J. Econ. Entom.*, 1932, **25**, 995.
48. Woodman, *J. Pomol. Hort. Sci.*, 1925, **4**, 78.
49. Penny, *J. Econ. Entom.*, 1921, **14**, 428.
50. Husain & Pruthi, *Rept. Proc. 4th Entom. Mtg., Pusa*, 1921, p. 148.
51. Flebut, *Mo. Bull. Calif. Dept. Agric.*, 1922, **11**, 6.
52. Flint, *J. Econ. Entom.*, 1923, **16**, 209; Davis, *Purdue Univ. Agric. Extens. Bull.* No. 114 (1923); Ackerman, *U.S. Dept. Agric. Circ.* No. 263 (1923); Melander, *Washington Agric. Exp. Sta. Bull.* No. 174 (1923); Burroughs, *Missouri Agric. Exp. Sta. Bull.* No. 205 (1923); Green, *Ind. Eng. Chem.*, 1927, **19**, 931.
53. Hutson, *J. Econ. Entom.*, 1932, **25**, 116.
54. Hartzell, Parrott, & Harman, *ibid.*, 1933, **26**, 474.
55. Baker, *U.S. Dept. Agric. Circ.* No. 295 (1933).
56. Gentner & Norris, *Oregon Agric. Exp. Sta. Bull.* No. 321 (1933).
57. Orchard, *Cheshunt Exp. Sta. Ann. Rept.*, 1928, 79.
58. Parker, "*Nurseryman and Seedsman*," 1921, No. 1426, p. 9; Speyer, *Cheshunt Exp. Sta. Ann. Rept.*, 1928, 76.
59. Catoni, *Rev. Agric. Puerto Rico*, 1921, **7**, 21.
60. Catoni, *ibid.*, 45; Moreira, *Rept. Internat. Conf. Phytopath. & Econ. Entom.*, Holland, 1923, p. 283.
61. Parker, *Bull. Bur. Bio-Tech.*, 1923, **2**, 37.
62. Gowdey, *Jamaica Dept. Agric. Entom. Circ.* No. 7 (1922).
63. Borden, *Mo. Bull. Calif. Dept. Agric.*, 1922, **11**, 36.
64. Primm & Hartley, *J. Econ. Entom.*, 1923, **16**, 435.
65. Gurney, *Agric. Gaz. N.S.W.*, 1924, **35**, 325.
66. Parker, *Bull. Bur. Bio-Tech.*, 1923, **2**, 105.
67. *Philippine Agric. Rev.*, 1923, **16**, 49.
68. Richardson, *J. Econ. Entom.*, 1930, **23**, 753.
69. Cleveland, *ibid.*, 1931, **24**, 349.
70. Lathrop & Sazama, *ibid.*, 1932, **25**, 83; Cutright & Houser, *ibid.*, 1933, **26**, 380.
71. Carter, *ibid.*, 1931, **24**, 1233.
72. Frost, *ibid.*, 1932, **25**, 381; 1933, **26**, 334; MacCreary, *Delaware Agric. Exp. Sta. Bull.* No. 184 (1933).
73. Hough, *J. Econ. Entom.*, 1932, **25**, 613; Aull & Dean, *ibid.*, 1933, **26**, 912.

74. Schoene, *ibid.*, 325.
75. Bishopp, *U.S. Dept. Agric. Circ.* No. 288 (1923).
76. Davidson, *U.S. Dept. Agric. Bull.* No. 1228 (1924).
77. *Queensland Agric. J.*, 1925, **24**, 134.
78. *Agric. Gaz. N.S.W.*, 1924, **35**, 290.
79. Hinds, *Ann.* (1925) *Rept. Agric. Exp. Sta. Louisiana State Univ. & Agric. & Mech. Coll.*, 1926, 19; Cory, *Maryland Agric. Exp. Sta. Bull.* No. 298 (1928).
80. Cousins, *Proc. 9th. W. Indian Agric. Conf., Kingston, Jamaica* (1924), 1925, 153.
81. Takashima, *J. Publ. Hlth. Japan*, 1927, **3**, 1.
82. Bruce, *J. Kansas Entom. Soc.*, 1928, **1**, 74; Hall, *ibid.*, 1929, **2**, 74; Caler, *ibid.*, 1931, **4**, 77.
83. Graham, *J. Assoc. Off. Agric. Chem.*, 1927, **10**, 124; de Ong, *J. Econ. Entom.*, 1928, **21**, 697; *Ind. Eng. Chem.*, 1930, **22**, 836; *J. Econ. Entom.*, 1931, **24**, 978; Spuler, Overley, & Green, *Washington Agric. Exp. Sta. Bull.* No. 247 (1931); Young, *Phytopath.*, 1931, **21**, 130; 1932, **22**, 31; 1934, **24**, 266; Swingle & Snapp, *U.S. Dept. Agric. Tech. Bull.* No. 253 (1931); Ginsburg, *J. Agric. Res.*, 1931, **43**, 469; Savage & Ballantyne, *Agric. Gaz. N.S.W.*, 1931, **42**, 947; Felt & Bromley, *J. Econ. Entom.*, 1932, **25**, 298; Green, *J. Agric. Res.*, 1932, **44**, 773; St. George & Beal, *J. Econ. Entom.*, 1932, **25**, 713; Snapp, *ibid.*, 786; Penny, *ibid.*, 1002; Ebeling, *ibid.*, 1007; Dawsey, *ibid.*, 1933, **26**, 735; Young & Morris, *J. Agric. Res.*, 1933, **47**, 505.
84. Hartzell, *J. Econ. Entom.*, 1933, **26**, 480.
85. Molz, *Centralb. f. Bakt.*, 1911, **30**, 181; Maag, *Schweiz. Zeitschr. Obst-u. Weinbau*, 1923, **32**, 53; Cory, *Maryland Agric. Exp. Sta. Bull.* No. 252 (1923); Lees, *J. Pomol. Hort. Sci.*, 1924, **3**, 174; Petherbridge & Dillon Weston, *J. Min. Agric.*, 1926, **33**, 332; Goodwin, Massee, & Le Pelley, *J. Pomol. Hort. Sci.*, 1926, **5**, 275; Tutin, *Long Ashton Ann. Rept.*, 1927, 81; Staniland & Walton, *ibid.*, 1928, 87; Theobald, *J. Pomol. Hort. Sci.*, 1928, **7**, 199; Jencic, *Arh. Hemiju*, 1930, **4**, 176; Soule, *U.S.P.* 1,809,255, 9/6/31; Cory & Sanders, *J. Econ. Entom.*, 1932, **25**, 566; Houben, *Chem.-Ztg.*, 1932, **56**, 601; Gante & Zimmer, *Z. Pflanzenkr. Pflanzenschutz*, 1932, **42**, 121; Goffart, *ibid.*, 1933, **43**, 49; Hartzell, *New York Agric. Exp. Sta. Bull.* No. 636 (1933); Parrott, *ibid.*, No. 637 (1933); Mesnil, *Compt. rend. Acad. Agric. France*, 1934, **20**, 29.
86. Cramp, *Cambs. C. C. "Farming,"* No. 3, Oct., 1934, p. 7.
87. Staniland & Walton, *J. Min. Agric.*, 1930, **36**, 476; Petherbridge & Hey, *ibid.*, 1931, **37**, 1078; 1185; Austin, Jary, & Martin, *J. S.-E. Agric. Coll. Wye*, 1932, 62; 1933, 62; Hey, *Murphy's Advisory Bull.* No. 2; Hurt, *Virginia (Blackburg) Agric. Exp. Sta. Bull.* No. 293 (1933); Gray & Brooks, *J. Min. Agric.*, 1933, **40**, 630.
88. Cf. Lodeman, *op. cit.*, p. 14.
89. Siegler & Popenoe, *J. Agric. Res.*, 1924, **29**, 259; but *cf.* van der Meulen, *J. Econ. Entom.*, 1930, **23**, 1011.
90. Tattersfield & Gimmingham, *Ann. Appl. Biol.*, 1927, **14**, 331.
91. Staniland, *Long Ashton Ann. Rept.*, 1926, 78.
92. Ginsburg, *J. Econ. Entom.*, 1931, **24**, 283.

93. Balachowsky, *Bull. Mat. Grasses,* 1931, **15,** 274.
94. Balachowsky, *Compt. rend. Acad. Agric. France,* 1933, **19,** 497.
95. Fleming, *U.S. Dept. Agric. Circ.* No. 280 (1933).
96. Cottier, *New Zealand J. Sci. Tech.,* 1932, **13,** 317.
97. Guba, *Mass. Agric. Exp. Sta. Bull.* No. 292 (1932).
98. Michelbacher, *Calif. Coll. Agric. Exp. Sta. Bull.* No. 548 (1932).
99. Lodeman, *op. cit.,* p. 156.
100. Cf. Hobson, *J. Agric. Sci.,* 1931, **21,** 101; Tattersfield & Hobson, *Ann. Appl. Biol.,* 1931, **18,** 203; Walker, *Virginia Truck Exp. Sta. Bull.* No. 75 (1931); Murphy & Peet, *Soap,* 1934, **10,** 95; 97; 99; 101; 103; Ginsburg, *J. Econ. Entom.,* 1932, **25,** 599.
101. Cousins, *loc. cit.; "The Chemistry of the Garden,"* 1916, p. 132.
102. Pickering, *J. Chem. Soc.,* 1917, **111,** 86.
103. Cf. Woodman, *loc. cit.; J. Soc. Chem. Ind.,* 1932, **51,** 358T.
104. Hartzell & Lathrop, U.S.P. 1,772,511, 12/8/30.
105. Ginsburg, *J. Econ. Entom.,* 1929, **22,** 360.
106. Volck, U.S.P. 1,914,903, 20/6/33.
107. Jones, *Welsh J. Agric.,* 1927, **3,** 293.
108. Markley & Sando, *Plant Physiol.,* 1933, **8,** 475.
109. Herbert, *J. Econ. Entom.,* 1924, **17,** 567.
110. English, *J. Agric. Res.,* 1930, **41,** 131; Dawsey & Haas (jun.), *ibid.,* 1933, **46,** 41; Swain & Green, *J. Econ. Entom.,* 1933, **26,** 1021.
111. Smith, *ibid.,* 1930, **23,** 376.
112. Cf. *J. Min. Agric.,* 1925, **32,** 549.
113. Robinson & Hartman, *Oregon Agric. Exp. Sta. Bull.* No. 226 (1927).
114. Hartman, Robinson, & Zeller, *ibid.* No. 234 (1928).
115. Robinson, *J. Econ. Entom.,* 1931, **24,** 119.
116. Robinson, *ibid.,* 1929, **22,** 693.
117. Pentzer, *Cornell Univ. Agric. Exp. Sta. Bull.* No. 604 (1934).
118. Wright & Woodman, *Chem. News,* 1932, **144,** 116.
119. Wright & Woodman, *ibid.,* 146; Davies & Smith-Homewood, *J.S.-E. Agric. Coll. Wye,* 1934, 39.
120. Barker & Lees, *Long Ashton Ann. Rept.,* 1914, 73.
121. McWhorter, *Phytopath.,* 1927, **17,** 201.
122. Martin & Salmon, *J. Agric. Sci.,* 1931, **21,** 638.
123. Martin & Salmon, *ibid.,* 1933, **23,** 228.
124. de Ong, *Ind. Eng. Chem.,* 1928, **20,** 826; *J. Econ. Entom.,* 1928, **21,** 502.
125. Pipal, *Indiana Sta. Bull.* No. 176 (1914).
126. Woodman & Jones, *Chem. News,* 1932, **144,** 21; Woodman, *H.E.A. Year Book,* 1933, 77.
127. Woodman & Wiley, *J. Soc. Chem. Ind.,* 1931, **50,** 187T.
128. Johnson, *Calif. Agric. Exp. Sta. Bull.* No. 528 (1932).
129. Martin, *J. Soc. Chem. Ind.,* 1931, **50,** 91T.
130. Jencic & Bajek, *Kolloid-Z.,* 1931, **55,** 212.
131. da Rocha & de A. Souza, *Rev. Soc. Brasil. Quim.,* 1933, **4,** 31.
132. *Min. Agric. Bull.* No. 82 (1934).
133. Hudson, private letter.
134. Marshall, *Calif. Dept. Agric. Special Pubn.* No. 101 (1930).
135. Tutin, *J. Pomol. Hort. Sci.,* 1932, **10,** 65.

136. Robinson & Whitaker, *Oregon Agric. Exp. Sta. Circ.* No. 106 (1931).
137. Clayton, *"Emulsions and Their Technical Treatment,"* 1928, 164 et seq.
138. Briggs, *J. Physical Chem.*, 1920, **24**, 120.
139. Woodman, *J. Pomol. Hort. Sci.*, 1925, **4**, 95.
140. Robinson, *loc. cit.;* cf. *Virginia Agric. Mech. Polyt. Inst. Bull.* No. 123 (1931).
141. Woodman, *J. Soc. Chem. Ind.*, 1932, **51**, 358T.
142. Woodman, *ibid.*, 1933, **52**, 4T.
143. Woodman, *J. Pomol. Hort. Sci.*, 1925, **4**, 184.
144. Volck, U.S.P. 1,914,902, 20/6/33.
145. Woodman, *Chem. News*, 1932, **144**, 225.
146. Woodman & Taylor, *loc. cit.; J. Physical Chem.*, 1930, **34**, 299.
147. Griffin, Richardson, & Burdette, *J. Agric. Res.*, 1927, **34**, 727.
148. Clayton, *op. cit.*, p. 31.
149. Robertson, *Koll. Zeits.*, 1910, **7**, 7.
150. Weston, *Chem. Age*, 1921, **4**, 604; 638.
151. Seifriz, *J. Physical Chem.*, 1923, **29**, 587; 738; 834.
152. Woodman, *ibid.*, 1926, **30**, 658; 1929, **33**, 88; *Chem. Age*, 1931, **25**, 146; Woodman *et alia, loc. cit.*
153. Mead & McCoy, *Colloid Sympos. Monog.*, 1926, **4**, 54.
154. Tartar, Duncan, Shea, & Ferrier, *J. Physical Chem.*, 1929, **33**, 435.
155. Kernot & Knaggs, *J. Soc. Chem. Ind.*, 1928, **47**, 96T.
156. Cooper *et alia, Biochem. J.*, 1912, et seq.; *J. Physical Chem.*, 1926, et seq.
157. Woodman & Gallagher, *J. Physical Chem.*, 1929, **33**, 1097.
158. Bancroft, *ibid.*, 1912, **16**, 746; Clayton, *op. cit.*, p. 49 et seq.
159. Wellman & Tartar, *J. Physical Chem.*, 1930, **34**, 379.
160. Woodman, *J. Soc. Chem. Ind.*, 1932, **51**, 95T.
161. Maclean, *"Lecithin & Allied Substances,"* 1918, 33 et seq.
162. Woodman, unpublished data.
163. Woodman, *J. Soc. Chem. Ind.*, 1933, **52**, 44T.; 1934, **53**, 57T.; 115T.
164. Briggs, *J. Physical Chem.*, 1914, **18**, 34.
165. Clayton, *Brit. Ass. Colloid Repts.*, 1918, **2**, 114.
166. Cf. Pratt, *Better Fruit*, 1922, **17**, 10; 11; 19.
167. Cf. Wardle, *"Problems of Applied Entomology,"* 1929, p. 150; Martin, *"Scientific Principles of Plant Protection,"* 1928, pp. 136, 145.
168. *Manufacturing Chemist*, 1932, **3**, 114.
169. Woodman, *J. Soc. Chem. Ind.*, 1930, **49**, 93T; 1933, **52**, 4T.
170. Cf. Bird, *J. Soc. Dyers & Col.*, 1931, **47**, 254; 1932, **48**, 30; 256.
171. Woodman, *J. Pomol. Hort. Sci.*, 1925, **5**, 43; *Chem. News*, 1926, **133**, 339; 353.
172. Gray, unpublished data, cf. Wardle, *op. cit.*, 151; Melander, Spuler, & Green, *Washington Agric. Exp. Sta. Bull.* No. 197 (1926).
173. Woodman, *J. Soc. Chem. Ind.*, 1933, **52**, 185T.
174. Woodman, *ibid.*, 1933, **52**, 351T.
175. Weichherz, *Chem.-Ztg.*, 1930, **54**, 702.

SECTION 9

SOME OBSERVATIONS ON A TYPICAL FOOD EMULSION

By J. W. Corran, B.Sc., Ph.D., F.I.C.

(Chief Chemist, J. & J. Colman Limited, Carrow Works, Norwich)

IT is evident to those who have a knowledge of emulsion chemistry that the Food Industry provides a fruitful field for the application of such knowledge. One could cite numerous examples to support this statement. The words "butter" and "margarine" at once suggest emulsions, and what foodstuffs have we that are of more importance than butter? One might answer "milk" and "eggs;" but milk itself is nature's finest example of an emulsion and eggs contain the most efficient edible emulsifying agent. Of lesser, but still of great importance are the applications of the principles of emulsification to the baking and the drug industries (for example, cod liver oil and paraffin emulsions). A complete understanding of the digestion of our food, particularly of fats, is dependent, amongst other things, on a knowledge of emulsions and emulsification. In fact, in a short paper it is quite impossible to do justice to a general survey of such a large field of application of emulsions as is presented by the Food Industry.

It is for this reason that it is proposed in the present contribution to confine attention to a particular food emulsion which, although not being as important as some of the foodstuffs referred to above, nevertheless is now an accepted food adjunct. Moreover, it presents some pretty examples of the problems encountered in making emulsions and, in consequence, will indicate some aspects in the preparation of emulsions which need not be regarded as peculiar to the product in question. The emulsion, it is proposed to use as an example, is mayonnaise.

In justification of this choice, it should be explained that the writer and his colleagues have had occasion, during the past few years, to investigate certain aspects of the preparation of mayonnaise and most of the data referred to later were obtained during that investigation.

Before proceeding to consider in a detailed way the emulsion called mayonnaise, it is as well to describe it in a general way. Mayonnaise is an emulsion in which a vegetable oil, to the extent of 60–80 per cent is dispersed in an aqueous phase (water and vinegar) with the aid of a number of emulsifying influences. The main emulsifying agent is egg yolk, which is, in consequence, a most important ingredient of mayonnaise. The American definition of Mayonnaise is as follows:—

> "*Mayonnaise, Mayonnaise Dressing, Mayonnaise Salad Dressing, is the semi-solid emulsion of edible vegetable oil, egg yolk, or whole egg, a vinegar and/or lemon juice, with one or more of the following:—Salt, other seasoning commonly used in its preparation, sugar and/or dextrose. The finished product contains not less than 50 per cent of edible vegetable oil.*"

The preparation, which we term Salad Cream or Salad Dressing, more favoured in England at present than Mayonnaise, differs from Mayonnaise in that the oil content is definitely less and in consequence the balance of the emulsifying agents is somewhat different.

It is absolutely essential, in order to prepare a mayonnaise for marketing purposes, that meticulous care should be paid to the question of the stability of the product. When one takes into consideration that oil is present in the greatest amount whereas the percentage of aqueous ingredients is relatively low, it is evident that, to disperse this large amount of oil in the aqueous phase, great care has to be taken, not only in the choice of emulsifying agents, but also in the method of mixing the various ingredients.

Given a certain formula for mayonnaise, it might well be thought that it would be an easy matter to obtain a product of the maximum stability. This, however, is not the case as will be shown later.

The following will indicate a typical commercial formula for a mayonnaise, omitting those flavouring ingredients, which do not exert an effect on the persistence of the emulsion:—

				Per cent
Oil	....	....	....	75.0
Salt	....	....	....	1.5
Egg yolk	....	....	....	8.0
Mustard	....	....	....	1.0
Water	....	....	....	3.5
Vinegar (6 per cent acetic acid)			....	11.0

It will be observed that the ingredients mentioned are oil and water (the dispersed and continuous phases respectively), egg yolk, mustard (emulsifying agents) and vinegar, which has a relation to the question of emulsification. In our consideration, it is proposed to postulate a satisfactory source of oil and vinegar, although it is perhaps desirable to mention that the nature and degree of purity of the oil exerts a definite, but as yet incompletely assessed, influence on the character of the mayonnaise emulsion.

We shall examine the emulsifying influences which bear on the question of the stability of the emulsion.

These influences are as follows:—

(1) Egg yolk.
(2) The relative volume of the phases.
(3) The emulsifying effect of the mustard.
(4) The method of mixing.

(5) The hardness of the water.

(6) Viscosity.

EGG YOLK

It has already been stated that egg yolk is the most efficient edible emulsifying agent in the production of oil-in-water (creamy) emulsions. Egg yolk, however, is not a simple substance, but consists of a mixture of protein, fat, water and mineral salts, *etc.*, of the order indicated in the following analysis:—[1]

				per cent
Protein	....	....	....	16.0
Fat	....	....	....	23.0
Lecithin	....	....	....	11.0
Cholesterol	....	....	....	1.5
Salts	....	....	....	3.0
Water	....	....	....	45.5

Although the protein content of the yolk has undoubtedly an emulsifying effect, the most important factor in this connection is to be found in the phosphatide content of the fat. Egg fat contains about 33 per cent phosphatide, which largely consists of lecithin. In addition, it contains the substance cholesterol in amounts of the order of 5 per cent. Whereas lecithin, in its natural state, is a very powerful agent in promoting the oil-in-water type of emulsion, cholesterol exerts just the reverse effect; [2, 3] that is, although cholesterol exerts an emulsifying effect, it does so in the sense of dispersing the water in the oil and producing a "greasy" emulsion. This explains why wool fat (lanolin) which contains a high percentage of cholesterol, possesses the capacity of absorbing a large amount of water. Thus, cholesterol exerts an effect which is antagonistic to lecithin. In practice, an undue excess of such an emulsifying agent will cause instability of a creamy emulsion. This effect is illustrated in Table 1,[4] which shows the characters of different emulsions of oil and water containing varying amounts of lecithin and cholesterol. When water is the continuous phase, this means that the emulsion is one of the "creamy" (oil-in-water) type, and *vice versa.*

TABLE 1

The Effect of Mixtures of Lecithin and Cholesterol on Emulsion Systems

Volume of oil phase cc	Volume of aqueous phase cc	% lecithin	% cholesterol	Ratio lecithin/ cholesterol	Continuous phase
5	6.0 -	0.33	0.017	19.4	Water
5	5.5	0.18	0.018	10.0	Water
5	5.4	0.148	0.0185	8.0	Indefinite
5	5.3	0.113	0.019	6.0	Oil
5	5.2	0.077	0.019	4.1	Oil
5	5.1	0.04	0.02	2.0	Oil

In this Table, it will be observed that lecithin and cholesterol, in the presence of each other, lower the other's efficiency and tend towards instability. At a certain point, the relative concentrations of lecithin and cholesterol are such that there is an equal tendency to the production of oil-in-water and water-in-oil emulsions respectively, the net effect being instability. From the above table, this point is seen to occur, when the lecithin/cholesterol ratio is 8. In a similar experiment, in which the cholesterol was present in the oil phase, the corresponding ratio at this "inversion point" was found to be between 1 and 2.

A knowledge of the antagonistic action between cholesterol and lecithin suggests an explanation of the fact that fresh egg yolk is a better emulsifying agent than preserved (frozen) yolk. In the fresh yolk, one can assume that the lecithin is present in a fairly pure condition and, hence, exerts its maximum emulsifying powers. On keeping, however, lecithin is liable to chemical changes of a hydrolytic nature. It may reasonably be postulated that this chemical change is accompanied by loss of emulsifying properties. Cholesterol, on the other hand, is relatively stable and it is not likely to change appreciably on keeping. Therefore, it is suggested that the relative effect of cholesterol in old egg yolk is greater than in fresh yolk and from the foregoing, it may be inferred that an increased relative influence of cholesterol will mean a less stable mayonnaise.

RELATIVE VOLUME OF THE PHASES

Several investigators, in the past, have performed work which suggests that the relative volumes of the phases have a distinct bearing on the type of the resulting emulsion. Thus Clayton [5] points out that in margarine manufacture, if one runs milk into a bulk of oil, with stirring, these conditions favour a water-in-oil emulsion. If, however, the oil is run into the milk, the opposite type of emulsion emerges.

In the case of mayonnaise, it is the usual practice to prepare a nucleus consisting of all of the oil emulsified in a fraction of the total aqueous phase, prior to adding the remainder of the aqueous phase (vinegar and water). This large concentration of oil is in itself a condition tending to give rise to the water-in-oil emulsion. The emulsifying agents prevent this occurring, but the fact still remains that the high concentration of oil, in the initial stages, is a factor of great importance in the case of such an emulsion, and is unfavourable influence on the net stability of the final product.

One might reasonably enquire why the oil should not be added to the whole of the aqueous phase. The reason is that the viscosity of the medium would then be so low that the efficiency of the ordinary type of beater used would not be adequate to disperse the oil effectively. On the other hand, if recourse be had to an homogeniser, the oil globules would be split up to such an extent that the emulsifying agents, in amounts generally used in commercial practice, would be insufficient to give stability in view of the increased surface of dispersed phase produced. It would seem that for such an emulsion, any process of homogenisation must be carefully controlled, since too much homogenisation will break the emulsion.

This criticism of homogenisation does not apply to emulsions such as salad cream, where the oil phase is less than in mayonnaise, being of the order of 30–50 per cent. In this case, homogenisation is possible and, indeed, is desirable, since the globules must be well broken up, in order to confer stability and allow the viscous additions such as starches, gums, and pectin to perform their rôle of keeping the oil globules apart.

THE EMULSIFYING EFFECT OF MUSTARD

When mayonnaise first became a food adjunct, it can reasonably be supposed that mustard flour was included from the flavouring point of view. During the past few years, evidence has been produced of the fact that mustard flour possesses emulsifying properties. Perhaps the most striking illustration of this is its antagonistic behaviour towards the emulsifying effects of calcium soap. Whereas ordinary, or sodium, soap promotes an emulsion of the oil-in-water (creamy) type, calcium soap promotes the reverse, or greasy type. Thus calcium soaps are, in this respect, antagonistic towards sodium soaps. In Tables 2 and 3, it is shown that mustard flour exerts an antagonistic effect towards calcium soaps, similar to that exerted by sodium soaps. [6]

In the experiments in these tables, 6 cc each of lime water and olive oil were shaken together. The calcium combined with the free fatty acid in the olive oil, with the result that this mixture, when shaken, gave rise to a water-in-oil, or greasy, emulsion. When, however, increasing quantities of mustard were dispersed in the olive oil, it was found that there came a point at which the power of the calcium to form a water-in-oil emulsion was overcome. The effect of adding more mustard flour was to produce a creamy emulsion. This is clearly indicated in Tables 2 and 3. A comparison of these two tables indicates that the fineness of the mustard flour has a definite influence on its activity in this respect. The coarse mustard flour is seen

TABLE 2

Weight of mustard added to oil	% Mustard	Type of Emulsion
0.00 g fine mustard flour	0	Greasy (water-in-oil)
0.02 g ,, ,, ,,	0.17	,, (water-in-oil)
0.04 g ,, ,, ,,	0.3	Unstable (mainly water-in-oil)
0.06 g ,, ,, ,,	0.5	,, (mainly water-in-oil)
0.08 g ,, ,, ,,	0.7	,, (mainly water-in-oil)
0.10 g ,, ,, ,,	0.8	,, (mainly water-in-oil)
0.12 g ,, ,, ,,	1.0	,, (mixture of two types)
0.15 g ,, ,, ,,	1.25	,, (mixture of two types)
0.20 g ,, ,, ,,	1.7	,, (mostly oil-in-water)
0.25 g ,, ,, ,,	2.1	Creamy (oil-in-water)
0.30 g ,, ,, ,,	2.5	,, (oil-in-water)
0.40 g ,, ,, ,,	3.3	,, (oil-in-water)
0.50 g ,, ,, ,,	4.2	,, (oil-in-water)

TABLE 3

Weight of mustard added to oil	% Mustard	Type of Emulsion
0.00 g coarse mustard flour	0	Greasy (water-in-oil)
0.05 g ,, ,, ,,	0.4	,, (water-in-oil)
0.10 g ,, ,, ,,	0.8	,, (water-in-oil)
0.15 g ,, ,, ,,	1.25	,, (water-in-oil)
0.20 g ,, ,, ,,	1.7	,, (water-in-oil)
0.30 g ,, ,, ,,	2.5	Unstable (mixture of types)
0.40 g ,, ,, ,,	3.3	,, (mixture of types)
0.70 g ,, ,, ,,	5.9	,, (mixture of types)

to be less effective than the fine flour. Incidently, the writer believes that this is the first occasion on which a fine powder has been shown to antagonize the effect of a colloidal emulsifying agent.

The applications of these results, to the case of the stability of mayonnaise, have been examined with the help of an instrument called the Mobilometer. The Mobilometer was first used for a similar purpose by Gray and Southwick.[7] It consists of a hollow, vertical, metal cylinder about 9″ high and 1½″ in diameter. It is fitted with a plunger consisting of a thin metal rod, with, at the lower end, a perforated disc which fits the cylinder closely and, at the upper end, a platform on which a weight can be placed. Its primary use is to measure the consistency of products like mayonnaise. Consistency is measured by the time taken by the plunger, weighted to a known degree, to fall a known distance through the mayonnaise. With a given formula, it is reasonable to assume that the higher the consistency or viscosity the greater is the extent of emulsification. This assumption has been made in all of the results which follow.

In addition to the measurement of consistency, the Mobilometer can also be used to obtain a measure of the stability of the mayonnaise emulsion. It is known that violent agitation of an emulsion such as mayonnaise, in which the margin of stability is not very high, often results in separation of the phases. Conditions approximating this violent agitation can be obtained by repeated plunges of the Mobilometer. In the case of a mayonnaise which is not very stable it is found that a number of consecutive plunges of the weighted plunger, fitted as it is with a perforated disc, will cause breaking of the emulsion.

In the experiments shown in Table 4, to determine the relative stability of mayonnaise, samples of mayonnaise have been made and kept for various lengths of time and, periodically, they have been submitted to this plunging treatment with the Mobilometer. Where a sample withstood a hundred consecutive plunges, under the influence of a known weight, (generally 1,000 grams) placed on the Mobilometer, it was called stable. If the sample broke within one hundred plunges, it was called unstable, and it was this criteria as to whether a sample would stand a hundred plunges of the Mobilometer, which was taken as a measure of the relative stability of the mayonnaise samples. Using this technique, the results contained in Table 4 were obtained. These results indicate in a practical way that the presence of mustard flour confers a measure of stability on the product.

TABLE 4

Formula	Age when sample broke in Mobilometer (measure of stability)	Number of experiments
(a) Mayonnaise: 3% frozen egg yolk. No mustard present	1 day; 1 day; 4 days	Three
(b) Ditto—with mustard flour added with egg	31 days; longer than 50 days	Two
(c) Ditto—with mustard flour added with vinegar	24 days; 24 days	Two
(d) Mayonnaise: 12% frozen egg yolk. No mustard present	19 days	One
(e) Ditto—with mustard flour added with egg	longer than 30 days	One

As well as indicating that mustard flour has a definite stabilising effect on mayonnaise, this table also shows that this stabilising action is more pronounced when the mustard is incorporated with the egg, during the first stage of the mixing process, than when it is added with the vinegar during the third stage.

THE MIXING PROCESS

The process of mixing a mayonnaise, in order to obtain a product of the greatest stability, is one worthy of the closest consideration of the mayonnaise industry. Not only can the order of adding the ingredients be varied, but, in addition, both the time and the degree of agitation are factors which exert a profound influence on the stability and state of the final emulsion.

Different conditions of these three factors are undoubtedly necessary for different emulsions, and it must be admitted that even to-day procedures are governed largely by empirical factors. Nevertheless, by a study of the mixing of an emulsion such as mayonnaise, one can obtain a certain degree of enlightenment which will undoubtedly help in the preparation of emulsions of differing types.

The general process, adopted in mixing mayonnaise, is to take the dry ingredients, namely salt and mustard, *etc.,* and mix them thoroughly with the egg yolk, in the presence of a small amount of the aqueous ingredients. The oil is then run in slowly, with rapid mixing, to form a nucleus of a very thick consistency. During this process, the nucleus, which is a concentrated emulsion of oil dispersed in water, becomes thicker and thicker, and the remaining oil is virtually beaten into it. The efficient formation of this nucleus is a most important operation in making mayonnaise. If too little water is added to the egg yolk and dry ingredients, the nucleus becomes too thick to be manageable, *i.e.,* it is not possible to beat all of the oil into it. If, however, too much water is added, the concentration of the emulsifying agents and the viscosity of the system are too low to permit of adequate dispersion of the oil in the nucleus.

When the nucleus is made, the final process is to dilute the concentrated emulsion with the remainder of the aqueous ingredients. This is a straightforward operation provided that the nucleus has been satisfactorily formed.

For the purpose of clearness, it is desirable to define the various stages in the preparation of mayonnaise and these are as follows:

First stage—Mixing of the egg yolk and dry ingredients (salt, mustard, *etc.,*) and part of the aqueous phase.

Second stage—Addition of the oil.

Third stage—Addition of the remainder of the aqueous phase. The mixing is carried out in the usual commercial type of beater such as, for example, the Hobart and Peerless mixers. The beater is generally of the wire whisk type and the machine is run at its fastest speed during the mixing, to give efficient emulsification. As an indication of the times taken for each .of the three stages mentioned above, for a gallon batch, the egg yolk-solid mixture was beaten for 5 minutes; addition of the oil took a further 10 minutes; the final addition of acid took 1 minute. At the end of this time, the finished mayonnaise was stirred for 1 minute with the beater running at its lowest speed. With the large size of commercial beaters, the times for the three stages would still be in the same proportion, but. they would not need to be increased in proportion to the size of the batch, as the degree of stirring, in the larger mixers, would be more efficient.

With this brief outline of the mayonnaise mixing process, it is proposed to refer to some results concerned with it. It is not suggested that the data given is comprehensive, but it is hoped that it will serve to show the need for more concentrated investigation of this particular aspect of the making of an emulsion. The results, to which reference will be made, deal with the mixing process, with particular reference to the first stage, in which the egg yolk and the dry ingredients are mixed with a small fraction of the aqueous ingredients.

VOLUME AND COMPOSITION OF THE AQUEOUS LIQUID ADDED DURING THE FIRST STAGE

Table 5 shows the effects of increasing the volume of aqueous liquid added to the egg yolk in the first stage. The consistency was measured by the Mobilometer and was taken as an index of the efficiency of emulsification.

It is evident from figures obtained by the Mobilometer that it is possible to add too much water or vinegar at this stage.

The consistency of the product, in which 30 per cent of the aqueous ingredients was added at the first stage, is definitely higher than when 47 per cent is added. At the same time, as has already been stated, the addition of too little water results in the nucleus becoming so thick that it is difficult, if not impossible, to complete satisfactorily the addition of the oil, *i.e.*, some of the oil remains unemulsified. The reasonable conclusion is that the amount of water, at the first stage, must be the minimum possible compatible with a workable nucleus. This minimum amount of water is itself dependent on certain variable factors, since the thickness of the nucleus is a function of the efficiency of emulsification, which is, in turn, dependent on the egg yolk and mustard as emulsifying agents. Egg yolk varies within limits as an emulsifier, for example, according to its freshness. However, in this special emulsion, it would appear that 30 per cent is a reasonable amount of the aqueous ingredients to add at first.

TABLE 5

% of aqueous phase added with egg yolk during first stage	Acid concentration of aqueous ingredients added during first stage (acetic acid)	Consistency of completed mayonnaise
47% of total	0	56 sec.
47% of total	1.6%	39 sec.
47% of total	2.6%	13 sec.
30% of total	0	212 sec.
30% of total	2.1%	116 sec.

Table 5 also indicates that the addition of acid (vinegar), during the first stage of the process, is undesirable, *i.e.*, that the addition of the vinegar should be made at the third stage, after the nucleus has been formed. It will be observed that the viscosity of the mayonnaise progressively decreases as more acid is added in the first stage.

TIME OF BEATING

The time of beating has a very definite influence on viscosity and, hence, the degree of emulsification. There is naturally a tendency, in the commercial production of mayonnaise, to cut all processes down to the minimum, with a view to increasing production. This is not always a wise measure, as will be suggested by the following table, in which times of beating refer to the first stage of the process, namely, mixing of egg yolk and dry ingredients:—

TABLE 6
(no acid added in the first stage)

Time of beating during first stage	% of total aqueous phase added during first stage	% acetic acid (in first stage)	Consistency of completed mayonnaise
½ min.	30	0	100 sec.
1 min.	30	0	133 sec.
3 min.	30	0	161 sec.
5 min.	30	0	233 sec.

TABLE 7
(acid added in the first stage)

Time of beating during first stage	% of total aqueous phase added during first stage	% acetic acid (in first stage)	Consistency of completed mayonnaise
½ min.	30	2.1	144 sec.
1 min.	30	2.1	59 sec.
3 min.	30	2.1	140 sec.
5 min.	30	2.1	95 sec.

In Table 6, the increased time of beating of the ingredients, during the first stage, is shown to exert a very definite effect on the consistency of the finished product, when no acid is added.

In Table 7, however, where acid is added during the first process, it will be seen that the initial viscosities showed inexplicable variations. Although, the difference may be due to the specific addition of acetic acid, it is more likely to be due to a pH effect. Whatever the explanation may be, it is shown in the above results that the length of time of mixing the ingredients, at the commencement of emulsification, has a very definite effect on the efficiency of the resultant emulsion.

In Tables 8 and 9, a comparison is made of the viscosities of mayonnaise prepared, firstly with no acid addition during the first stage and 5 minutes mixing of the emulsifying agents; and secondly, with a 1.6 per cent acetic acid addition and ½ minute mixing time. The results in Table 8 were obtained at 18°C., and those in Table 9 at 26°C. The ½ minute mixing and vinegar addition during the first stage would appear to represent a common practice of American mayonnaise manufacturers.

TABLE 8
(at 18°C.)

% Egg yolk	% Acid in initial mix	Time of beating	% Liquid added	Consistency of mayonnaise
8	0	5 min.	30	212 sec.
12	0	5 min.	30	615 sec.
8	1.6	½ min.	30	83 sec.
12	1.6	½ min.	30	190 sec.

TABLE 9
(at 26°C.)

% Egg yolk	% Acid in initial mix	Time of beating	% Liquid added	Consistency of mayonnaise
8	0	5 min.	30	130 sec.
12	0	5 min.	30	205 sec.
8	1.6	½ min.	30	71 sec.
12	1.6	½ min.	30	144 sec.

In both tables, it is evident that 5 minutes beating with no initial acid addition is productive of a more viscous mayonnaise than is the case with a mixing process of ½ minute and a 1.6 per cent acetic acid addition in the first stage. Also, it is evident from a comparison of the viscosities (consistencies) in the two tables that temperature exerts a definite influence. Thus a mayonnaise prepared at the higher temperature has a slightly lower viscosity than that prepared at the lower temperature. The viscosities were measured at room temperature.

VISCOSITY

Viscosity is a factor which plays a most important part in the stability of emulsions. In fact, certain substances owe their emulsifying properties to their ability to increase the viscosity of a system. Thus, in salad creams, if emulsification were accomplished by means of the same ingredients as in mayonnaise, the viscosity of the emulsion would be relatively low, and creaming or separation of the phases would occur more or less rapidly. To prevent this, it is the usual practice to add stabilizers of a viscous nature, such, for example, as starch, gum tragacanth, pectin, acacia, etc. When the oil globules have been broken up by means of homogenisation, the viscous emulsifiers confer on the system a standard of stability which will not show separation of phases for times as high as several years.

The viscosity of mayonnaise is not, however, brought about artificially, but is due to the high concentration of oil dispersed in a low volume of water. If the natural viscosity of mayonnaise were not so high it would be extraordinarily difficult to obtain a product of any degree of stability.

HARDNESS OF THE WATER

Finally, a minor, but nevertheless important factor is the hardness of the water, due, as it is, to the presence of salts of divalent metals such as calcium. Calcium soaps, as pointed out by Clowes,[8] give rise to greasy emulsions of the water-in-oil type and it thus follows that the softer the water, the more stable is the resulting mayonnaise likely to be.

REFERENCES

1. Mathews, *"Physiological Chemistry,"* 3rd Ed., 316.
2. Seifriz, *Amer. J. Physiol.,* **56**, 124 (1923).
3. Bhatnagar, *J. Chem. Soc.,* **119**, 1760 (1921).
4. Corran and Lewis, *Biochem. J.,* **18**, 1368 (1924).
5. Clayton, *Margarine J.,* **2**. No. 13, 503 (1920), (see also Clayton, *"Emulsions and their Technical Treatment,"* 2nd Ed., p. 174).
6. Corran, *Food Manufacture,* **9**. No. 1, 17 (1934).
7. Gray and Southwick, *Food Industries,* **1**, 300 (1929).
8. Clowes, *J. Phys. Chem.,* **20**, 407 (1916).

EMULSIONS AND EMULSIFICATION IN THE WOOL TEXTILE INDUSTRY

By J. B. SPEAKMAN, D.Sc., F.I.C.

and

N. H. CHAMBERLAIN, PH.D.

(Textile Chemistry Laboratory, Leeds University)

THE wool textile industry has two main interests in the subject of emulsions and emulsification: (*a*) the preparation of oil and wax emulsions for application to wool in carding, combing and finishing processes; (*b*) the removal, by emulsification, of the natural grease present in raw wool and of the oils applied to wool in manufacturing processes. As regards the latter, an oil rich in oleic acid (oleine) is normally applied in woollen carding, and its removal from the woven fabric is accomplished by converting the oleic acid into soap by means of soda ash. The soap produced, besides emulsifying any glycerides and unsaponifiable matter present in the oil, serves to cleanse the fabric. In the worsted trade, however, olive oil containing not more than 5 per cent of free fatty acids is used, and scouring cannot be carried out by means of soda ash alone. Soap is used in conjunction with soda, but there appears to be a difference of opinion regarding the optimum pH for scouring, one observer [1] giving a value of 9.5, while two others [2, 3] agree in giving a value of 10.7. The removal of wool grease from raw wool is normally carried out under essentially similar conditions to the removal of olive oil, *i.e.*, by means of soap and soda to-

193

gether. In recent years, however, raw wool scouring has been carried out by means of the suint present in the fleece.[4] Suint, in part, consists of potassium salts of fatty acids, which can take the place of soap. As would be expected, the composition of suint varies with the source, and concentrations varying from about 2 to 6 per cent are needed to produce the same reduction in oil-water interfacial tension as is given by 0.45 per cent potassium oleate.[5] Since the suint, present in a given quantity of wool, is insufficient to emulsify the whole of the grease it contains, commercial scouring is realised by recovering the suint for repeated use. Recovery is accomplished by circulating the liquor of the scouring bowls through centrifuges, to remove dirt and grease. Maintenance of the high-speed centrifuges necessary to remove the grease is, however, rather costly and it would be a great advantage if the complex emulsion or sludge of suint, wool fat and dirt could be broken by means of a coagulant. Up to the present, however, no suitable reagent has been discovered. Such are the everyday details of emulsification in the wool textile industry, so far as the removal of oils from wool is concerned, but the subject has an important theoretical interest in connection with the properties of thin films of oil.

THE PROPERTIES OF THIN FILMS OF OIL IN RELATION TO SCOURING PROCESSES [6]

The amount of olive oil, applied to wool in combing, is 3 per cent by weight, and if this is assumed to be uniformly distributed over fibres having a diameter of 20μ (64's quality), the thickness of the oil film is of the order of 0.2μ. Even on the woollen system of manufacture, where up to 20 per cent of oil may be applied, the thickness of the oil film does not exceed 1.4μ. It is here that theoretical interest is aroused, because Hardy, in his studies of boundary lubrication and related adhesion phenomena, obtained evidence of molecular orientation in liquid films up to 5 or 7μ thickness.[7] In the case of the thin films of oil normally present on wool, a highly organised structure must, therefore, develop by the processes of molecular orientation and dialysis and it is to be expected that adhesion phenomena will play an important part in determining the difficulty of removing an oil from wool by emulsification. In particular, since Hardy found adhesion to increase with the chain-length and polar character of aliphatic compounds, and to depend on the character of the surface, to which they are applied, it is of some interest to examine the part played by these factors in scouring processes.

(a) The Character of the Surface

Using plane surfaces separated by films of aliphatic alcohols, Hardy found adhesion to be greater with steel surfaces than with copper.[8] It is, therefore, to be expected that the difficulty of removing an oil by emulsification will depend on the nature of the surface to which it has been applied. The well-known difficulty of removing mineral oil from wool by emulsification with soap makes this oil particularly suitable for use in experiments designed to discover the part played by adhesion phenomena in scouring. 5 per cent by weight of an oil, consisting of 97 per cent mineral oil (d $25°/4° = 0.8672$) and 3 per cent oleic acid, was applied from ethereal solution to wool and cotton fabrics, which were afterwards scoured twice with a solution of soap and soda under constant mechanical conditions. The amount of oil retained by each scoured fabric was determined by ether-extraction in a Soxhlet apparatus, giving the following results.

Fabric	Residual Oil (% on wt. of fabric)
Wool	2.42
Cotton	0.58

The structure of a fabric must play some part in determining the ease of removal of oil, and since, it is impossible to give identical structures to wool and cotton fabrics, the above results may seem to be inconclusive. Actually, however, they are decisive because with mineral oil on wool it would always be difficult, if not impossible, to reduce the oil content to as low a value as 0.58 per cent under the experimental conditions used. It must, therefore, be concluded that adhesion phenomena play an important part in emulsification scouring, to an extent depending on the character of the surface to which the oil is applied. The greater ease of removing mineral oil from cotton than from wool has an important practical application in the case of wool-cotton union fabrics.

(b) The Length of the Molecule

Within any one homologous series of compounds (acids, alcohols or paraffins), Hardy found that adhesion increases as a linear function of the chain length (weight) of the molecule. If adhesion is important in scouring processes, the difficulty of scouring should similarly increase with increasing molecular weight in the case of the paraffins. A water-white mineral oil (d 25°/4° = 0.8672) was, therefore, subjected to repeated fractional distillation, and the various fractions obtained were used to oil strips of a white worsted fabric. 10 per cent by weight of oil was applied in each instance, and the strips of oiled fabric were twice scoured as before. Residual oil was determined by ether-extraction, the amount of soap acids in the extracted oil being estimated and deducted from the total oil to give the figures shown in Table 1.

In the case of the paraffins, therefore, the difficulty of scouring increases with increasing chain-length (boiling point), and the form of the curve showing the amount of residual oil as a function of boiling point, is such as would be expected if scouring is opposed by adhesion which increases in proportion to the length of the paraffin molecule. Because the oil-water interfacial tension is sensibly independent of the molecular weight of the paraffin,

TABLE 1

Boiling Range of Fraction. ° C. (Pressure = 10 mm. Hg)	Residual Hydrocarbons (% on weight of wool)
165–175	1.80
175–185	2.90
185–200	3.59
200–220	4.54
220–240	4.82
240–260	5.37
260–280	5.90
280–300	6.10

(c) *The Polar Character of the Oil*

Hardy has shown that the degree of adhesion, shown by thin films of lubricant between metal surfaces, depends on the polar character as well as on the length of the molecules, being greater with alcohols than with paraffins having the same number of carbon atoms in the molecule.[8] As regards scouring, the importance of adhesion, arising from the polar character of the oil, is best appreciated from the results obtained with mixtures of mineral oil and polar compounds. Strips of a white worsted fabric were oiled with 5 per cent by weight of various mixtures of mineral oil and oleyl alcohol (iodine value = 82.6). After scouring in the usual manner, the residual oil was determined by ether extraction, giving the data shown in Table 2, which includes the results of oil-water interfacial tension measurements.

It is clear that the main difficulty, in removing mineral oil by emulsification, lies in the high oil-water interfacial tension. Once the latter has been reduced by the addition of about 6 per cent of oleyl alcohol, scouring becomes simple. Of greater interest in the present connection, however, is the fact that although further increase in the content of oleyl alcohol is accompanied by a slight fall in interfacial tension, the difficulty of scouring increases rapidly with increasing oleyl alcohol content. Pure oleyl alcohol is itself even more difficult to remove from wool than mineral oil, in spite of the low value for oil-water interfacial tension. In the case of mixtures of mineral oil and oleyl alcohol, therefore, scouring must be opposed by adhesion which increases with increasing alcohol content.

Similar results were obtained with mixtures of mineral oil and Δ-i-octadecenylamine (B.P. 200°–210°C. at 17 mm). The amine is solid at 25°C. and tends to separate from solution in mineral oil at room temperature, especially when present in high con-

TABLE 2

Percentage by weight of Oleyl Alcohol in Mixture	Oil-Water Interfacial Tension (dynes/cm)	Residual Oil (% on weight of wool)
0.0	47.9	2.74
2.5	20.9	1.81
5.0	19.1	0.61
6.0	18.9	0.58
10.0	20.2	0.57
15.0	19.6	0.83
20.0	19.1	1.14
40.0	...	2.20
55.0	16.1	2.88
70.0	15.5	3.25
85.0	14.7	3.36
100.0	14.4	2.66

centration. To overcome the difficulty, 5 per cent by weight of oleic acid or cyclohexanol was added to the mixtures containing large amounts of the amine. Strips of a white worsted fabric were oiled, as before, with 5 per cent by weight of the various mixtures, and the amounts of oil retained after scouring were estimated by ether extraction, giving the results summarized in Table 3.

A blank experiment carried out with mineral oil, to which 5 per cent by weight of cyclohexanol had been added, gave the amount of oil retained after scouring as 2.10 per cent. There is clearly a marked similarity between octadecenylamine and oleyl alcohol as regards their influence on the scouring of mineral oil, but adhesion phenomena are much more pronounced in the

TABLE 3

Per cent by Weight of Amine in the Mineral Oil-Amine Mixtures before Dilution with 5% Oleic Acid or Cyclohexanol	Residual Oil—Per cent on Weight of Wool Oiled with:—		
	Mineral Oil-Amine Mixture	Mineral Oil-Amine-Cyclohexanol Mixture	Mineral Oil-Amine-Oleic Acid Mixture
0.0	2.74	...	...
2.5	1.32	1.26	...
5.0	...	0.79	...
10.0	...	0.78	0.81
20.0	...	1.78	1.83
30.0	...	2.61	2.55
50.0	...	4.56	4.62
75.0	...	5.51	...
100.0	...	...	4.49

case of the amine. With the mineral oil mixture containing 75 per cent of amine, more oil is retained by the fabric after scouring than was applied, owing to solution of soap acids in the oil during scouring. Results such as these suggest that mixtures of polar compounds and mineral oil might be made the basis of a flexible type of washable, waterproof finish for textiles.

(d) *Distribution of Dissolved Polar Compounds between the Wool-Oil and Oil-Water Interfaces*

Since the difficult scouring of mineral oil is due mainly to the high oil-water interfacial tension, scouring should be facilitated by the addition of any compound capable of reducing the oil-water interfacial tension, just as in the case of oleyl alcohol. Although, oleic acid is even more effective than oleyl alcohol in reducing the oil-water interfacial tension, mixtures of mineral oil and oleic acid are not easily removed from wool by emulsification, as shown by the data of Table 4. In all cases, 5 per cent by weight of oil was applied to the fabric before scouring.

TABLE 4

Percentage by Weight of Oleic Acid in Mixture	Oil-Water Interfacial Tension (dynes/cm)	Residual Oil (% on Weight of Wool)
0	47.9	2.74
5	23.7	...
10	19.7	...
20	13.1	2.07
40	15.0	1.22
60	15.0	0.56
80	...	0.18
100	14.6	0.38

Oleic acid, in 20 per cent concentration, should be particularly effective in promoting the scouring of mineral oil, according to surface tension measurements, but this is far from being the case. The defect of oleic acid is that when scouring commences, the fatty acid is converted into soap and is removed to the water phase. Scouring is then simply the scouring of mineral oil by soap, no polar compound being present in the oil to aid the process. Results such as these emphasise the necessity for using oil-soluble, not water-soluble or alkali-soluble, polar compounds with mineral oil, to promote its removal from wool by emulsification.

Transferring attention now to such oil-soluble polar compounds, the case of mixtures of mineral oil and olive oil may be discussed. For scouring experiments, 5 per cent by weight of oil was again applied to the fabric, and the results are summarised in Table 5, together with measurements of oil-water interfacial tension.

On the basis of surface tension measurements, by analogy with the results obtained with oleyl alcohol, it would be expected that the mixture containing 40 per cent of olive oil would scour with fair ease. Actually, however, scouring is very imperfect. Since olive oil is itself easily removed from wool by emulsification, it is difficult to explain the difficulty of scouring the 40 per cent mixture in terms of high adhesion, although the adhesive properties of mixed oils are sometimes anomalous. What seems more probable is that the olive oil is distributed between the two interfaces—wool-oil and oil-water—in such a way that the reduction in oil-water interfacial tension is not so great as in the case of the free oil. In other words, the olive oil appears to collect preferen-

TABLE 5

Percentage by Weight of Olive Oil in Mixture	Oil-Water Interfacial Tension (dynes/cm)	Residual Oil (% on Weight of Wool)
0	47.9	2.74
5	27.3	...
10	26.2	...
20	23.0	2.23
40	21.2	1.78
60	21.2	0.95
80	22.7	0.31
100	25.3	0.27

tially at the wool-oil interface. Conversely, in the case of oleyl alcohol, the latter appears to collect preferentially at the oil-water interface, as might be expected, although when the concentration of oleyl alcohol exceeds 6 per cent sufficient is adsorbed at the wool-oil interface, to increase adhesion and oppose scouring. A study of the distribution of oil-soluble, polar compounds, between the wool-oil and oil-water interfaces, is now in progress.

(e) Emulsifiable Mineral Oils

As a result of the preceding experiments, it may be stated with some certainty that the ease of removal of an oil, from wool, depends on the distribution of oil-soluble polar compounds between the wool-oil and oil-water interfaces, on the magnitude of the oil-water interfacial tension, and on adhesion. Emulsification of an oil in bulk, however, is conditioned mainly by the magnitude of the oil-water interfacial tension; molecular cohesion is not, as a rule, sufficiently well-developed to oppose emulsification, although Seifriz [9] did, indeed, find that when mineral oil was emulsified by means of casein, the oils of low molecular weight ($d = 0.664 — 0.828$) gave oil-in-water emulsions, whereas oils of high molecular weight ($d = 0.857 — 0.895$) gave water-in-oil emulsions. The ease of emulsification of an oil, in bulk, is, therefore, no necessary criterion of its behaviour when applied to wool, as was proved by an examination of several trade preparations of emulsifiable mineral oils. All the oils were readily emulsifiable, some by mere pouring into water, and the following are results of scouring tests carried out on strips of a worsted fabric oiled with 5 per cent by weight of the various oils.

TABLE 6

Oil Number	Residual Oil (% on weight of wool)
1	2.53
2	1.55
3	1.89
4	1.06
5	1.38

For a successful wool oil, the residual oil should not exceed 0.5 per cent, a requirement which is fulfilled by none of the above oils, despite the fact that all could be emulsified, in bulk, with great ease.

THE NEW DETERGENTS AND EMULSIFYING AGENTS

So far, in this paper, attention has been restricted to the principles of scouring as determined by the peculiar properties of thin films of oil. Soap, aided by soda, has been used as the scouring agent, because although so many new detergents have been introduced to the textile trade in recent years, none of these has found widespread application in wool scouring processes.

Among the advantages of the new products are neutrality in solution, insensitivity to hard water and ability to scour in acid solution. Such properties are achieved, in effect, by replacing the —COONa group of soap by a sulphonic or sulphuric ester group, as illustrated by the formulæ of typical products:—

(1) $C_{16}H_{33}.O.SO_2.ONa$ (Lissapol A). Kindred products are Gardinol, Sulphonated Lorol and Sulphonated Ocenol.

(2) $C_{17}H_{33}.CO.N(CH_3).CH_2CH_2SO_3Na$ (Igepon T).

The fact that such substances are neutral in solution, in contrast with soap, is an advantage in scouring materials such as wool, silk and acetate silk, which are easily attacked by alkali. Recent research shows, however, that the optimum pH for scouring is at 9.5 or thereabouts.[10] In alkaline solution, scouring is assisted by the soap produced from the free fatty acid in the oil or grease being 'emulsified, but since wool scouring, by means of soap and soda, is normally carried out at or below pH 9.5, the new detergents can claim no advantage over soap, in this respect. A number of attempts have been made to compare the merits as detergents of the new compounds and soap, but the results are open to criticism. For example, Hannay [11] failed to take account of pH, and the new detergents were placed at a disadvantage. Götte,[10] on the other hand, in comparing soap with the sulphonated alcohols, adjusted the pH of the solutions in both cases by means of buffers, so that soap was placed at a disadvantage. A fair conclusion seems to be that there is no satisfactory evidence of any difference in efficiency between soap and the new detergents at pH 9.5.

Until recently, the fact that the new detergents could be used successfully in hard water gave them a great advantage over soap. With the introduction of sodium metaphosphate in the form known as "Calgon," [12] however, soap can now be used in hard water and new detergents are not needed to cope with the difficulty. The great advantage of the new products is their all-round utility, including stability in acid solution, which allows them to fulfil many purposes in dyeing where soap is inadmissible.

Akin to the new detergents are emulsifying agents such as Perminal EML, Emulphor O, Emulphor A and Emulphor EL, which are finding extended use in the preparation of oil emul‧ sions intended for application to wool, prior to processes such as rag pulling, carding and combing. Oil is essential in these processes to minimise fibre breakage and to increase the cohesion of loose rovings. As regards the lubrication aspect of wool oiling, the difficulty has been to ensure uniform application of oil. The surface area of the fibres, in 1 lb of 64's merino wool, is of the order of 80 square yards, and even if 12.5 per cent of oil was to be added in woollen carding, this would imply the necessity of distributing so small a quantity of oil as 2 ozs. uniformly over an area of 80 square yards. With oil alone, uniform oiling is impossible, but success is much more probable if the bulk of liquid to be added is increased by converting the oil into an emulsion with water. In addition, the water, then introduced with the oil, tends to minimise fibre breakage by increasing the extensibility of the fibres.[13] These are the main reasons governing the increasing use of emulsions, instead of oil, for oiling wool in the processes already mentioned. Originally, oils such as olive oil were emulsified by means of ammonia, but the emulsions lacked the stability necessary in industrial practice. The difficulty was overcome by the use of stearamide in conjunction with a little soap, and emulsions, prepared in this way, are still finding extended use in the worsted trade. Similarly, blended oils, containing not more than 30 per cent of free fatty acid, were used in the form of emulsions in the woollen trade, but no success was realised with oils rich in oleic acid (98 per cent oleine), until the new emulsifying agents were introduced. The latter (e.g., Emulphor EL) are stable in acid solution, and if they are dissolved in the oleine, it can be emulsified by mere stirring into water.

The stability of the emulsion is excellent, and its preparation is so simple that the more general adoption of emulsion oiling in the woollen trade seems likely. Although, there is no substitute for the new emulsifying agents in the case of oleines, it should be understood that the products (*e.g.,* Emulphor A) are equally successful with glycerides where emulsification is commonly effected by other means. An additional advantage of the new emulsifying agents is that certain of them (Emulphor O, Emulphor FM) are antioxidants. When oil is distributed, as a thin film, over wool, the tendency for oxidation to occur is very high. Besides leading to spontaneous combustion, oxidation causes the oil to become sticky, and it is then very difficult to remove in scouring. Dyeing faults, due to this cause, are fairly common in the industry, so that antioxidants are often added to oils which would otherwise be dangerous. In so far as they combine the two functions of emulsifying agent and antioxidant in the one compound, the new emulsifying agents are ideal for use with wool oils.

Once the oil has served its purpose in processes prior to weaving, it is removed in piece scouring processes which have already been discussed. It should, however, be noted that where an oil-soluble emulsifying agent has been used in the preparation of emulsions for application to wool, the emulsifying agent afterwards serves a useful purpose in scouring. The logical extension of this idea is to make the wool oil itself water-soluble, and a sulphonated oil of this type, Whitcol SES, is now finding considerable use in the woollen industry. The so-called "ionised oils" go further and combine bleaching properties with solubility in water.

As regards finishing, wax emulsions, prepared with the aid of the new emulsifying agents, are used in waterproofing. Of greater interest in this connection, however, is rubber latex, which is also used for fixing the pile of pile fabrics, such as carpets.

References

1. Kertess, *J. Soc. Dyers and Colourists,* 1932, **48**, 8.
2. Rhodes and Bascom, *Ind. Eng. Chem.,* 1931, **23**, 778.
3. Götte, *Koll. Zeit.,* 1933, **64**, 222.
4. Duhamel, French Patent, No. 188,286.
5. Stott and Mengi, *J. Soc. Chem. Ind.,* 1934, **53**, 211T.
6. Speakman and Chamberlain, *Trans. Faraday Soc.,* 1933, **29**, 358.
7. Hardy, *Phil. Trans.,* 1932, **230**A.1.
8. Hardy and Nottage, *Proc. Roy. Soc.,* 1926, A**112**, 62.
9. Seifriz, *J. Phys. Chem.,* 1925, **29**, 587.
10. Götte, *Koll. Zeit.,* 1933, **64**, 327.
11. Hannay, *J. Soc. Dyers and Colourists,* 1934, **50**, 273.
12. Smith, *Amer. Dyestuff Reporter,* 1934, **23**, 313.
13. Speakman, *J. Soc. Chem. Ind.,* 1934, **53**, 173T.

SECTION 11

THE STABILITY OF EMULSIONS IN THIN FILMS

By L. A. JORDAN, D.Sc., A.R.C.S., F.I.C.

(Director, Research Association of British Paint, Colour and Varnish Manufacturers)

THE industrial background of this contribution is provided by emulsion paints of the oil-in-water type which occupy an important place in painting practice. The processes of manufacture, application, and drying, to form a thin but coherent film of paint, all give rise to special problems, but there is much that can be treated in a general way. It must be admitted at once that the paint technologist has made but little contribution towards the study of emulsions. The drive on the subject has really come from the biological side in the desire to know more of proteins in thin films and as membranes. The relative simplicity of the emulsion system has proved suitable for experimental study in the biological field, and that work is now being applied to technical problems.

It is now generally agreed that the emulsifying agent, used to produce oil-in-water emulsions, is effective because it is adsorbed upon the oil-water interface preventing coalescence of the dispersed globules. Cataphoresis experiments have provided quantitative proof of the correctness of the view that a protective layer of emulsifying agent does exist. Perhaps the best known example is the emulsification of paraffin droplets with gelatin,[1] which show the isoelectric point of gelatin (pH = 4.7) and thus behave as gelatin. Also it follows that the protective layer of emulsifying agent must control some at least of the properties of the disperse

207

phase as well as maintain the stability of the emulsion as a whole. However, the mere existence of this layer, with its important electrokinetic property (which determines behaviour under electric stress in a system of known pH value), is not sufficient to explain the many variations of stability of emulsions found in practice, as those familiar with the production and properties of such emulsions well know.

The adsorbed layer idea being accepted, attention can profitably be focussed upon the conditions of formation of the layer and the effect of age thereon, for the ageing effects, produced on emulsions, are reflections of the ageing effects on the protective adsorbed layer which controls the properties of emulsions.

The emulsifying agents most commonly used are soaps, but a wide variety of materials including liquids can be adsorbed at an oil-water interface. It is easy to understand how molecules, like those of soap, can be orientated and show structure, but even when the adsorbed film consists of liquid, the forces operating are so powerful that such liquids show structure under the stress. One condition precedent for emulsification is adsorption in one phase and solution in the other, the emulsifier forming the interface.

It is also generally supposed that the adsorbed film is much thicker than monomolecular. If so, the molecules most remote from the theoretical interface will be less subject to stress and have less effect on the system. Nevertheless, the thickness of the adsorbed film is an important problem.

McBain[2] and colleagues have shown that an emulsifying substance, soluble in one of the phases adjacent to the interface, gives films thicker than monomolecular, but the experimental technique used gives little or no opportunity for any process of film ageing to take place before an estimate is made of film thickness. In short, no ageing consideration having been provided for, it is reasonable to suggest that the extra thickness found (above monomolecular) is due to some other effect, possibly entanglement of material. There may be multimolecular layers, but we do not consider them necessary to explain the stability of an oil-in-water emulsion.

E. K. Fischer and W. D. Harkins [3] have pointed out the importance of the determination of the thickness of the film, and its ultimate effect upon the emulsion stability, after ageing. Their work on paraffin and water is illustrative of the many attempts made to determine the thickness of the film. The emulsifying agent, they used, was a fresh soap solution (containing sodium hydroxide to prevent hydrolysis and the liberation of oil-soluble fatty acids) and by a reliable optical technique, they were able to calculate the interfacial area, and the particle size distribution.

They observed that the initial soap concentration gave little indication of the lower limit of soap necessary for a stable emulsion, *i.e.*, that the final concentration of soap, after adsorption has taken place, is the important factor, for the amount of soap removed is dependent upon the interfacial area. A dilute soap solution was found to exhibit a somewhat larger molecular area (of the order 40-50 sq. Å,) than a concentrated one, but experiments upon ageing showed that corresponding with the increase in maximum particle size of the dispersed phase, a condensation of the protective film occurred, from a highly expanded film of 45 sq. Å to 20 sq. Å, with, of course, a corresponding increase in the quantity of soap packed in the film. Such a condensed film produces a stable emulsion, and confirms the earlier work of Harkins and Beeman [4] that an emulsion, in which the droplets are protected by an expanded film, is unstable, and that stability is dependent upon the production of a tightly packed and condensed, *i.e.*, orientated, monomolecular film.

It is concluded that this work "definitely contradicts the idea that surface and interfacial films are several molecules thick in all cases in which the adsorbed substance is soluble in one of the phases. Soap films, in particular, have been recently supposed to be polymolecular, but it is now shown by accurate work that they are monomolecular, and either expanded or condensed."

Another powerful experimental means of attack upon the properties of the interfacial layer has been devised by R. L. Nugent [5] who applied the Mudd [6] interfacial technique to the examination of the protective protein film in a paraffin-in-water emulsion. The Mudd technique essentially consists of microscopically observing the movement of an oil-water interface approaching a suspended particle or droplet in the aqueous phase.

Should the particle or droplet possess an oil-attractive surface, then it would pass easily and directly into the advancing oil phase, but particles or droplets, protected with a stable condensed film, would offer resistance to passage into the oil, dependent upon the rupture or displacement of the protective film.

In short, it offers a visual means of determining the resistance to rupture of the film surrounding an individual droplet, which, in turn, must govern the emulsion stability.

Although, perhaps, the actual emulsion dilution procedure adopted by Nugent, [5] by which he could observe individual droplets upon the microscopic slide, may be subjected to criticism, it is difficult to explain his observations otherwise. The behaviour of the emulsified droplet, protected by gelatin, is determined by the viscous properties of the interfacial layer, and the resistance of this layer to rupture is determined by the usual gelatin viscosity—pH curve, showing a minimum at the isoelectric point.

It may now be postulated that the stability of any emulsion is dependent upon the formation of a tightly packed orientated stable monomolecular layer and the resistance of this layer to dis-orientation or rupture is the determining factor in stability.

The technical importance of the above conclusions and of the factors which control the behaviour of emulsions is well illustrated by the properties of emulsion paints as used in industry.

These paints consist essentially of a pigmented oil-in-water emulsion, the pigment being wholly water-wet. The aqueous phase contains a quantity of protein (glue), while the oil phase (varnish) usually used has a relatively high viscosity of about 30 poises. Emulsifying agents are invariably used, and are usually soaps of a complex type or various sulphonates and derivatives of naphthalene and protein.

The emulsion is made by adding the warm oil to the glue solution containing the emulsifier. Emulsification occurs with ease, often spontaneously, and the emulsions are always stable so long as they are not disturbed.

Pigmentation is achieved by mechanically dispersing the pigment (often pre-wet by some of the gelatin solution) uniformly throughout the aqueous phase. Adsorption in the pigment surface will be entirely aqueous and not oily in character.

This type of pigmented emulsion can be diluted slowly with water to any extent without breaking, and at a convenient consistency can be brushed out in the form of a film, thus fulfilling the purpose for which it was manufactured.

The paint films produced in this way are of the order of 50μ in thickness. It is obvious, for reasons of storage and transport, that the thinning with water is only done immediately prior to use, but the thinning process must be easily achieved with the minimum of stirring or effort on the part of the consumer.

Now, technical difficulties occur, particularly at two points (a) in manufacture during the dispersion of the pigment and (b) during the brushing out of the film.

To obtain good brushing properties, it is essential that the pigment should remain water-wet; failure to produce a satisfactory film occurs through premature rupture of the protective adsorbed layer around the oil disperse phase. This premature rupture may occur under the shearing stress of the brush, or occasionally during pigment incorporation. That this type of failure is due entirely to the lack of resistance of the protective layer to the penetration of the pigment particle, can be seen from a study of pigment/liquid relationships. The figures in the accompanying table were obtained by a study of the wetting characteristics of lithopone, a commonly used pigment in technical water paints. The pigment was examined by the Bartell[7] cell technique.

Liquid	Surface Tension (dynes/cm) of the Liquid	Contact Angle (Calculated)	Adhesion Tension (dynes/cm) between Liquid and Pigment
Benzene	28.23	0°	28.23
Linseed Oil	33.75	32° 30′	28.5
Water	72.6	57° 30′	38.9

It would appear that the tendency of the water, to penetrate into the pigment mass, would be greater than that of the oil, the adhesion tension actually measuring the penetrability.

However, we are not dealing with water, as such, but with an aqueous solution of emulsifying agent, etc. The surface characteristics of such a solution are profoundly different from those of water; for example, the surface tension is about half, and the interfacial tension against oil about one-hundredth of that of water, and as one would expect, under such circumstances, the true adhesion tension is different also.

Although it is difficult to demonstrate practically an actual change over of lithopone from an aqueous medium, such as the above, to an oil phase, the surface relationships studied indicate that the pigment/oil system would be more stable than a pigment/aqueous medium system. Further, a lithopone/oil paste made up with an oil, such as is used in this type of paint, is unaffected even by a liquid with such a high adhesion tension as water, due probably to specific adsorption of constituents of the oil.

In any case, the wetting of the pigment by the oil will be prevented by a sufficiently efficient layer of emulsifying agent. Thus everything depends on the stability of the protective layer, and not only must a very stable protective layer be provided, but experience shows that it is produced. The formation of a stable layer is perhaps best achieved by a sufficient concentration of emulsifier, or a sufficiently long period of ageing of the emulsion before pigmentation. For reasons, which need not be discussed here, it is undesirable to use a high concentration of emulsifier.

The degree of stability is best determined by noting the time taken, before breakdown of the emulsion occurs, during the grinding process or mechanical dispersion of the pigment. The breakdown is easily observed and the changes that occur can be readily followed by a simple microscopic technique. A properly aged emulsion will, under these circumstances, remain stable for a period of 24 hours, and such an emulsion can be diluted and brushed out in thin films satisfactorily. The same emulsion, in its fresh condition, may live only four hours.

It may, as a result, be stated that the emulsifier is the central point of investigation, the desirable material being effective rapidly and at low concentration.

REFERENCES

1. Limburg, *Rec. Trav. Chim.*, 1926, **45**, 885.
2. McBain and Davies, *J. Am. Chem. Soc.*, 1927, **49**, 2230; McBain and DuBois, *J. Am. Chem. Soc.*, 1929, **51**, 3534.
3. Fischer and Harkins, *J. Phys. Chem.*, 1932, **36**, 98.
4. Harkins and Beeman, *J. Am. Chem. Soc.*, 1929, **51**, 1674.
5. Nugent, *J. Phys. Chem.*, 1932, **36**, 449.
6. Mudd and Mudd, *J. Expt. Med.*, 1924, **40**, 633.
7. Bartell and Osterhof, *Colloid. Symp.*, Vol. 5, 113.

SECTION 12

EMULSION PAINTS

By S. Werthan

(Research Division, The New Jersey Zinc Company
[of Pennsylvania])

INTRODUCTION

THE same general principles that govern other types of emulsions are applicable to emulsion paints, although the emulsion must possess additional properties not generally required of most industrial emulsions.

The emulsion must be sufficiently stable so that it will not be broken either by the pigment or by the mechanical work involved in the pigmentation. The packaged paste-paint must maintain its stability, during prolonged storage, even though subjected to marked temperature changes, involving freezing and extreme summer heat. The emulsion must not break during reduction of the paste-paint for application nor during application. Stabilization, however, must be sufficiently well regulated so that the emulsion will break shortly after application of the paint, thereby releasing the water, permitting it to escape, and the film to dry.

Considering these requirements and the fact that emulsion paint is not a new development, since its origin may be traced back to the ancient Egyptians, who used sour milk and lime as a coating, one might expect that emulsion paint formulation

214

would have reached the stage of an exact science. This is not the case, since paint chemists have generally depended on available data and practical experimentation for the development of their formulations.

Several years ago, the casein paint manufacturer, in order to improve his product, incorporated a small percentage of an oxidizing oil into his paste-paint. This may be considered the start of the present-day oleoresinous emulsion paste-paints. Since the caseinates and free alkali (in combination with fatty acids of the oil or resin), present in the casein solution, provided excellent emulsifying agents and protective colloids, little difficulty was encountered in emulsifying the oil, resin or varnish present in oleoresinous paste-paints. For this reason, the paint manufacturer was able to successfully formulate emulsion paints, without giving consideration to the science of emulsions. The demand, caused by the adoption of emulsion paints for important classes of war finishes, has kept him too occupied with the formulation of marketable products to consider theoretical or fundamental aspects of the subject. However, in the process of solving the practical problems involved in improving emulsion paints, fundamental information is being developed and it can be anticipated that within the very near future, the paint chemists will contribute their full quota to the science of emulsions. It is with the thought that through the publication of the results of practical tests, the increase in the technical knowledge on the subject will be expedited that this brief discussion of some of the tests made is presented.

OLEORESINOUS EMULSION INTERIOR FLAT WALL PAINT

Emulsion paints may be of the water-in-oil or oil-in-water type. Only O/W emulsions will be considered here and, to a large degree, will be limited to white and tint base oleoresinous emulsion interior flat wall finishes. Emulsion paints are usually marketed as paste-paints, which are reduced with water for application.

The components of an oleoresinous emulsion paint vehicle usually include resin, oil, protein, emulsifying agent, volatile hydrocarbon, anti-foaming agent, drier, preservative, and water. A typical formula used consists of:

Ester Gum	93
Bodied Linseed Oil	75
Casein	42
Oleic Acid	36
Ammonia Solution (28–29% NH_3)	16
Mineral Spirits	93
Pine Oil	32
Liquid Drier	8
Chlorinated Phenyl Phenols	1
Water	604

As would be anticipated by the high content of casein, oleic acid, and ammonia, this formula produces a fine, well stabilized emulsion.

The paste-paint is prepared by pigmenting a hundred parts of the emulsion with a hundred parts of lithopone and/or zinc sulfide and ten parts of diatomaceous silica.

Using this base-formula, such variables as types of mixing equipment, method of solubilization of the casein, partial or total replacement of the casein, method and rate of formation of the emulsion, variation in resin-oil ratio, method of pigmentation, etc., have been studied. In most cases, these variables were considered from the practical angle of their effects on the properties of the paint. Because of space limitations, only a few of the experiments will be discussed.

PREPARATION OF THE EMULSION PAINT VEHICLE

It is general practice to solubilize casein by cooking in a steam-jacketed kettle. Many paint plants do not have jacketed kettles.

Comparative tests were made in which the casein was solubilized in three ways—(1) cooked, (2) cut with a cold aqueous ammonia solution, and (3) cut with a hot aqueous ammonia solution. If the alkalinity and the temperature of the casein "solution" (these are not true solutions) are equalized before combination with the oil phase, comparable emulsions are obtained by these three procedures. They are equal in consistency, size of oil globules, and properties of the paints made with them.

The paint chemist finds that there are literally hundreds of compounds recommended as emulsifying agents. Excepting that he prefers a material, which loses its emulsifying action in the dry film, thus producing a paint which will withstand washing, his selection is only governed by the efficiency, economy, and availability of the material. Soaps have generally proved very satisfactory. Since the dried and even the aged film of paint, which contained a sodium or potassium soap emulsifier, will frequently tend to re-emulsify when wetted, the soaps of ammonia and its derivatives are usually preferred. Some of the derivatives that have been found satisfactory are triethanolamine, tetramethyl ethylene-diamine, pentamethylene-diamine, morpholine and 2-amino-2-methyl-1-propanol. These have frequently shown advantages over ammonia in efficiency and freedom from strong ammoniacal odor. Still, because of availability and low cost, the simple ammonium soaps of the fatty acids, such as ammonium oleate, have been used generally. Since an emulsifying agent is most efficient when formed in situ, ammonia is added to the water phase and the oleic acid blended with the oil phase, the soap forming as the two are mixed.

Special machines, colloid mills, homogenizers and emulsifying machines, are frequently used in the manufacture of emulsions. The equipment of the average American paint plant does not include any of these machines. However, it did not take long for the paint manufacturer, to learn how to prepare his paint emulsions with his available equipment.

In preparing the emulsion in the laboratory, in a change-can paint mixer, the casein is placed in the container, and water is slowly added in small portions, to give the casein sufficient time to wet. The alkali (ammonia solution) and the preservatives are then stirred in. This forms the water phase. The varnish (oil, resin, and mineral spirits), pine oil, oleic acid, and liquid drier are mixed together, forming the oil phase. The emulsion is prepared by slowly flowing the oil phase into the water phase, with constant agitation. The water phase may be poured into the oil phase, but the reverse has been found a more reliable means for producing a fine particle size, stable emulsion. Some care should be exercised in the addition of the oil phase. The rate will somewhat depend on the equipment and the degree of stirring. It is desirable, at the beginning, to add the oil phase in relatively small portions and make sure that it has been emulsified, before an additional portion is added. The degree of emulsification, that is, the size of the dispersed droplets and the uniformity of size distribution, is related to the rate of addition of the oil phase and the length of agitation. This was established both by following consistency changes and by microscopical examination, and is illustrated by the typical curve (*Figure 1*) and the photomicrographs (*Figures 2–5*) covering the preparation of the emulsion. The emulsion is prepared in a constant-speed propeller blade type of change-can mixer, generally used in American paint plants for reducing and tinting paints. The water phase is placed in the container and agitation started and continued throughout the test. The oil phase is added slowly in three approximately equal portions. The addition of the first portion requires approximately 20 minutes and, two minutes later, the first sample is taken. The relative consistency reading, as shown on the curve (*Figure 1*), is practically the same as for the original water phase (0 minute). The photomicrograph (*Figure 2*) shows that the dispersed globules are quite large and non-uniform. Their average particle size is 2.2 microns. Immediately after taking the sample, the second portion of the oil phase is added, over a period of five minutes, and two minutes later, a sample of the emulsion is taken (*Figure 3*). The dispersed globules are now more uniform and smaller in size (1.6 microns), whereas the consistency of the emulsion is appreciably increased. The third

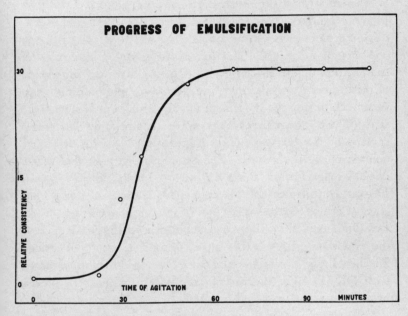

Figure 1

THIS CURVE DEMONSTRATES THE RELATION BETWEEN DEGREE OF EMULSIFICATION AND CONSISTENCY.

sample is taken after adding the last third of the oil phase over a period of about five minutes, and stirring for an additional two minutes, to insure adequate emulsification. There is an increase in consistency and a slight decrease in droplet size. From then on, additional samples are taken at fifteen-minute intervals, until it is definite that no further significant increase in consistency will occur. This is paralleled by little change in droplet size. Figure 4 is a photomicrograph of the emulsion after 51 minutes of agitation, when practically maximum consistency has been reached. Its average droplet size is 0.55 micron. From then on, there is little change in particle size. Figure 5 is representative of the remainder of the samples taken after 66 or more minutes of agitation, the average particle size of the dispersed globules is 0.5 micron.

Although no special technique is required for microscopical examination of the emulsions, the violent Brownian movement of the dispersed globules makes photomicrography difficult. Any treatment, to stop the movement of the particles, may alter their size. These photomicrographs were obtained by preparing mounts of the emulsion diluted approximately with an equal volume of distilled water. The photomicrographs were taken at 400X magnification, using a Bausch & Lomb No. 4597, 6-volt, 108-watt coil filament Mazda lamp with 7.4 mm. of signal blue glass (Corning Glass Works No. 5562) for illumination. With this illuminant, it was found possible to stop the movement of the emulsion particles with a 1/25-second exposure on Super Panchro Press film. The film was developed for six minutes with DK-60A. For the particle size measurements, the photomicrographs were enlarged to 1200X.

This experiment establishes that there is a maximum degree of emulsification for any specific formula and equipment. The practical value is that consistency measurements can be used both as a control for the mixing process and for the uniformity of the product.

The types of mixing equipment, generally available in American paint plants that might be considered for the manufacture of emulsion paints, are the High-Speed or "Lightnin'" Agitator, Change-Can Mixer, Pony Mixer, and Lead Paste Mixer.

Emulsions were prepared with the same formula using available laboratory or small size commercial paint mixing units.

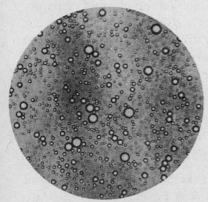

Magnification 400X

Figure 2—SAMPLE CONTAINING ⅓ OF THE OIL PHASE AND TAKEN 22 MINUTES AFTER STARTING AGITATION.

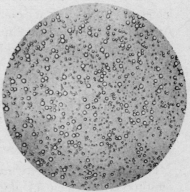

Magnification 400X

Figure 3—SAMPLE CONTAINING ⅔ OF THE OIL PHASE AND TAKEN 29 MINUTES AFTER STARTING AGITATION.

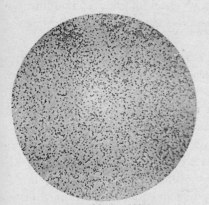

Magnification 400X

Figure 4—SAMPLE CONTAINING ALL OF THE OIL PHASE AND TAKEN 51 MINUTES AFTER STARTING AGITATION.

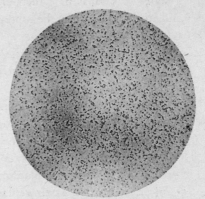

Magnification 400X

Figure 5—SAMPLE CONTAINING ALL OF THE OIL PHASE AND TAKEN 81 MINUTES AFTER STARTING AGITATION.

Even though, because of differences in the units, the size of the batches had to be varied, the results were quite informative. In each case, a stable and uniform emulsion was obtained. Approximately, 15 minutes of agitation was required with the Lightnin' Agitator, 50 with the Pony Mixer, 65 with the Change-Can Mixer and 90 in the case of the Lead Paste Mixer. These results indicate that with a balanced formula, containing sufficient quantities of efficient emulsifying agent and protective colloid, paint emulsion vehicles can be prepared using practically any of the common types of paint-mixing equipment.

CASEIN SUBSTITUTIONS

Tests were made to determine the effects on the emulsion of substitution for casein of alpha soya protein, sodium alginate, gelatin, glue, methyl cellulose, and colloidal clay (Bentonite). While the experiments were very limited in scope and while in no case sufficient data were developed to warrant drawing definite conclusions, they do indicate some interesting possibilities.

The photomicrographs (Figures (a) to (h), inclusive) are of a series of emulsions which are identical in their composition and in the method of their preparation except for the following substitutions for the casein.

(a) Standard formula using casein.

(b) Equal weight replacement of the 42 parts casein by alpha soya protein.

(c) 13 parts sodium alginate replaced the 42 parts casein.

(d) 42 parts alpha soya protein and 13 parts sodium alginate replaced the 42 parts casein.

(e) The 42 parts casein replaced by 4.2 parts gelatin.

(f) Equal weight replacement of the 42 parts casein by glue.

(g) Eight parts casein replaced by an equal weight of methyl cellulose.

(h) Half of the casein replaced by an equal weight of Bentonite.

SUBSTITUTIONS FOR CASEIN CONSTITUENT OF RESIN-OIL EMULSION

(Magnification 400X)

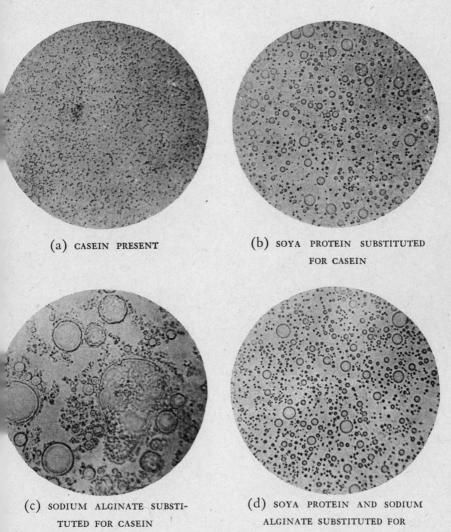

(a) CASEIN PRESENT

(b) SOYA PROTEIN SUBSTITUTED FOR CASEIN

(c) SODIUM ALGINATE SUBSTITUTED FOR CASEIN

(d) SOYA PROTEIN AND SODIUM ALGINATE SUBSTITUTED FOR CASEIN

(e) GELATIN SUBSTITUTED FOR
CASEIN

(f) GLUE SUBSTITUTED FOR
CASEIN

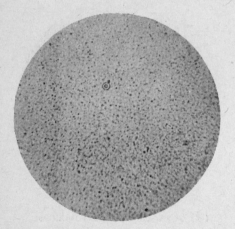

(g) PARTIAL REPLACEMENT OF
CASEIN BY METHYL CELLULOSE

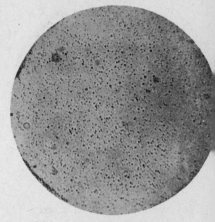

(h) PARTIAL REPLACEMENT OF
CASEIN BY COLLOIDAL CLAY

It will be noted that the standard formula containing casein produced a fine, uniform emulsion (photomicrograph (a)). The emulsion obtained with the soya protein (b) is coarser and less uniform. The sodium alginate apparently is not so satisfactory a protective colloid as either the casein or soya protein, since the oil particles coalesced to form large droplets and aggregates (c). The combination of soya protein and sodium alginate (d) produced an emulsion approximately the same in appearance as the emulsion made with soya protein. Gelatin, although used in a much smaller quantity, produced almost as uniform, though very slightly coarser emulsion (e) than casein. As would be expected, the emulsion containing glue (f) was very similar to the one containing gelatin. The replacement of part of the casein by methyl cellulose (g) did not change the size or uniformity of the dispersed oil globules, although they appeared to be very loosely flocculated. Substitution of colloidal clay for half of the casein (h) did not change the size nor the uniformity of the globules.

The following few observations, regarding the properties of the emulsions, may be of interest.

The emulsions, containing the soya protein or the sodium alginate, were slightly thinner but dried harder and with less gloss than the standard emulsion, containing casein. Both the casein and the soya protein emulsions dried to opaque, milky films while the sodium alginate produced an almost clear film.

The combination of soya protein and sodium alginate had the same effects on the properties of the emulsion as the soya protein alone, except that the consistency of the emulsion was definitely increased.

The gelatin substitution resulted in lower consistency, harder, dry, and a less opaque film with definitely lower sheen than the standard casein emulsion. Excepting that the emulsion containing the glue was thinner, it checked the standard very closely in its properties.

The partial replacement of casein by Bentonite lowered the consistency of the emulsion, increased the hardness of the dried film, lowered its gloss, and slightly decreased its opacity.

The only observed effect of the partial substitution of methyl cellulose was an increase in the consistency of the emulsion.

The individual properties of the paints, prepared by pigmenting these emulsions, will not be discussed, except to state that when all properties were considered, none rated as high as the one made with the (casein-containing) standard emulsion. The results, however, do indicate that these types of materials may be used to extend and, in some cases, replace casein in oléoresinous paint emulsions and that their investigation should prove very fruitful for the emulsion paint chemist.

OLEORESINOUS COMPONENT OF THE EMULSION

Although there are apparently no limitations to the viscosity of an oil that can be emulsified, especially if it is first reduced with a volatile diluent, it was found that the heavily bodied oils (viscosities 75 to 150 poises) produce paints possessing desirable consistency, application and film properties. It was also found that bodied oil and ester gum or another oil and mineral-spirits-dispersible resin produce comparable emulsions whether the resin is dispersed by heating it with the oil or by cutting it in the mineral spirits and then blending with the oil. Varying the ratio of the resin-to-oil over a range of a 10- to 40-gallon length varnish, but maintaining the total of oil and resin solids constant, does not change the properties of the emulsion nor of the resultant paste-paint, although, as with normal varnish vehicle paints, the hardness or brittleness of the film increases with decrease in the varnish length.

It has been generally recognized that control of the pH is important in casein water paints. Work done in the laboratory has not indicated that control of the pH of the oleoresinous emulsion or emulsion paint is a satisfactory means for maintaining uniform properties in various batches of the product. The standard emulsion made possesses a fairly high pH (8.7 to 8.8). Although, the consistency of the reduced emulsion paint tends to vary directly with the pH values of the emulsion and of the paste-paint, there have been so many exceptions, that we have not been able to use pH values as a control. Batches of emulsions with pH values varying as much as from 8.5 to 9.1 have frequently shown no significant differences in the properties of the paints. Variations in the quantities of the emulsifying agents, protective colloids, preservatives, etc., seem to exert more influence on the properties of the paint than pH variations. The relation of pH values of the resin-oil emulsions, of the paste-paints and of the reduced paints to the other properties of these materials, appears to be another fruitful field for further investigation.

THE PIGMENTED EMULSION

There may be considerable controversy and speculation whether the pigment of a pigmented emulsion occupies the oil or the water phase. The dispersed oil particles, in a standard emulsion (Figure 5), are quite uniform and small in size (average 0.5 micron). The size of the individual particles of the average paint pigments will approach this figure. In many cases, the pigment in a paint is not completely dispersed, but a considerable proportion is present as loosely held aggregates or undispersed lumps of one or more microns in size. For the pigment to be in the oil phase, the oil particles would have to expand like balloons to envelop the pigment particles or they would have to coalesce around a pigment particle. Under the microscope, with dark field illumination, the pigment in the emulsion paint appears well dispersed and is in rapid motion, and emulsified oil particles are also easily identified. Various microscopic methods have been tried to establish whether the pigment is just dispersed in the water phase or coated by the oil phase. These included the use of selective wave lengths of light with colored as well as transparent pigments, staining of the pigmented emulsion with dyes of selective solubilities, and the use of special single pigment paints. Quite conclusive evidence has been obtained when an oil-soluble fluorescent dye (Fluorescent Yellow AA, Calco Chemical Company) was incorporated in the emulsion by dissolving it in the oil before emulsification.

The emulsified oil particles are found to fluoresce brilliantly in the misroscope when the field of the microscope is illuminated with ultra-violet light. A 100-watt type CH-4 mercury vapor lamp is used as the ultra-violet source with 5 mm of H.R. Red Purple Ultra (Corning Glass Works No. 5874) to remove most of the visible light from the mercury arc. In the pigmented emulsions, it is then easy to identify (1) small strongly fluorescing oil globules, (2) small more feebly fluorescing oil-coated pigment particles, and (3) larger feebly fluorescing undispersed lumps of pigment coated by oil on the dark field formed by the non-fluorescent water phase.

The same feeble fluorescence of pigment particles, coated with the fluorescent oil, is observed when a few drops of the fluorescent oil phase are stirred into about two grams of pigment, thus coating the pigment particles, without leaving an excess of oil. The water phase of the emulsion is used as a mounting medium for the coated pigment particles. All oleophilic pigments that have been examined appear coated with the oil phase in emulsion paints. Unfortunately, the fluorescent light, from the microscopic particles, is not intense enough for photomicrography.

Emulsion paint can be prepared by (1) pigmenting the emulsion, (2) pigmenting part or all of the oil phase and then emulsifying the pigmented paste, and (3) pigmenting part or all of the water phase and then emulsifying. Using the standard formula, paints are prepared according to the three procedures. There are no detectable differences in the paste-paints nor the reduced liquid paints. It has been found that the dried paint films vary slightly in opacity and resistance to scrubbing with water. The paint prepared by pigmenting the oil phase possesses a slight advantage in the resistance to wet abrasion, whereas the one prepared by pigmenting the water phase has a slight advantage in dry opacity. The paint prepared by pigmenting the complete emulsion is intermediate in both properties.

The oil-soluble fluorescent dye is added to each of the paints. Under the microscope, dispersed oil particles and oil-coated pigments are present in all three. The only difference is a very slight variation in the number and size of the oil-coated, loosely held pigment aggregates; the paint prepared by pigmenting the water phase contains the most and the one prepared by pigmenting the oil phase the least. In other words, the thoroughness of the pigment dispersion follows the order, pigmentation of the oil phase, pigmentation of the complete emulsion, and pigmentation of the water phase. These slight differences in pigment dispersion agree with the slight differences observed in the opacities and wet abrasion resistances of the paint films.

There seems to be a tendency for dispersion of the pigment to continue in the paste-paint, during storage, and the differences in these three paints will probably disappear on prolonged storage. Progressive dispersion of undispersed pigment, in emulsion paste-paint, during storage, may be one of the causes for the progressive decrease in the reduced paint consistency as the age of the paste-paint increases, which is a quite common phenomenon with oleoresinous emulsion paints.

EMULSIONS IN THE LEATHER INDUSTRY

By W. R. ATKIN, M.Sc. AND F. C. THOMPSON, M.Sc.

(Leather Industries Department, The University Leeds)

OILS and greases are used in leather manufacture chiefly for the purpose of rendering leather either more waterproof or more soft and pliable. In addition, oils are used in oil tannages, such as the manufacture of chamois leather, and also for some miscellaneous purposes such as "oiling off" before drying. The more important processes, involving oils and fats, may be classified under four types:

(1) Oil tannages
(2) Impregnation
(3) Currying and
(4) Fat-liquoring

and will be referred to or discussed in this order.

The first type of oil treatment is oil tannage, in which, the oil or fat is not merely a lubricating or waterproofing agent, but actually the tanning material, which converts the collagen of the hide or skin into leather. Many theories have been put forward to explain this process. The most likely hypothesis is that the amino groups of the skin proteins combine chemically either with oxidised fatty acids produced from the oils, or with aldehydes also formed as a result of the oxidation of unsaturated oils. The chief oil-tanned leather is the so-called chamois leather made from the fleshes or inner layers of sheep-skins, by treatment with

230

fish oils, in the presence of moisture, and, generally, some alkali. In its dyeing properties, chamois leather is very similar to formaldehyde leather, now so much used for white washable gloves. In addition to combination with amino groups, there also occurs considerable coating of the leather fibres with grease, and this contributes both to softness and to water-resistance. Fish oils are not absolutely necessary for the production of leather. Certain leathers, for use in textile factories, are prepared by kneading tallow into hides by the use of special machines. Some tanning occurs in such a process, but most of the effect produced is due to a coating of the individual fibres with grease.

The second manner of applying grease to leather is the process of impregnation. The leather, *absolutely dry,* is immersed in hot, melted greases or waxes. The grease is quickly absorbed and the final product may contain 40 or 50 per cent of fatty matter. This is a method of waterproofing leather and has been much used for chrome sole leather and, occasionally, for vegetable tanned sole leather also. Great care must be used in this latter case, since vegetable tanned leather is exceedingly sensitive to heat in the moist or damp state. Rosin may be incorporated in the grease mixture and prevents soles from being slippery in wet weather.

The processes of oil-tannage and impregnation, though important in leather manufacture, are thus briefly dismissed, since there is no direct application of emulsification theory to these methods of applying grease to leather. However, the third process, that of currying, is of very much greater interest in this connection.

Currying is very widely practised, and may be carried out by either of two methods, namely, hand-stuffing and drum-stuffing. In the former process, a suitable oil and fat mixture is spread evenly over the damp leather, which is then put away, in some place, not too cold, so that the penetration of oil may take place. A typical mixture is the traditional dubbin made of cod oil and tallow. The solid tallow (which largely crystallises out) seems

to be chiefly a means for holding the liquid cod oil in place, and
may, though without any practical advantage, be replaced by
other inert materials made into pastes with the cod oil. Whilst
laid away, the leather slowly dries, and the cod oil penetrates into
the interior. In the drum-stuffing process, the damp leather is
drummed with a suitable mixture of oils and low-melting greases,
which are absorbed by the leather with fair rapidity. From the
physical point of view, both these methods of currying offer
serious obstacles to investigation, and there are also chemical
complexities to be considered, both in the constitution of the
materials used and in the chemical changes which take place
after the oil has been incorporated in the leather. Consequently,
little has been contributed to the scientific understanding of currying, though mention should be made of the chapter on the subject
in Procter's book [1] "Principles of Leather Manufacture" and of
some important work by R. H. Marriott.[2]

To the layman, the most striking feature of the currying
process is the indispensible necessity for having the leather damp.
The exact degree of dampness is very important and a matter
for the experienced judgment of the foreman. Roughly, however, if water is easily squeezed out of the leather it is too wet,
and if it is impossible to squeeze water out at all, then the
leather is not damp enough. Those not practically acquainted
with leather manufacture are usually surprised to find how
important the dampness of the leather really is, and also to be
informed that wet boots should be greased first and dried afterwards and not vice versa; and this in spite of the fact that perfectly dry leather appears to absorb oil quite easily as a rule, if
there is no special finish on the surface to interfere. However,
it is this necessity for moisture which gives the clue to what
really happens in currying.

The most rational view of the process is that it depends chiefly,
and in the first instance, on the spreading of the oil. A non-
volatile liquid, such as a triglyceride oil, spreads very slowly, if

at all, on a strictly solid surface. Indeed N. K. Adam [3] takes the point of view that unless a liquid is volatile, and can volatilise and then condense in a neighbouring place, the spreading of a liquid on a solid is an exceptional occurrence due to special causes. A liquid spreads on another liquid because of the thermal agitation of the molecules of the lower liquid at the interface; molecules of the upper liquid are dragged outwards and remain further out if the surface energy relationships of the system show that there will be a diminution in total surface energy after spreading. In the case of a liquid resting on a solid, however, whatever the surface energy relations might be (and these can only be guessed at), there is no free thermal agitation of the solid molecules at the interface, but only vibrations of molecules about fixed centres; there is, consequently, no mechanism for actually spreading the drop of liquid into a thin film except the feeble force of gravity which tends to flatten the drop. A dry leather fibre, from this point of view, therefore, does not possess a surface over which oil can readily spread. However, the oils used in currying will spread over a water surface, and also, though sometimes a little less readily, over the surface of a tannin solution. This latter fact was noted by Marriott, and is probably to be accounted for by the lowered surface energies of tannin solutions as compared with water. If a leather fibre, therefore, is sufficiently wet, so wet as to have what is essentially a water surface, oil will spread over it easily. It may be mentioned that pure mineral oil has some disadvantages for currying, which are, no doubt, due to its poor spreading qualities. However, if leather is too wet, the penetration of oil will not be good. Under such circumstances, not only are the fibres wet, but the spaces between the fibres, i.e., the pores of the leather, are filled up with water, and oil will tend to spread over the water-air surface on the exterior of the leather, rather than penetrate by spreading over each individual fibre. This means that currying does not begin, until the water-content of the leather is reduced by evaporation. This, therefore, represents the first stage of the currying process, namely, the formation of oil films on the fibre surfaces, which, of course, is not strictly emulsification, though closely related to it. Emulsifying agents such as sulphated oils and dégras appear to assist penetration very materially.

The second stage of currying is the slow drying which ensues after the penetration of the oil. (Actually, in hand-stuffing, both stages take place more or less simultaneously.) This causes the movement of oil, carried by water towards the drying surface or surfaces. This goes on until the amount of water present is quite small and free or liquid water may be considered to be absent. This is the cause of the interesting and important fact that the amount of grease, in the outer layers of the finished curried leather, is always notably greater than in the middle layer. This is the case when the grease is applied on one side of the leather only, as has been demonstrated several times. The grease content, in the outer layer, opposite to the side on which the grease is applied, is higher than in the centre, notwithstanding the fact that all the grease, in the distant layer, must have traversed the central portion, before arriving at the opposite side. This has an interesting domestic application. If muddy boots are allowed to dry before being cleaned, grease is lost by being carried into the deposit of drying mud. If this occurs a few times, with heavily greased boots, a notable difference, in the feel of the leather, is apparent. Football boots can be largely degreased in this way.

A method of currying, sometimes practised, is to begin by incorporating grease into absolutely dry leather. This is the impregnation process already referred to in this paper. However, leather so treated has not at all the feel and other properties of curried leather. The grease has been taken up more or less as water is taken up by a sponge and is present probably in a form much more "massive" than after currying. In order to convert such leather into curried leather it is necessary to drum it for a considerable time with water, a process not very obvious at first sight when it is remembered that the impregnated leather is practically waterproof. However, in time, water penetrates, perhaps through tiny fissures caused by the drumming, spreads over the fibres, and finally brings about a re-arrangement of the oil into films which cover and lubricate the individual fibres. The leather thus attains the same condition as when curried.

It is not possible to say anything definite with regard to the thickness of the oil-films, but even if they are no more than monomolecular, the enormous surface areas of the fibres and fibrils will account for a considerable quantity of oil. However, in the absence of data it is hardly profitable to consider this question further, though the writers incline to the view that a monomolecular film is first formed, and that further spreading occurs over this film.

Very important changes take place in the oil, after incorporation in the leather. Oil can only be re-extracted in its entirety with difficulty, and the re-extracted oil always shows a somewhat increased acid value, a much increased saponification value, and a greatly diminished iodine value. Important as these changes are, they are chiefly subsequent to the currying process, except in hand-stuffing, where the leather is laid in grease for prolonged periods. In this case the currying no doubt involves some degree of oil tannage, *i.e.,* chemical combination of the altered oil with the leather, whereas in the case of drum-stuffing, such oil-tannage will take place during drying and storage. These questions, however, have not, so far as can be seen at present, any direct connection with emulsification or spreading phenomena, except, of course, that the chemical changes are much accelerated by the physical state of the oil.

The fourth type of application of grease is by drumming the leather in the wet or damp state in a dilute oil-in-water emulsion, which is technically known as a "fat-liquor." This term often provokes a smile from people unconnected with the leather trade, but the word "liquor" is used extensively in the industry and the expression "fat-liquor" followed naturally on such terms as lime-liquors and tan-liquors. The process of fat-liquoring has become more and more extensively used with the development of chrome tanning, during the last forty years, and many people, even in the trade itself, are of the opinion that incorporation of grease by drumming the leather with emulsions dates from the intro-duction of the chrome tanning process. Actually, the process dates back to the time of the Egyptian wars of the "eighties." An American tanner, James Kent, first used this process in the manufacture of "Dongola" leather, in which he treated leather, tanned by a combination tannage of alum and vegetable tannin, with the alkaline liquor obtained by washing the surplus oil from chamois leather. It is possible, however, to make out a case for an even earlier use of emulsions in the leather industry, namely the employment of egg-yolk in the manufacture of alum tawed leather, which provided the original glazed kid and glove kid leathers. The egg-yolk is of course a natural fat-liquor or emul-sion, in which the emulsifying agents are the proteins and lecithin present in the egg-yolk. The usual fat-liquors are oil-in-water emulsions in which the oils employed are triglyceride oils, mineral oils, or mixtures of these, emulsified either by soaps or sulphated oils.

The leather, suitably washed and neutralised in the case of chrome tanned leather, is drummed with the emulsion and nearly all of the oil is quickly absorbed by the leather, practically clear water being left behind. The theory generally accepted for the absorption of the oil is that it is due to the neutralisation of opposite electrical charges. Chrome-tanned leather has a basic chromium salt combined with the free carboxyl groups of the hide, which also, of course, possesses amino groups which have already combined with the acid produced in the chroming liquors by hydrolysis. Thus the chrome leather possesses positive charges due to $-NH_3{}^+$ groupings. These have an affinity for the nega-tively charged oil droplets where the charge resides in the outer pellicle of emulsifying agent, whether it is soap or sulphated oil. This theory is sufficient to account for the initial rapid absorption of the oil. Since the process is carried out in drums, the mechanical tumbling that the leather undergoes causes considerable flexing of the wet skins, and thus the penetration of the fat-liquor is greatly facilitated.

Reference has been made above to the neutralisation of the chrome leather. This, and a thorough washing, after tannage, are essential if soap is to be used as an emulsifying agent, otherwise two dangers are likely to be encountered. If soluble chromium compounds are left in the leather, chromium soaps will be formed, leaving sticky messes on the skins, and also the emulsion will break, causing greasy patches. This danger is obviated by washing, but further trouble with soap fat-liquors may be encountered owing to excess acid left in the skins cracking the soap. The acid should be neutralised with salts of weak acids, such as sodium bicarbonate or borax, but care has to be exercised as it is possible to over-neutralize chrome leather. Even after neutralisation, further acidity develops on standing, due to hydrolysis of the chromium compounds combined with the hide, and the extreme liability of basic chromium compounds to coordination causes this hydrolysis to be progressive and not reversible. Consequently, fat-liquoring must not be delayed after neutralisation, or the fat-liquor is split either outside or on the surface of the leather. These dangers of soap fat-liquors have been in part obviated by the use of sulphated oils which are capable of emulsifying even in slightly acid solutions.

So far, we have been concerned with the introduction of oil into the leather as an emulsion. If fat-liquored leathers are split into sections and fat determinations are made, it is always found there is least grease in the middle layer.[4] Merrill extended the work initiated by Wilson and investigated the fat-liquoring properties of sulphated neatsfoot oil on chrome tanned calf skin. His results may be summarised as follows:—

(1) The outer layers always contained more grease than the inner layers of the leather.

(2) The depth of penetration of grease with this fat-liquor was practically the same in the wet leather as in the dried-out leather.

(3) Increase in the amounts of grease, applied as fat-liquor, caused an increased absorption of oil in the outer layers and particularly the grain. It was only with larger amounts of applied grease that there was observed an increased absorption in the middle layers.

(4) When fat-liquors at different pH values were employed, there was greatest absorption in the outer layers and least in the middle with lower pH values. An increase of pH led to a more even distribution of grease.

This last observation was confirmed by Merrill and Niedercorn,[5] who noted a much greater take-up of grease with more acid leathers.

The reason for this piling-up of grease in the outer layers is that the emulsion is broken after relatively little penetration of the leather. Two factors may bring about this breaking:

(a) The acidity of the leather has some effect, but this is minimised with a greater degree of neutralisation of the leather, although delayed hydrolysis and oleation will operate against neutralisation.

(b) The absorption by the basic chromium salt combined with the leather, of either fatty acid anions of soap or of the negatively charged sulphated oils which owe their charge to the sulphate group.

Chromium salts, especially when basic, readily form complexes either with the anions of organic acids, such as acetic, or with sulphates. If the stabilising emulsifying agent is absorbed by the chromium complex, the emulsion is broken, and the grease cannot penetrate into the interior to any great extent, unless large amounts of emulsifying agent have been used. It is a well known fact that of the total grease absorbed by a chrome leather only a part can be extracted by solvents.

It should be clearly understood that Merrill's results were obtained with sulphated neatsfoot oil, which contains a large amount of neutral oil and relatively little of the sulphated portion. Consequently, its emulsions are fairly easily broken by combination of the sulphated portion with the chrome tanning compounds. If a really soft leather is required, as for example in the case of certain special leathers for textile machines, success may be achieved by fat-liquoring, drying-out, and then re-fat-liquoring. Care should also be taken to ensure the presence of sufficient emulsifying agent, in order to avoid the complete splitting of the emulsion, before satisfactory penetration has been obtained.

Fat-liquoring may also be carried out on vegetable tanned leather, although the splitting of the fat-liquor is not so easily brought about. The emulsifying agent, in this case, apparently combines with the free amino groups present in the leather and this may be facilitated by the usually acid condition of such leathers. Usually, when vegetable tanned leather is fat-liquored, the proportion of grease in the middle layers is definitely higher than with chrome leather.

REFERENCES

1. Procter. *"Principles of Leather Manufacture,"* 1922.
2. Marriott. *J. Inter. Soc. Trades' Chem.,* 1933, **17**, 270.
3. N. K. Adam. *"Physics and Chemistry of Surfaces."*
4. cf. Wilson. *"Chemistry of Leather Manufacture,* Vol. 2," (1929).
5. Merrill and Niedercorn. *Ind. Eng. Chem.,* 1929, **21**, 364.

SECTION 14

RUBBER LATEX

By H. P. Stevens, M.A., Ph.D., F.I.C.,
and
W. H. Stevens, A.R.C.S., F.I.C.

(Consultants to the Rubber Growers' Association)

UNTIL the last few years, rubber suspensions were hardly used industrially, rubber being exported entirely in the solid state. The idea of utilising rubber latex or the "milk," in the form in which it exudes from the tree, is very old and dates back to the time of Hancock, the "father" of the rubber manufacturing industry, but the difficulties of transport prevented an early development. There is a number of different species of rubber bearing trees, and the nature of the latex obtainable from these differ fundamentally. Although, most of them must be regarded as suspensions rather than emulsions, there are one or two varieties, such as that obtained from the *Ficus elastica,* which are true emulsions. Under the microscope, the particles in suspension are seen to be spherical and to merge into one another like drops of oil.[1] The particles of this latex vary in size up to about 5μ.[2] Under the microscope, the globules are seen to readily unite to lakes. Macroscopically, the latex creams readily, especially when heated. This is the easiest way of breaking the emulsion, as acids and other coagulants, for *Hevea* latex, have no effect. In this connection, it should be noted that the proportion of acetone soluble (resin), contained in this rubber,

240

is much higher than in *Hevea* rubber whereas the protein content of the serum is much less.

Another latex, which creams readily, is that obtained from the *Castilloa elastica*. The particles are spherical but do not unite readily as do those of the *Ficus*. This may arise from the much larger solid content of the serum which also may account for more rapid creaming. The particles, too, on the average, are larger than *Hevea*. Here again the emulsion is difficult to break and the rubber is obtained by creaming which may be conveniently hastened by centrifugation. The cream, deposited on the inner walls, consists of a layer of discreet particles which readily unite under moderate pressure. This rubber also contains a large proportion of "resin" (acetone extractable).

There is little in the literature concerning the latex from *Funtumia elastica*. All we know is that the particles are very small and have a globular appearance. The latex can be shipped substantially unaltered, without preservative. The latex is usually coagulated by boiling. Also, formaldehyde has been recommended as a coagulant.

The latex obtained from the *Manihot glaziovii* appears to be a suspension and not an emulsion as according to Tobler,[3] the latex contains rod-shaped particles of irregular contour up to 10μ in length. There are, however, particles which tend to a spherical shape. This latex is reported as more viscous than others and is diluted with ammonia solution where collection in liquid condition is desired. In its behaviour to coagulants, *Manihot* latex behaves similarly to *Hevea*. Alkaline substances stabilise, whereas acids and acid salts coagulate. The separated particles unite in somewhat similar fashion to those of *Hevea*.

Unfortunately, none of these latices has been thoroughly investigated, in the light of modern knowledge. Most of the data are contained in papers published before the war. Since then, *Hevea* latex has become of such predominating importance that work on other latices and the rubber produced from them has been entirely neglected. The above mentioned latices were the course of commercially valuable rubber. To-day, very little of such rubber reaches the market. There are an enormous number of latex yielding plants, particularly in the tropics, and the latices contain a variety of substances other than rubber, very frequently substances of a resinous character. Of the physical properties of these latices, little or nothing is known, although, from the standpoint of the colloid chemist, they are of as much interest as those of commercial importance.

The latex of *Hevea Braziliensis* is one of the least stable and contains readily putrescible nitrogenous constituents. It cannot, therefore, be shipped without preservatives. Microscopically examined, it is seen to consist of particles approximately spherical but mainly slightly ovoid. There are occasional particles which resemble a falling drop, that is they are drawn out to a point.[4] Sometimes, this character is so pronounced that the particles have the appearance of carrying a tail. It has been suggested that the irregular shape of the particles results from the partial coalescence of two or more particles of different size. The particles vary greatly in size from about 2μ in diameter downwards, perhaps the greater number appear to about $\frac{1}{2}\mu$, and there are many which are barely visible. It is the largest particles which show greatest variation from the spherical. Naturally, the particles are in Brownian movement. The specific gravity of the rubber hydrocarbon is about 0.92, and the latex creams very slowly when set aside. The cream is readily re-dispersed on shaking the vessel. But little is known about the constitution of the particles. According to Hauser,[5] they consist of a solid sack containing a viscous liquid. Hauser has described his experiments at length in a monograph entitled "Latex." By means of a micromanipulator, he was able to pierce the particles and he has published microphotographs showing the puncturing of the rubber particles. If the coalescence of the particles be studied under the microscope, it will be seen that they largely retain their shape so

that the tiny masses of coagulum preserve an irregular outline.
The serum contains a variety of water soluble substances, that
present in the largest amount being quebracitol (1-methyl inositol). There are also nitrogenous (protein constituents) fatty acids,
lipin, *etc.* Some of these are dissolved in the serum and some
presumably adsorbed on the particles. Some may form independent particles in suspension.

A typical analysis of the total solids yields:—

Moisture per cent	2.4 to 3.6
Acetone soluble per cent	2.0 to 4.0
Protein (N × 6.65) per cent	4.2 to 4.8
Ash per cent	1.4 to 1.8
Rubber hydrocarbon by difference per cent	85.8 to 89.0

The percentage of rubber, in the latex as drawn from the tree,
is usually 35 to 40 per cent, but varies with the conditions of
tapping, as does also the amount of non-rubber constituents.
There has been considerable speculation as to the persistence of
the rubber particle as an entity in the rubber obtained from the
latex, but an examination of sections of rubber is said to reveal
a structure. It would seem very probable that the pressure, exerted
in compacting the fresh coagulum, would obliterate most of
such structure. Moreover, it is probable that the initially fluid
contents of the sacks, if indeed, they are viscous fluids and not
gels, must undergo some change, possibly of a chemical character, by which the fluid is transformed to a gel. That such changes
do take place is apparent from the behaviour of the fluid particles
which comprise *Ficus elastica* latex. In the process of drying the
cream, obtained when the latex is set aside, the fluid rubber must
change to a gel. Similar considerations apply to other latices
where the particles are apparently fluid. In this connection observations made in Mexico by C. O. Weber may be recalled. He
collected *Castilloa* latex in a flask containing ether, and, on
separating the aqueous layer, obtained a mobile etherial rubber

sol. This suddenly became viscous, and the change was attributed by him to the conversion of the original mobile fluid sol of the latex particles into one containing the rubber sol owing to polymerisation of the original particle constituents. One of us attempted to repeat this experiment some years ago in the East, both with *Hevea* and *Ficus* latices, but without success. In the former case, immediate coagulation of the latex took place, followed, in both cases, by formation of a normal rubber sol or gel.

Hevea latex, as obtained direct from the tree, is readily coagulated by any reagent of an acid nature, presumably owing to the negative charge on the particles. On the other hand, this does not explain all cases of coagulation, and other theories have been put forward. Opinions differ as to the pH value of latex as it exudes from the tree. It is obvious that, on cutting into the cortex to sever the latex vessels, other vessels will also be cut, so that the exuding latex will be contaminated with sap from other vessels. Rae [6] has determined the hydrogen ion concentration of a number of *Hevea* latices taken at different periods of the year, and obtained figures varying from 5.8 to 6.7. Normally, the latex becomes increasingly acid on standing, and lactic acid bacteria get a hold, with the result that within twenty-four hours, the liquid is largely coagulated, the extent depending on the proportion of surface exposed to the air. Alkaline substances prevent this change. For purposes of export, approximately one half per cent of ammonia is added. If this addition is made promptly, at collection, the latex appears to remain uncoagulated in closed vessels almost indefinitely, although chemical changes take place between the ammonia and the soluble serum constituents, the fatty acids being converted into soaps and the proteins being degraded. Although more acid is required for coagulating such preserved latex than is required for coagulating fresh latex, owing to the need to neutralise the ammonia content, it may be said that such preserved latex is actually less stable than that as obtained direct from the tree. The reason for this is that the protein layer adsorbed on the rubber particles, which is the stabiliser of the dispersion, is slowly attacked by the ammonia and rendered soluble (amino acids?), with the result that the stability of the system is lowered. This is well known from the extreme sensitivity to coagulants of latex which has been preserved and kept for a long time. This sensitivity is readily cured by an addition of weak casein solution. It has also been shown that rubber prepared from latex, ammoniated and stood aside three days before coagulation in the East, has a lower protein content than rubber from latex not so treated.[7]

Preserved latex may be coagulated with salts such as aluminum sulphate while retaining the alkaline reaction (say to litmus) due to the ammonia present. Sodium silicofluoride acts similarly. Latex, whether fresh or preserved, is also coagulated by hydrophyllic substances, both organic and inorganic. As examples may be mentioned acetone and alcohol, in the first class, and finely divided mineral matter, such as carbon black, in the second class. Coagulation by alcohol or acetone is connected with the water soluble constituents of the latex, for, on removal of these, coagulation with alcohol becomes difficult or impossible. The finely divided mineral matter, no doubt, acts by withdrawal of water. Such mineral matter must be first dispersed in an aqueous solution with a suitable stabiliser, such as an alkaline caseinate; the resultant dispersion can then be mixed with latex without any difficulty. Substances, relatively coarse particled, such as Portland cement and lime, also readily coagulate latex for the same reason.

There has been, in recent years, a tendency to distinguish between coagulation and gelling or setting of latex; the former term being applied to a sudden breaking of the dispersion and the latter to a gradual process analogous to the formation of a junket from milk. This has led to a distinction between coagulating and gelling agents. This distinction is false, as the same agent can act in both respects. Thus, with preserved latex, acids are regarded as coagulants, because it is not possible or very difficult to produce a gelling or setting of the whole volume of latex by stirring in an acid solution. If this is done, at first, no change takes places, the acid being wholly utilised in neutralising the ammonia; eventually a stage is reached, at which, local conditions are such that in spite of vigorous stirring, the pH value reaches a figure at which the dispersion is broken and local coagulation sets in. It is possible, however, to produce a uniform "gelling" or "setting" with acid alone if this is added sufficiently diluted to a stage just short of that necessary to cause coagulation. If now the mixture be gently heated, the whole sets to a uniform gel. Similarly, in the East, where all latex is converted to rubber by gelling or setting, diluted acid, either acetic or formic of about 5 per cent concentration, is added to the latex diluted to a rubber content of about 15 per cent. The amount of acid added is approximately one part to five hundred of latex according to the concentration of the latex and the nature of the acid employed. No change is initially produced and the mixture can be handled; for instance, it can be baled out into coagulating pans. In about half an hour, a substantial change is apparent and the whole sets to a porous gel or junket-like mass. Hence, acids are as much gelling as coagulating agents and it is merely a matter of adjusting conditions to give the required result. Where latex is coagulated, it is necessary, for technical reasons, to distinguish between coagulation proper and flocculation. In the former, the latex is converted into a compact mass of coagulum which is indistinguishable from that gelled. It is, however, possible to produce a discreet coagulation in which the particles of coagulum are very small. This is termed flocculation. In fact, the particles may be so small that, at first sight, the latex appears unaltered. This effect is produced by using well diluted latex and acid, or best by means of metallic salts, such as aluminum sulphate or chloride or salts of other polyvalent metals. As stated above, the breaking of the dispersion can take place without complete neutralisation of the ammonia. This form of coagulating is of importance for the commercial utilisation of latex.

Much of the work on preserved latex has been carried out with concentrated and purified latex as this is usually preferred for manufacturing processes. The purification involves removal of part of the water soluble ingredients and this results in loss of stability or perhaps rather increased sensibility to coagulating agents. Part of the ammonia is also lost but may be replaced. There are various methods of concentration. That chiefly used is the centrifugal process carried out in a modified milk separator. As part of the rubber particles are lost in the whey, the resulting concentrate may differ not merely in serum content but also in the nature of the rubber content. Presumably, it is the smaller sized particles which are lost in the whey, although Twiss reports that the microscopic appearance of the latex is not substantially altered.

The latex may also be concentrated by evaporation, although, this necessitates the addition of relatively large quantities of stabilisers, in particular, soft soap. Latex can be commercially concentrated by creaming without centrifugal aid if "creaming agents," such as gum tragacanth, are added. This is analogous to the effect on animal milk. The cream must be handled carefully, as any mechanical pressure causes the particles to adhere and a coagulated film of rubber results. Here again, the composition both of the serum and the rubber are altered, the latter, unless the separation is clean, with a clear under-layer.

As might be expected, the behaviour of these concentrates, in regard to coagulating agents, varies and also differs from the original latex. Moreover, the consistency of the concentrates varies according to the method of preparation. The evaporative process yields stiff creams or pastes for concentrations, at which centrifuged latex is quite mobile, probably on account of the large proportion of stabilisers which they contain. These evaporated latices are also the most stable and will stand a considerable amount of handling, even in paste form, without coagulation setting in. Put briefly, the larger proportion of protective colloid prevents coalition of the particles. Rubber being naturally adhesive, contact between particles must result in amalgamation and consequently, to revert to the question of the persistence of latex particles, after conversion to dry rubber, this can only result where a protective layer remains intact. That such a layer of protein does remain is shown by swelling a small piece of dry coagulum in benzene. The film of protein, being impervious, protects the rubber. The solvent only gradually finds its way into the rubber. Eventually, the films become enormously distended. No doubt, they are largely ruptured, but their structure and character are still retained (see India Rubber Journal, December 12, 1925, p. 1059, where photographs of the swollen rubber will be found). It would not be safe to assume that the film consists entirely of protein, all we know is that it is insoluble, gives protein reaction and contains a large proportion of nitrogen. Latices of different botanical origins vary in regard to the nitrogen and protein content of the resultant rubber. *Manihot* and *Ficus* rubbers have been examined in this regard. These rubbers swell like *Hevea* in benzene, but the amounts of soluble and insoluble nitrogen vary considerably as the following table shows.[8]

		Soluble %	Insoluble %	Total %
Hevea	....	0.07	0.39	0.46
Manihot	....	0.31	1.21	1.52
Ficus	....	0.08	0.03	0.11

Hevea stands in an intermediate position to the *Manihot* and *Ficus*. Is it a mere coincidence that the particles of *Manihot* are solid, of *Hevea* partly solid or highly viscous, and of *Ficus,* fluid? The swelling action in benzene, to reveal structure, applies only to a coagulum which has not been subjected to mechanical treatment. Crepe rubber, which is prepared by washing a coagulum on differentially geared rollers, dissolves with little or no swelling, but the debris of protein films, in time, settle to the bottom of the vessel containing the sol. On the other hand, the protein films may be hardened by adding a solution of tannic acid to the latex previous to coagulation. Such rubber is very resistant to swelling by solvents. It is obvious that the nature and condition of the protein film, surrounding the particles, must exert a considerable influence on the breaking of the suspension or emulsion, whichever we are dealing with. How far will they account for the behaviour of the latices to coagulating agents? *Hevea* latex is described as negatively charged. *Manihot* and *Ficus* are presumably similarly charged, but *Ficus* is not susceptible to acid coagulants. *Funtumia* has an acid reaction, so have certain latices yielding balata or gutta percha, but these are not coagulable with alkalies, contrary to expectation. It would seem, therefore, that there is still something to be said for the older theory, namely, that coagulation of rubber latex is brought about by the action of the acid on the protein film surrounding the particles, or that this acid activates a coagulating enzyme. There is little or no protein film round the *Ficus* or *Funtumia* particles. It may, therefore, be argued that the latex is, therefore, indifferent to acids or alkalies, and the drops of liquid rubber forming the particles readily amalgamate. Unfortunately, so little work has been done on latices other than *Hevea* that we have few facts to go upon. A wealth of data has been accumulated in respect to compounded latices derived from *Hevea,* mainly centrifuged latex with both organic and inorganic compounding ingredients, but most of these is to be found in patent specifications and are difficult to summarise. It has already been stated that fine powders coagulate latex by withdrawing moisture, consequently, where it is desired to apply a film containing loading or pigments, the latter must first be wetted, preferably by an aqueous solution of a stabiliser or protective colloid. The number of such substances available is very large. Some of the more common materials comprise glue, caseinates, starch paste, sulphonated oils and soaps. Some of the newer products are known under trade names such as "Nekal," "Igepon," "Laurel." Water-soluble substances can be added, in solution, to the latex, and do not usually coagulate unless of an acid nature. Sodium silicate has been used to a considerable extent in this way. The addition of these substances, therefore, involves the addition of water. Hence the advantage of starting with a latex from which part of the water has been removed. The compounded latex may even then be found to be too dilute for the required purpose, in which case a concentration, at this stage, becomes necessary.

Other substances, frequently added to latex, consist of emulsions, particularly of oils and waxes, both mineral and vegetable. A small quantity of a mineral oil emulsion, such as one prepared from transformer oil, is a frequent addition to be found in illustrative formulæ in patent specifications. Mineral oils emulsify very easily in latex, vegetable oils are more difficult to incorporate, but the scope for combination with drying oils is obviously wide. Similarly with resins and waxes which, of course, must be properly dispersed before adding to the latex.

There are various means by which the compounded latex may be converted to rubber. These comprise coagulating or gelling the dispersion with subsequent removal of water. The methods of coagulating and gelling are similar to those already discussed when treating of uncompounded latex, but some call for special mention, in particular the method of heat sensitisation. It has been found possible to pretreat the latex with certain reagents including metallic salts such as calcium sulphate and organic substances such as substituted guanidines, so that, on raising the temperature, coagulation or rather gelling sets in. The effect of a raised temperature, in promoting gelling, has already been mentioned in the process of gelling preserved latex with dilute acids. The effect may be connected with the buffering action of the ammonium salt first formed. The action can take place without neutralisation of the ammonia in the latex. The method is of great importance technically, because it facilitates the process of manufacture known as "dipping." This consists of dipping a mould or "former" into the latex and, after removal, drying the thin film, subsequently re-dipping and repeating the process until a sufficiently thick film is obtained. Various modifications have been introduced to reduce the necessary number of dippings, as for instance, coating the former with a coagulating medium or employing a hollow porous former and abstracting serum by suction, so as to leave the latex particles heaped on the surface. Or again, by adding gums, starch paste and other substances, to increase the viscosity of the latex. But the use of heat sensitised latex is perhaps the most convenient of all as it only requires the heating of the former before dipping into the cold sensitised latex. A compact coagulum or rubber gel forms on the surface of the former, without affecting the remainder of the latex, while a sufficiently thick layer of rubber on the former can be obtained with a single dip.

Finally, mention should be made of the electrical method of depositing rubber. If the object to be coated is provided with a conducting surface and forms the anode, the negatively charged rubber particles are deposited thereon when a current is passed. Only a low-tension current is necessary. The process has not been found of as great commercial importance as originally anticipated on account of the secondary reactions which take place, particularly electrolysis of the liquid and evolution of gas, which causes porosity of the deposited rubber. Various proposals have been made for overcoming these difficulties, but perhaps the most ingenious is that which involves the alteration of the sign of the charge on the particles converting the anode into a cathode process. This can be effected by cautious addition of a relatively large excess of acid to fresh or stabilised preserved latex. Taking a quantity of latex and adding gradually increasing quantities of dilute acid, the first effect is to cause coagulation.

The liquid then passes through an intermediate zone when no coagulation takes place, and eventually through a still more acidic range when the charge on the particles is reversed.[9]

REFERENCES

1. Beadle and Stevens. *Communications to the 8th Internat. Congress of Applied Chemistry*, 1912, **9**, 17.
2. D. Spence. *India Rubber Journal*, 1908, **36**, 233.
3. Pringsheim. *Jahrb. wiss. Bot.*, **54**, 2, 265–308.
4. Petch. "*The Physiology and Diseases of Hevea Braziliensis*," 1911, p. 19.
5. E. A. Hauser. *Z. wiss. Mikros.*, 1924, **41**, 4.
6. Rae, *Analyst*, 1928, **53**, 330.
7. Stevens and Parry. *India Rubber Journal*, 1934, 542.
8. Beadle and Stevens. *India Rubber Journal*, 1913, **45**, 313 and 345.
9. G. S. Whitby. "*Plantation Rubber*," 1920, p. 48.

SECTION 15

SOME PHYSICAL PROPERTIES OF DISPERSIONS OF ASPHALTIC BITUMEN

By LEONARD G. GABRIEL, B.Sc., M.INST.P.T.

(Chief Chemist, Messrs. Colas Products Ltd.)

THE manufacture of asphaltic bitumen emulsions is, at the same time, one of the simplest and one of the most difficult technical operations to carry out satisfactorily. With modern dispersive apparatus there is little difficulty in obtaining a finely dispersed emulsion; it is the meeting of numerous detailed requirements, all essential to satisfactory use, that presents the difficulties.

Various technical emulsions, other than those of asphaltic bitumen, are produced commercially, although in most cases, not in the quantity in which road emulsions (by far the most important type of asphaltic bitumen emulsions) are manufactured. In regard to the production of fine dispersions, the problem with many of these emulsions is more difficult than with asphaltic bitumen, but usually the specifications for the properties of such emulsions are, by no means, so numerous or so stringent.

The raw material, employed for the dispersions, which form the subject of the present paper, is known officially as "asphaltic bitumen," and is not to be confused with "asphalt," a term implying a compound of asphaltic material with fine mineral filler. Nor should the remarks here made be taken to apply to coal tar, or tar-pitch compounds. The emulsification properties of such materials are widely different from those of true asphaltic bitumen, and need special consideration. The "asphaltic bitumen," commonly employed for emulsification, consists of a petroleum residual pitch. The crude oil, as it comes from the well, after perhaps a preliminary "topping" to remove the most volatile fractions, is then further distilled under appropriate conditions, and the residue from this distillation is the "asphaltic bitumen" of commerce.

The usual method, by which the physical consistency of such bitumens is specified, is by means of a determination of "penetration." A needle of standard design is allowed to sink into a prepared sample of the asphaltic bitumen, under a load of usually 100 grams at 25°C. for 5 seconds. The depth of penetration, in tenths of a millimeter, gives a measure of the softness of the asphaltic bitumen. A common grade of bitumen, employed for the manufacture of road emulsions, has a penetration between 200 and 300, under the above conditions. .

The semi-solid, highly viscous nature of the base of these emulsions leads to their having certain peculiarities which differentiate them from other types of emulsion. Thus, the coagulation of bitumen emulsions is very easily watched and determined, owing to the formation of a semi-solid lump of the coalesced disperse phase, which shows no spontaneous tendency to re-disperse, and which is physically easily distinguishable from the original emulsion, and from the aqueous phase. With fluid oil emulsions, such as those of benzene or carbon tetrachloride, for example, it is a matter of some difficulty to determine the exact degree of coagulation which may have taken place in a given emulsion.

On the other hand, the specific gravity of most grades of asphaltic bitumen, suitable for emulsification, does not depart from unity by more than about 0.06, and consequently, the tendency of the emulsions to separate into layers is very much less than with most fluid disperse phases. This fact has an important bearing on the use of asphaltic bitumen emulsions in the road industry, because it enables emulsions to be stored for comparatively long periods, without the onset of any extensive coagulation of disperse phase, following from excessive sedimentation. This is especially important as, unlike the case of emulsions of fluid disperse phase, re-dispersion is not possible, without resort to intensive mechanical agitation.

The chemical nature of the asphaltic bitumen also has a bearing on the properties of emulsions prepared from it. Not much is known definitely regarding the chemical composition of the individual components which go to make up the complex entity which we are discussing. Its general constitution is, however, fairly well recognised: it consists of a viscous, oily medium, having dispersed in it, in a very fine state of subdivision, particles of carbon, or of compounds very rich in carbon, which particles are protected (peptised) by certain compounds present in the oily medium. The asphaltic bitumen is, therefore, itself a disperse system. Further, it contains certain acidic compounds which exert an important influence on some properties of the emulsions. Due to this fact, the emulsification of asphaltic bitumen can, in no sense, be compared with that of a pure neutral oil, and it will readily be recognised that the high viscosity of the bituminous disperse phase serves as a further complicating factor, in that diffusion phenomena in the bitumen itself are retarded, and the interaction between acidic constituents of the bitumen and, for instance, free alkali of the aqueous phase, becomes a gradual reaction, taking hours or days to reach completion. Further reactions due to the peculiar properties of the asphaltic bitumen will be discussed at greater length later in the paper.

It will, therefore, be realised that the production of a disperse system of finely divided asphaltic bitumen, in a suitable aqueous phase, presents no great difficulties, but that when it is desired to control the properties of the finished dispersion, and possibly to predict them in advance, the problem becomes much more difficult and involved.

It will be well to state, at this stage, what roughly are the requirements from a commercial asphaltic bitumen emulsion in use. The main desiderata can be summarised under the following headings:

(i) Stability.
(ii) Lability.
(iii) Homogeneity.
(iv) Viscosity, or Consistency.

Under stability, we have to consider the life of the emulsion under conditions of quiescent storage, and also its resistance to outside influences, such as extreme heat or cold, which possibly bring about premature coagulation. Emulsions are required to keep in good condition for from six months upwards, and only the most perfunctory agitation can be relied upon to redistribute any sediment of disperse phase which may have formed. In closed containers the emulsions are stable to ordinary atmospheric heat, but the normal type of road emulsion will usually exhibit some coagulation if cooled to such a temperature that actual freezing (solidification) takes place. This is usually at about $-3°$ to $-4°C$.

"Lability" is a term which has been adopted by technicians in the industry, to indicate the readiness of the emulsion to break down under conditions of use, and deposit its bitumen in a cohesive form, suitable as a road binding agent. Not the least of the problems to be met in the production of these emulsions is that although the general stability of the emulsion in storage must be considerable, nevertheless there are quite stringent requirements to be met regarding the readiness with which the emulsion should break when applied to the road. Luckily the two sets of opposed criteria have not proved irreconcilable, as forces, other than those of gravity, come into play to coagulate the emulsions in use. These forces may be summed up as

(1) evaporational, (2) chemical, (3) mechanical, and their relative incidence and importance will be seen later. For the present, it may be mentioned that, for road-building purposes, asphaltic bitumen emulsions are employed in three principal ways:

(a) For spraying or painting on a road surface, followed by application of chippings and rolling.

(b) For pouring into, or grouting a layer of unbound stone.

(c) For mixing on the road, or before application to the road, in some form of mixer, with aggregate of suitable type.

In (a) and (b) the evaporational effect comes into play and concentrates the emulsion to a certain extent, so that it becomes susceptible to mechanical disturbance, which in the end produces the necessary coagulation. In (c) the evaporational effect is of less importance, but mechanical disturbance is more intense and there is often a pronounced chemical coagulative effect of the stone employed. This is particularly so if the aggregate is very fine, and the specific surface correspondingly large.

The requirements regarding homogeneity are, in the main, that the particles of disperse phase larger than microscopic sizes shall be non-existent, or of strictly limited amount, so that the emulsion can be passed through spraying jets and other narrow orifices. Further the general microscopic dispersion should be fine enough to ensure no gradual coarsening of the dispersion which would lead, in time, to a partial coagulation.

The viscosity of road emulsions is of considerable importance in determining covering power, and rate of spraying under given conditions. With a given asphaltic bitumen, the viscosity of emulsions varies with the bitumen content, according to laws which will be dealt with later. Different types of asphaltic bitumen give different characteristic viscosities, which are, however, amenable to control by processes discovered in the author's laboratory, and forming the subject matter of various patents. Bituminous emulsions, in common with most, if not all, disperse systems show the phenomena of an apparent viscosity varying with the applied rate of shear, *i.e.*, structure viscosity. Measurements must, therefore, be made under conditions which eliminate this effect, if the results are to be comparable.

The standard methods for testing road emulsions are all described in British Standard Specification 434—1931, and need not be more fully mentioned here. The test for "Lability" was not available when these specifications were issued, and the form of this test, which it is hoped will shortly be adopted as standard, is, therefore, included in the Appendix of this paper.

MANUFACTURING METHODS

Modern manufacture of dispersions of asphaltic bitumen is easy to describe in general terms, but very difficult to particularise. With the more fluid oil phases frequently used for the experimental preparation of emulsions, a relatively uniform fine dispersion is somewhat difficult to produce, except under more or less carefully chosen conditions. With asphaltic bitumen of the softer grades, however, quite a wide range of conditions can be made to yield emulsions having a fairly uniform and fine dispersion, though the consideration of the finer points of the physical properties, important in the use of the emulsions, for the purposes for which they are designed, leads to a very careful control of production conditions, the details of which are largely closely guarded by the manufacturers who have worked them out.

Fig. 1 shows a size-frequency curve of a typical dispersion prepared by a normal commercial process. Beyond the size-range conveniently covered by a high power photomicrograph, such as was used for preparing the above curve, there are a certain number of larger particles which are revealed by a careful sieving operation. The origin of these is somewhat difficult to assign; whether they are formed during the dispersion operation and persist as such, or whether they are formed during the early life of the emulsion, due to coalescence of perhaps still freely fluid asphaltic bitumen, *i.e.,* before the final cooling of the emulsion to atmospheric temperature.

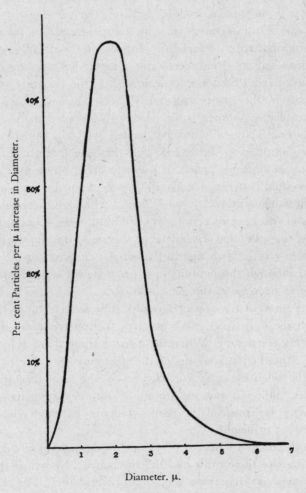

Fig. 1

THE COLLOID MILL

The colloid mill, or homogeniser, as it is sometimes ambiguously termed, is a very convenient apparatus for the commercial production of the type of emulsion under discussion. As will be seen in a subsequent section, however, the use of such intense mechanical disintegration is by no means necessary when dealing with normal types of asphaltic bitumen. Colloid mills need not be described in detail here, the construction and operational features having been amply dealt with in the literature. Certain features of the manufacture may, however, be touched upon. The asphaltic bitumen is, of course, always used in the molten condition. The mill must be flooded with the aqueous phase before introducing the asphalt and the asphalt must be cut off before the aqueous phase, in order to avoid jamming the mill.

In certain patterns of mills, the gap between the working faces is adjustable within fairly wide limits. Although there are exceptions in the cases of certain asphaltic bitumens, it is fairly generally the case that considerable variations in the gap width produce very little change in the general character of the dispersions, although throughput for a given power consumption will probably decrease as the gap is closed.

The speed of rotation of the mill must be kept up to that for which the mill is designed, usually a peripheral speed of about 10,000 ft. per minute. When the speed is allowed to fall by 25 per cent, a marked coarsening of the dispersion is liable to occur, *i.e.,* the quantity of coarse particles in the total dispersion increases, although the maximum of the size frequency curve probably remains in the same position, although decreasing somewhat in height.

Much research remains to be done on the process of dispersion by means of these mills and the mechanism, by which the subdivision occurs, requires a good deal of elucidation. The prevalent idea seems to be that shear between the rotor and stator faces constitutes the comminuting factor, but this is, by no means, certain. It should be borne in mind that the average size of the final disperse particles is much less than the gap width of the mill at its closest setting. This is usually about 4-thousandths of an inch, and may be much more, whereas the average particle size is of the order 1-2μ.

SLOW SPEED MIXING PROCESSES

Although, the Colloid Mill is, perhaps, the most convenient way of preparing these dispersions, it is by no means necessary to employ such intensive methods to produce a well-dispersed product. Owing to the complex chemical nature of the asphaltic bitumen, matters may be so arranged that a relatively gentle mechanical agitation can be supplemented by the dispersive effect of a chemical reaction carried on in situ, with the result that although the ultimate dispersion may possibly show a size-frequency curve somewhat changed in shape, the average particle size is not greatly affected, and the product answers commercial requirements.

Brief reference has already been made to the composition of asphaltic bitumen and the presence of acidic bodies has been mentioned. The nature of these acids has been, in part, elucidated, and their exact nature varies naturally from crude to crude, and from one variety of asphaltic bitumen to another. The manner, in which they act, will be largely dependent on their molecular weight, which will govern the colloidal behaviour of their alkali compounds when dissolved or dispersed in water.

The function of the naphthenic acids, in the actual dispersion process, as carried out in a slow stirring mixer, is, however, apparently merely that of a soap-forming agent, reacting with the alkali present in the aqueous dispersing medium to give surface active compounds capable of maintaining the asphaltic bitumen in the emulsified condition. The fact that this reaction occurs while the agitation of the bitumen with the aqueous phase is taking place seems to allow for the easy penetration of the bitumen by the alkaline aqueous medium, and this in some way, perhaps not so easily imagined in detail, assists materially in the comminution of the bitumen.

The result is, in practice, that a stirrer, running at no more than 60 r.p.m., is adequate for the production of well-dispersed bituminous emulsions. The aqueous phase may consist of a dilute alkali solution, or it may contain, in addition, some form of soap or colloid, to act as a stabiliser. It is a matter of some theoretical interest that it is usually not possible to get satisfactory dispersion in the absence of free alkali.

The order of addition of the two phases is of considerable importance. Generally speaking, it is much more effective to commence with the alkali solution in the mixer, heated to somewhere near the boiling point, and to add the molten bitumen slowly with stirring. It is possible, in this way, to prepare one-ton batches of emulsion containing from 50 to 60 per cent of bitumen, in about 1 to 3 minutes, depending somewhat on the precise apparatus and materials being used. Usually, a certain amount of soap or other stabiliser is added at the conclusion of the emulsification operation, although with some types of asphaltic bitumen, and particularly if the emulsion is soon to be used, this is not strictly necessary. Processes of this type are covered by a series of patents granted to Montgomerie.[1]

A prior patent, the first important process for the manufacture of commercial bituminous emulsions, embodies the same idea, but in a somewhat more complicated form. The fatty acid, destined to form the soap used for emulsification, is dissolved, first of all, in the molten bitumen in the mixer. A relatively concentrated alkali solution is then run into this mixture with stirring, when the emulsion is formed. Finally, this is diluted with water to the required concentration, usually 50 to 60 per cent of asphaltic bitumen. It is apparently an advantage to keep the concentration of soap rather high during the actual formation of the dispersion. This process and its variants are covered by a series of patents granted to Mackay.[2]

Another interesting examplification of the favourable influence of high soap concentration on dispersive processes is afforded by a process described by Préaubert.[3] Here emulsions of exceedingly fine dispersion are produced by the simple process of stirring the disperse phase with soap in high concentration. The stirring of similar grades of asphaltic bitumen with soap in low concentrations (2-5 per cent) under similar conditions does not lead to the formation of satisfactory dispersions.

PROPERTIES OF COMMERCIAL ASPHALTIC BITUMEN EMULSIONS

(a) Content of Asphaltic Bitumen

Medicinal preparations, in emulsion form, are frequently comparatively dilute, whereas other emulsions, such as some polishing preparations, contain high amounts of disperse phase. The normal bituminous road emulsion contains a medium percentage of asphaltic bitumen. Actually, this is usually between 55 and 65 per cent, although some emulsions contain as little as 50 per cent of bitumen. The governing consideration, in this respect, is the achievement of a viscosity which is suitable for the purposes to which the emulsions are put.

The viscosity of the emulsion is not altogether governed by the bitumen content, but this is one of the leading factors, and as the types of bitumen available are usually limited, the bitumen content frequently gives a guide to the viscosity. This will be discussed in a later section.

(b) Dispersion

A study of photomicrographs of commercial bitumen emulsions will enable the general dispersion of the products to be judged. A more accurate quantitative idea of the mean size and size variation of the particles may be obtained from a study of the size-frequency curve shown in Fig. 1. Here the peak of the curve occurs at 2μ, and the arithmetic mean diameter of the particles is 3μ. This figure fairly well represents general practice.

(c) Viscosity

There is some variation of viscosity between different commercial emulsions, but in general it may be stated that the viscosity varies between 3-4° Engler and 10-12° Engler. Some of the more concentrated emulsions with over 60 per cent of bitumen, go up to higher figures, but for normal road work 20°E. is about the limiting value. It is customary to use the Engler viscometer for measuring the viscosity of these emulsions, so that values are here given on that scale. Reference will be made later to the problems arising from the control and measurement of emulsion viscosity.

(d) Sedimentation

Separation of the components of an emulsion, due to the action of gravity, though not serious in a medicine bottle, becomes a more involved matter when in the larger bulks in which road emulsions are handled. Owing to the frequent difficulty in redistributing accumulations of sediment in drums and larger storage receptacles, even small amounts of sedimentation have to be avoided as far as possible, by care in manufacture, so that a minimum of coarse particles are produced, and by adopting adequate precautions for agitating the emulsion from time to time.

Due to the fortunate proximity of the specific gravity of the average asphaltic bitumen to that of the aqueous phase (which may normally be taken as 1.0 with sufficient accuracy), the tendency to sediment is by no means so pronounced as in the case of emulsions of light mineral or vegetable oils. Nevertheless, sedimentation does occur in the course of a few days or weeks to the point where agitation has to be resorted to. The specific gravities of the asphaltic bitumens, usually employed, are of the order 1.02—1.04. Where the emulsion is being stored in drums, rolling or up-ending the drums is the usual method of re-incorporation adopted. The large storage tanks of an emulsion factory are usually fitted so that the emulsion can, if so desired, be circulated by a system of pumps.

(e) Normal Useful Life

Road emulsions have an almost indefinite life, conditioned only by the fact of the gradual accumulation of sediment. If this is periodically redistributed, there is no reason why the emulsion should not last for ever, in an air-tight drum or container. Usually, however, this redistribution is not carried out periodically, and a certain amount of very concentrated emulsion collects at the bottom of the drum. Above a certain degree of concentration, it becomes impossible for the sediment to be moved without producing a complete coagulation of the concentrated emulsion, resulting in the formation of a quantity of lumps of bitumen, which, however, does not necessarily hinder the use of the remainder of the emulsion after straining off the lumps. In practice many manufacturers guarantee their products for periods of up to six months.

SOME SCIENTIFIC ASPECTS OF THE PHYSICAL PROPERTIES OF ASPHALTIC BITUMEN EMULSIONS

(a) Measurement of Viscosity

As in the case of most disperse systems, the apparent viscosity of asphaltic bitumen emulsions varies with the rate of shear obtaining during the measurement. As the rate of shear rises, so the apparent viscosity falls, the rate of fall diminishing until above a certain rate of shear, the viscosity becomes sensibly constant. This is clearly exemplified in the curve shown in Fig. 2, where the rates of shear are plotted as abscissæ and apparent viscosities as ordinates. It will be seen that, at a velocity of rotation

/ of about 240°/sec., the apparent viscosity has become almost constant.

The above measurements were all made in a concentric cylinder apparatus designed in conjunction with Mr. E. Hatschek. In actual practice, such an instrument would rarely be available and, moreover, its operation calls for more care and attention than could possibly be given to a routine operation. It becomes imperative, therefore, to find some more ready means of making these measurements. Efflux viscometers of the types used for oils would, at first sight, be suitable, and are generally available to the road industry. Capillary viscometers are generally unsuitable, owing to the opaque nature of the emulsions, which precludes observation of the position of a falling column of emulsion, and to cleaning difficulties which present themselves even when a rising column is used.

Of the oil viscometers tested, the Engler instrument seems to give the greatest degree of accuracy, and when employed according to the directions given in British Standard Specification 434—1931, can be made to give results of a good degree of accuracy and reproducibility. For emulsions, within the usual range of commercial viscosities, the rate of shear is high enough not to affect the viscosity, and moderately accurate computations of absolute viscosity may be made from Engler values by using the following relation:

$$\eta = 0.07497\,E - \frac{0.0734}{E}$$

Where

$\eta =$ Kinematic viscosity in c.g.s. units at 20°C.
$E =$ Viscosity in ° Engler at 20°C.

(*b*) *Interdependence of Viscosity and Asphaltic Bitumen Content*

It has been recognised in the industry for some time that, in general, the bitumen content of an emulsion did not, of itself,

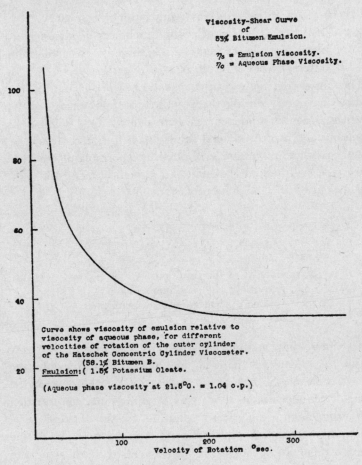

Viscosity-Shear Curve
of
53% Bitumen Emulsion.

η_s = Emulsion Viscosity.
η_0 = Aqueous Phase Viscosity.

Curve shows viscosity of emulsion relative to
viscosity of aqueous phase, for different
velocities of rotation of the outer cylinder
of the Hatschek Concentric Cylinder Viscometer.
(58.1% Bitumen B.
Emulsion:(1.5% Potassium Oleate.

(Aqueous phase viscosity at 21.5°C. = 1.04 c.p.)

Velocity of Rotation °sec.

Fig. 2

govern the viscosity. With different types of asphaltic bitumen,
different characteristic viscosities, at given concentrations of
bitumen, were obtained, although with any one type of asphaltic
bitumen, the viscosity increased quite markedly with rising bitumen content. Two problems, therefore, presented themselves for
investigation:

(1) How did viscosity increase with bitumen content?

(2) What caused the characteristic differences in viscosity between equally concentrated emulsions prepared from different types of bitumen?

The answer to both queries has been worked out in the author's laboratory during the last three or four years.

Viscosity/concentration curves were plotted for a number of emulsions and had the general form shown in Fig. 3. It will be found that these curves are well fitted by a formula of the Hatschek type, with the interpolation of a numerical factor "h," usually spoken of as a "hydration" factor, thus:

$$\eta_s = \frac{\eta}{1 - \sqrt[3]{h\,\phi}}$$

Where

η_s = viscosity of the emulsion
η = viscosity of the continuous phase
ϕ = volume concentration of disperse phase
h = numerical factor

It is interesting, in this connection, to note that the viscosity of the disperse phase material does not enter this expression, and in view of the fact of its high value, in the case of the asphaltic bitumens used, this seems to afford final confirmation of the suggestion of Hatschek[4] that the viscosity of the disperse system is independent of this factor. On the question of the interpretation of "h," it will be convenient to touch at a later stage.

As different types of asphaltic bitumen give different characteristic viscosities when emulsified, it follows that "h" will differ widely in those cases. The solution of the second of the two above problems would result in the establishment of one uniform value for h, but not in the elimination of h from the equation as we shall see. In point of fact, a value of h of about 1.3—1.4 applies to many different disperse systems, and even to froths, as has been shown by Sibree.[5] It would be easy to suppose that this constant was a mere numerical factor connected with the mathematical derivation of the formula, were it not for the fact that Trevan[6] found that for suspensions of red blood corpuscles, the equation could be applied with h equal to unity. We have, further, shown in our own unpublished work that h can be varied sharply by changing the shape of the size-frequency curve. This can readily be done by adding to an initial dispersion of normal size-frequency characteristics a further portion of disperse phase (molten asphaltic bitumen) under such conditions that this becomes relatively coarsely dispersed (many particles of 10—20μ and over). In this way, dispersions of very low viscosity can be produced and under favourable conditions, fluid emulsions with 80 per cent of asphaltic bitumen (perhaps 90 per cent by volume of disperse phase) can be prepared.[7]

In attacking the different fundamental viscosities exhibited by emulsions of different types of asphaltic bitumen, a start was made by examining the adsorption equilibrium in the aqueous phase of these emulsions. Measurements were made on two types of emulsion, prepared with sodium and potassium oleate solutions of varying concentrations. The asphaltic bitumens, used for these emulsions, were the 200 penetration grades from two different crudes, which we may designate A and B respectively. The results obtained are summarised in Table 1.

TABLE 1

Adsorption of Soap in Emulsions

Concentration of Initial Soap Solution	Grams Adsorbed per 100 Grams Bitumen			
	Bitumen A		Bitumen B	
	Na_2O	K_2O	Na_2O	K_2O
1.0%	0.014	0.017	−0.008	−0.032
1.5%	0.009	0.011	−0.010	−0.022
2.0%	0.012	0.008	−0.014	−0.018

It is seen that in all the Bitumen A emulsions, a normal soap adsorption is recorded, whereas in the Bitumen B emulsions, the concentrations measured are in excess of those used in the original emulsifier solutions. This is a somewhat surprising result, and is coupled with the fact that the bitumen B emulsions are much more viscous than the corresponding bitumen A emulsions. Quite clearly, some of the aqueous phase water has become "fixed," or "bound" in the more viscous emulsions, and no longer appears as bulk aqueous phase.

Various mechanisms could be advanced for this "fixation" process, such as true solubility of water in the bitumen, mechanical dispersion of water in bitumen, hydration of the bitumen particles, or finally the behaviour of the bitumen as a gel imbibing water. The effect is of considerable magnitude as can be seen by supposing that in the bitumen B emulsion, we have to allow for a positive adsorption of soap equal approximately to that shown by the bitumen A emulsions. In these circumstances, the B bitumen would have "fixed" about 14 per cent of its weight of water.

The measurement of adsorbed soap is a tedious and not too accurate method of determining the "bound" water of an emulsion, so that more accurate and convenient methods of direct measurement had to be found. Eventually two methods based on the same principle, were perfected, and applied. It was known that large quantities of potassium chloride could be added to bitumen emulsion without inducing coagulation, and it was, therefore, decided to add the potassium chloride in sufficient quantity to produce a saturated solution in the aqueous phase, and measure the heat of solution, thus calculating the amount of water present capable of effecting solution. By means of a specially designed calorimeter, employing a Beckmann thermometer, this could be done with great accuracy.

The second method was worked out relying on adding potassium chloride as before, but coagulating the emulsion subsequently with acid and estimating the potassium chloride in the separated aqueous phase. Both methods gave closely concordant results. The results so obtained on three types of emulsion are given in Table 2. They show a characteristic "water absorption" for each type of bitumen, although there are variations among the different emulsions of the same type.

TABLE 2

"Bound" Water in Emulsions

Type of Bitumen	Total Water % on Emulsion	Free Water % on Emulsion	Bound Water % on Bitumen
A	57.4	56.4	2.4
	45.9	44.8	2.0
	40.9	39.1	3.1
	30.4	26.1	(6.0)
B	68.1	65.9	7.3
	59.2	54.0	13.0
	49.4	40.5	17.5
	40.1	32.0	13.7
C	69.0	58.9	33.7
	61.5	48.3	35.1
	50.4	40.4	20.5

If the free water contents (total water content less the water absorbed into the bitumen particles) are now plotted, we get all our emulsions lying on one of two curves, as shown in Fig. 3, A, B, while curve C represents the curve yielded by the Hatschek expression.

$$\eta_s = \frac{\eta}{1 - \sqrt[3]{\phi}}$$

For reasons which cannot be discussed in the space available, the curve B is believed to be of doubtful authenticity, and the curve A applies to all normal emulsions (those not exhibiting an excessively high and unstable water absorption).

This work, therefore, led to the systematisation of the anomalous viscosities exhibited by different types of asphaltic bitumen. As the work progressed, also, various items of evidence were secured to show the character of the "water absorption" phenomenon. By a process of elimination the "swelling gel" hypothesis, mentioned previously, alone remained as not disproven and it, therefore, became necessary to consider this more fully. Bitumen swelling in water could obviously not be classed very readily with such hydrophile gels as gelatine swelling in water, nor does the analogy of rubber swelling in organic solvents appear profitable. Lowry and Kohman,[8] however, showed that rubber is capable of swelling in water, and that the equilibrium water absorption exhibited by the rubber after swelling is proportional to the amount of water-soluble substances (very minute in extent) present in the rubber. They assumed that the rubber was permeable to water but not to water-soluble substances, and that water passed into the rubber until the osmotic pressure of the aqueous solution in which the rubber was soaking was equal to the difference between the osmotic pressure of the solution of water solubles in the rubber, and the pressure due to elastic forces.

Following this line, it was shown that bitumen of the types used also contained small amounts of water-soluble substances. It was also found that the quantities of water-soluble substances in bitumens A, B and C were in the same order as the water absorptions exhibited in their emulsions. Exhaustive experiments, both on emulsions and on soaked films of these bitumens deposited on glass and metal, served to show that the water-soluble substances undoubtedly controlled the water absorption in both cases and that an osmotic equilibrium existed between the aqueous solution within the film or particle, and that without. It must, of course, be realised that the bitumen does not act as a semi-permeable membrane in the ordinary sense (as, for instance, copper ferrocyanide), but is permeable only to the solvent and not to the solute. Bancroft [9] visualises this type of system when he writes:

"It is clear that we can get osmotic phenomena in two distinct ways, depending on whether we have a continuous film or a porous one. In the case of a continuous film it is essential that the solvent shall dissolve in the membrane and that the solute shall not."

and again [10]

"It has already been shown that a semi-permeable membrane is like a continuous film in which the solute does not dissolve, or is a porous film giving marked negative adsorption, and having pores so small that all the liquid in the pores is adsorbed."

As an illustration of the relatively small amounts of water soluble substances which give rise to these important phenomena, Table 3 gives the data for a number of bitumens, and some average figures for water absorption shown by typical emulsions.

TABLE 3

Water Solubles and Water Absorption

Bitumen	Water Solubles	Water Absorption 57% Emulsion
A	0.025%	2%
B	0.052%	14%
C	0.316%	35%
D	0.345%	33%
E	0.043%	1%

It will be appreciated, of course, that strict proportionality between the amounts of water soluble substances, and the water absorption developed is not to be expected, as, among other factors, the size of the particles of these substances plays an important rôle. To be effective, these particles must be of such a size that when they have attracted their quantum of water, forming a little globule of aqueous solution within the emulsion particle, this globule shall not be of such a size that it causes the break-up of the bitumen particle, with discharge of the solute into the aqueous phase of the emulsion. If this takes place, to any extent, the effect will evidently be in the opposite direction to the initial effect. It is, therefore, clear that the size distribution of the water-soluble particles is of the greatest importance. The doubtful curve B in Fig. 3 is attributed to the presence of a

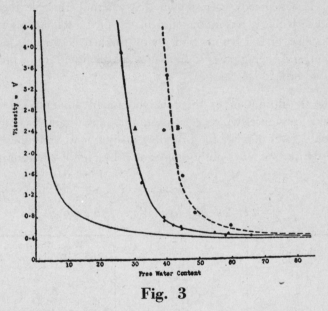

Fig. 3

large excess of heavily swollen particles which are readily broken up by agitation in the calorimeter, when determining the water absorption, thus giving unduly high values for the free water contents.

Before leaving this brief account of the work which had led to the solving of our two initial problems, it should be mentioned that further application of these ideas has resulted in an almost complete explanation of the complex changes of viscosity of this class of emulsion, on thermal treatment, and that practical processes have been worked out, enabling a complete control to be obtained over the viscosity of these emulsions, independent of their bitumen content and without the employment of substances to increase the viscosity of the aqueous phase. These processes may be found described in sufficient detail in the patent literature.[11]

(c) The "Stability" of Asphaltic Bitumen Emulsions

In no type of emulsion work is it so important to be precise over the meaning to be attached to the term "stability" as in the branch dealing with asphaltic bitumen road emulsions. This is because the function of these emulsions is to break down quickly when applied to the road surface, to yield bitumen which will function as a binding agent. There is, of course, little or no binding or adhesive power associated with the emulsion as such.

The user of these products is, therefore, vitally concerned that they shall not exhibit an undue stability in this sense. On the other hand, such emulsions are often kept for periods of months and years in drums or other containers before use, and it is imperative that they should not coagulate during these periods of time. Quite obviously, the term "stability," as applied to these emulsions, has a whole range of meanings, dependent on the factor which is in question, tending to lead to the breakdown of the emulsion, whether it is time, road conditions, or chemical or mechanical forces. Some causes of stability, in various directions, will be briefly touched upon.

Stability, in quiescent storage, obviously depends on the sedimentation behaviour of the dispersed particles. There being but a small density difference between the phases, sedimentation, in any case, will not be rapid, but over the lapse of time, the results may easily prove serious unless everything is done to minimize the segregation. Actually, we are not able to apply Stokes' Law direct, owing to the high volume concentration of disperse phase. Very curious phenomena are observed in the quantiative study of these systems, and the sedimentation becomes a packing phenomenon, rather than one of particles falling through a fluid medium. The gradual formation of a layer of coagulated bitumen, at the bottom of the container, seems to be due to the rupture of adsorbed soap films consequent upon the formation of a closely packed layer of particles, resulting from sedimentational packing. In concentrated sediments from emulsions made, using emulsifying agents which yield adsorbed films of great strength, remarkable anti-thixotropic phenomena may be observed.

The chemical stability and general chemical reactions of emulsions are largely a question of the chemistry of their aqueous phases, and of the substances used as emulsifying agents. Interesting work has been done by Weber and Bechler [12] on the reactions of various emulsions with different types of road stone. No generalisations of importance arise, however, from this work. The effects appear largely specific and the composition of the emulsions used by them, is not given.

Much attention has also been devoted to the reaction of calcium chloride solutions on road emulsions, as a means of obtaining a measure of their readiness to break down on the road. Unpublished work from the laboratories of Messrs. Colas Products Ltd. shows that these reactions of electrolytes, insufficient in quantity to decompose all the soap emulsifier, are exceedingly complex in respect of the amount of disperse phase coagulated, and this is a subject which is being followed up.

The conditions of breakdown of emulsions, applied to the road, have recently been considerably elucidated. This has resulted from the observation of the fact that when these emulsions are concentrated to a certain critical disperse phase concentration, coagulation can be induced by simple mechanical disturbance, as, for instance, stirring. It can be shown that except in a few special cases, the loss of water from an emulsion, exposed in a thin layer on the road surface, is principally due to evaporation. There may be minor amounts lost by the capillary action of porous stone or road surfaces, and there may also be minor chemical coagulative effects due to reactive aggregates. Principally, however, water is lost by evaporation, and while this evaporation is in progress, the road surfaces will normally be rolled or exposed to the action of traffic. In both cases, the mechanical disturbance necessary to produce coagulation when the critical concentration is reached, is present. The coagulation can actually be observed in the tracks of passing car wheels, under suitable conditions.

Another case of emulsion breakdown, in which the operative mechanism is not so clear, is that of frost coagulation. It is possible to produce emulsions by the choice of a suitable emulsifying agent, which can be frozen solid, and re-thawed without suffering coagulation. The normal soap-type emulsions employed for road work are, however, completely coagulated by such treatment. Considerable super-cooling of the emulsions is often possible, but once solidification has taken place, partial or complete coagulation results. The reasons for this behaviour are quite obscure and would form an interesting subject for research. One curious observation should be recorded: if an emulsion of this type is frozen solid and thawed with stirring, to coagulate it, it will be found that the aqueous liquid separating is almost pure water. The emulsifier seems to have completely disappeared and can only be recovered in very small part by continued boiling of the separated bitumen with water. This effect would certainly merit further investigation.

CONCLUSION

In this paper, the methods of manufacture of commercial asphaltic bitumen emulsions, as applied to road work, have been described. The point has been emphasized that the making of a dispersion of sorts is not at all difficult, but that the full knowledge of the properties of these dispersions, and the attainment of control over these properties, gives rise to a good deal of research and investigation. The problems of viscosity measurement and the elucidation of the anomalous viscosities obtained in emulsions of some types of asphaltic bitumen, have been discussed in some detail. The application of the Hatschek expression, with the interpolation of a numerical factor, is established.

Turning to the subject of the stability properties of emulsions, much work remains to be done to secure a full knowledge of the causes of observed phenomena. Freezing behaviour in particular requires elucidation.

Emulsions of asphaltic bitumen, in many ways, show superiority over the conventional fluid oil emulsions as instruments of research into the physical chemistry of emulsions, in general, if only because of the readiness with which coagulation can be detected and measured. At the same time, the complex chemical composition of these products has to be borne in mind as a complicating factor. Pure research on these interesting emulsions has, up till now, been practically non-existent, and it is hoped that this paper may serve to draw attention to a field of study until now the preserve of the industrial specialist.

REFERENCES

1. Montgomerie, Brit. Pat. 226,032, etc.
2. Mackay, Brit. Pat. 202,021, etc.
3. Préaubert, Brit. Pat. 9,422, 1,905.
4. Hatschek "Viscosity of Liquids," p. 202.
5. Sibree, Trans. Farad. Soc., 1934, 30, 325.
6. Trevan, Biochem. J., 1918, 12, 60.
7. See Brit. Pat. 362,577.
8. Lowry and Kohman, J. Phys. Chem., 1927, 31, 23.
9. Bancroft, "Applied Colloid Chemistry," p. 127.
10. Bancroft, loc. cit., p. 221.
11. See Brit. Pat. 389,810.
12. Weber and Bechler, Asphalt und Teer, 1932, 32, 45, etc.

APPENDIX

TEST FOR RATE OF BREAK OF EMULSION ON THE ROAD

The Lability Test

The following apparatus is required for the Lability Test:

1. One porcelain crucible 2.5 cm in height and 3 cm in diameter.
2. One small glass rod of about 3 mm diameter and 4 cm long, with a round end.
3. A glass rod about 10 cm in length. One end of this rod is drawn out to a point, and a small ball of glass formed on the tip. This ball is then flattened out at an angle to the rod, forming a round flat disc, the undersurface of which is ground until perfectly flat. It is advantageous, also, to grind one side of the disc to give a straight, sharp edge (see diagram attached).
4. One glass plate which has been carefully cleaned with petroleum spirit, dried, moistened with soap solution, and again dried with a clean, soft cloth, or with jap paper.
5. The apparatus for projecting an air current, on to the emulsion under test, may consist of a glass tube of 4-5 mm internal diameter.

Method

Approximately 1 gm of emulsion is placed in the porcelain crucible and concentrated by stirring with the small glass rod under a gentle current of air, at a temperature of 18°—20°C., so that the initial coagulation point is reached in 30—45 minutes. The air current is projected on to the surface of the emulsion at an angle of 45°.

279

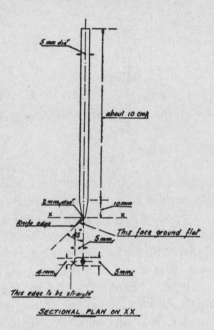

SECTIONAL PLAN ON XX

Under normal humidity conditions, the air need not be dried.

The emulsion should be stirred gently but continuously, to avoid the formation of a skin over the surface and maintain the emulsion in a substantially homogeneous condition; the stirring should be carried out in such a way as to avoid coating the sides of the vessel with emulsion.

On starting the test and at suitable intervals thereafter, testing for coagulation shall be carried out as follows.

The crucible is removed from the air current and the sample is given a final gentle stirring to ensure homogeneity. A small portion of the concentrated emulsion is then removed from the crucible by means of the small glass rod used for stirring during the concentration and placed on the glass plate.

A white paper placed under the plate enables the end point to be distinguished more clearly.

The small portion of emulsion removed on the tip of the rod is rubbed out with a circular motion on the glass plate, using the glass rod with the specially shaped end, care being taken to use only a very light pressure on the rod, since a heavy pressure tends to cause premature coagulation.

Adjacent to the rubbed out emulsion on the plate are placed a few drops of the distilled water and the water is gradually worked into the emulsion with a gentle stirring motion.

Recognition of End Point

The end point will be recognised by the presence on the tip of the rod, or in the diluted emulsion on the plate, of a substantial proportion of coagulated binder, in clumps easily visible to the unaided eye.

If, however, the end point has not been reached, the crucible is replaced under the air current and concentration continued for a short while, when a further test for the end point is made in the same way.

NOTE: Attention has already been drawn to the necessity of avoiding coating the sides of the vessel with emulsion; it is, however, impossible to avoid a slight amount of coagulation on the tip of the rod when testing for end point, and, therefore, in the above interpretation of end point, attention is specifically drawn to the necessity for the presence of a substantial proportion of the coagulated binder present either on the tip of the rod or in the diluted emulsion on the plate.

As soon as the end point has been reached, the bulk of the emulsion is transferred to a weighed, covered, flat metal dish, 1″ to 1½″ in diameter, and is heated at 105 to 110°C. for 1¼ hours.

The dish is then cooled and re-weighed, the difference between the initial and final weights being the water content of the residual emulsion and should be expressed as a percentage of the latter. The figure recorded shall be the average of three examinations, non of which should differ from this average by more than ± 10 per cent of the final water content.

It is of the greatest importance that all apparatus should be maintained thoroughly clean throughout the test. After each rubbing out, the tip of the glass rod should be wiped clean on filter paper and should be kept under the surface of distilled water, when not in use.

SECTION 16

THEORY OF EMULSIONS AND EMULSIFYING AGENTS

By George M. Sutheim

EMULSIONS were made and used long before there was any attempt to explain their formation and behavior. Up to the middle of the 19th century, the concepts of what emulsions actually are were quite hazy. Yet, the fact that milk is an emulsion was clearly recognized, as the word emulsion itself was derived from the Latin, "emulgere," which means: to milk out.

Two reasons may explain why the theoretical knowledge of emulsions is of comparatively recent date. First, emulsions, in those early days, were rather unimportant. Aside from small quantities of salves and unguents, made by hand in pharmacies according to carefully guarded secret formulas, and some foodstuffs, prepared as emulsions for immediate use in the kitchen, no appreciable quantity of emulsions was produced. Second, and more important, it was the trend of the time to concentrate on the investigation of the chemical composition of any substance, and to pay little attention to its physical structure. In the light of present-day knowledge, however, it is clear how little can be learned from the study of the chemical composition of an emulsion; it is known now that it is the physical pattern, the state of dispersion and the surface phenomena that govern the emulsion system. In spite of the enormous increase in chemical knowledge during the second half of the 19th century, the science of physical chemistry made only slow progress. The way had to be prepared by fundamental investigations, like those of Thomas Graham on colloids (1861) and Willard Gibbs on absorption (1877), but up to the turn of the century, the significance of their work was not well understood. Then, however, the picture changed rapidly. Equipped with the tools of theories on surface tension, absorption, dispersions and many other side lines, formulating a theory of emulsions became possible and, thus, within the first twenty years of this century, a number of successful attempts were made to explain the "why" and "how" of emulsions. But even in this day, there are many blank spots on the map and a great deal of research will be necessary before the last of these blank spots disappears.

A satisfactory theory of any system has to perform the following functions: it has to explain (1) the formation of the system, (2) its properties, and (3) its reaction to changes. The example of a satisfactory theory is the modern kinetic theory of matter. It may not be true in every respect, being strictly valid only for ideal gases, but it is a fine working theory.

For the time being, there is no equally satisfactory theory of emulsions. There are a number of valuable special theories covering particular phenomena, such as the formation of the emulsion or the reversal of the phases, but a single general theory of emulsions, which can be relied upon to answer all the questions is still lacking.

More specifically than the three points just mentioned, a general theory of emulsions is expected to explain:

(1) the formation of the emulsion;
(2) the reasons for the formation of either O/W or W/O emulsions;
(3) the maintenance of stability;
(4) the phenomena of instability, such as creaming, breaking and phase reversal;
(5) the influence of chemical factors, such as the action of acids, bases, electrolytes and antagonistic ions;

(6) the influence of physical factors, such as temperature changes, mechanical disturbances or ultrasonic waves;

(7) the role of the emulsifying agents.

In addition, the theory should be tested to determine whether or not it is able to account for some of the minor peculiarities of emulsions, for example, the formation of dual or multiple emulsions or the phenomenon of spontaneous emulsification.

The first approach in producing a working theory of emulsions is to limit the field. This seems to be a rather simple task, but if the definitions given by various authors are examined, it becomes evident that the concept of "emulsions" is, by no means, as clean-cut as it should be. To illustrate this point, some definitions chosen at random, are given. (The italics are the author's, indicating important points of divergence.)

(1) An emulsion is a *very fine dispersion* of one liquid in another with which it is immiscible. (Alexander: "Colloidchemistry, Principles and Application," p. 102.)

(2) . . . emulsions are *stable* and *intimate mixtures* of the oil or oily material with water. (Carbide and Carbon Chemicals Corp.: "Emulsions," 6th Ed., p. 8.)

(3) An emulsion is a system containing *two liquid phases,* one of which is dispersed as globules in the other. (Clayton: "Theory of Emulsions," 4th Ed., p. 1, quoting one of the earliest definitions given by Selmi, in 1845.)

(4) Emulsions are *mechanical mixtures* of liquids that are *immiscible under ordinary conditions,* and which may be separated into layers on standing, heating, freezing, by agitation or the addition of other chemicals. (Encyclopedia Britannica, 14th Ed.)

(5) An emulsion is a *two-phase liquid system,* consisting of *fairly coarse* dispersions of one liquid in another with which it is not miscible. (Hatschek: "An Introduction to the Physics and Chemistry of Colloids," p. 38.)

(6) Emulsions: The product of the dispersion of one liquid in another liquid, the dispersed-phase particles being *larger than colloidal size.* (Lange: "Handbook of Chemistry," 5th Ed., p. 1646.)

(7) An emulsion is a two-phase system consisting of fine droplets of one liquid in a second liquid with which it is *incompletely miscible.* (Lewis, Squires and Broughton: "Industrial Chemistry of Amorphous and Colloidal Materials," p. 250.)

(8) An emulsion, as is well known, consists of a *stable* dispersion of one liquid in another liquid. (Roberts: "A New Theory of Emulsions," J. Phys. Chem., **36**, 3087 [1932].)

(9) Emulsions are *intimate mixtures* of two immiscible liquids, one of them being dispersed in the other in the form of fine droplets. (Sutheim: "Introduction to Emulsions," p. 1.)

(10) Emulsions: A *suspension* of fine particles or globules of a liquid in a liquid. (Webster's Collegiate Dictionary, 5th Ed.)

If this selection of definitions, all of which are rather good, is examined, it will be seen that there is scarcely one point upon which all the authors are in full agreement. The emulsion, as a physical system, is explained as a dispersion, a suspension, an intimate or mechanical mixture, or a two-phase system; none of the terms covers exactly the same concept. The two phases are said to be immiscible, yet one definition emphasizes incomplete miscibility and another one states that the two liquids are immiscible under ordinary conditions. The dispersed particles are described as fine, very fine, larger than colloidal size or fairly coarse. Only two of the definitions make a statement about the stability of the system, all the others omit this important point. All definitions agree that the two emulsion phases are liquids; yet this is just the point that will require some further examination.

The reason for this apparent lack of harmony is the fact that some of the terms used in the definitions are not sharply defined. Consequently, the terms involved should be examined and an effort made to settle upon a single meaning that is accepted by the majority of authors.

The State of Dispersion.

The state of dispersion is the most general form in which matter occurs, if the term is interpreted in the broadest sense, namely as the distribution of one substance in another. Whenever particles of different kinds are present in a system, one type must necessarily be distributed, or dispersed, in some way in the other. Only absolutely pure substances, if such exists, cannot be regarded as dispersions, since they consist of particles of only one kind. Any other system, such as a salt solution with the sodium chloride dispersed in water, an oil paint with the pigment dispersed in the vehicle, or a cloud with the water droplets dispersed in the air, belongs to the category of dispersions. Emulsions, of course, are also dispersions, since one type of particles, the droplets of the internal phase, are distributed in another type of particles, the external phase.

Yet, this is a highly unsatisfactory classification. If systems as different as a salt solution, a cloud or an emulsion are, physically speaking, of one family, we feel that some more specific classification must be found to differentiate between them. To bring some order to the chaos, Wolfgang Ostwald (1907) proposed a classification which is almost universally accepted. He classified the dispersed systems according to two properties: (1) the degree of dispersion: coarse, colloidal and molecular, and (2) the state of aggregation of both the dispersed portion and the dispersion medium: solid, liquid and gaseous.

The Degree of Dispersion; the Particle Size

The term "degree of dispersion" used before is nothing more than another name for the particle size of the dispersed portion. The dispersed particles of any systems, whether they are of molecular dimensions or as large as plainly-visible grains of sand, always have a definite size which can be measured by some method and recorded in exact figures. Thus, by replacing the expression "degree of dispersion" by "size of the dispersed particles," the classification into coarse, colloidal and molecular dispersions takes on a definite meaning. There is no longer any need to speak in vague, meaningless terms, such as fine, very fine or fairly coarse. Exact, numerical statements can be made.

It is agreed upon to refer to dispersions as coarse, if the dispersed particles are of larger diameter than 0.1μ, to call a dispersion colloidal if the particles are in the range of $0.1\mu–1m\mu$, whereas any particle whose diameter is smaller than $1m\mu$ will be classified as molecularly dispersed. Of course, there will be no sharp line of demarcation between two different types of dispersions. It is unreasonable to expect a substance, dispersed into particles of say 0.1μ, to show such and such properties, and the same substance having particles of 0.09μ diameter to be entirely different. All that can be said is this: within the realm of a certain type of dispersion the properties attributed to that type will prevail. For instance, the properties which are called colloidal will prevail within the colloidal range; they are most accentuated in the center of that range and vanish gradually towards both ends. It may happen, however, that even beyond the colloidal limits, that is, within the realm of an adjacent type of dispersion, some colloidal properties appear; the limitations, as emphasized before, are not sharp and are solely dictated by the usefulness of such division.

The particles in most of the commonly used emulsions are in the coarse range. Particles as large as 25μ are quite often found, yet the bulk of globules in good emulsions is in the $1–5\mu$ range. Still smaller particles occur in emulsions treated by special homogenizing machinery or when the interfacial tension between the two emulsion phases is exceedingly low; then, the particle size may be as low as 0.25μ, which, by definition, is close to the colloidal range. Thus emulsions are found to be coarse dispersions, where the word coarse is now no longer to be taken as a vague description, but quite precisely as above 0.1μ.

Still smaller particles of oil are dispersed in water or vice versa. The condensation water of steam engines, for instance, contains quite frequently oil droplets well below the borderline particle size of 0.1μ. Are these systems still emulsions? These extremely-fine droplets of oil dispersed in water behave, in most respects, less like ordinary emulsions, and more like colloidal dispersions. The droplets are usually found in very low concentrations, they show optical and electrokinetic properties typical of colloidal dispersions and do not exhibit the characteristic emulsion proper-ties. On the whole, they behave just as particles within the col-loidal range would be expected to behave and, therefore, it seems quite appropriate to classify this type of dispersions of oil in water, as colloidal dispersions. This, in fact, is usually done; these "dilute emulsions" of extremely fine oil particles are called oil hydrosols, a technical term for a colloidal dispersion of oil in water.

One more word about the terms, coarse and fine. That emul-sions are coarse dispersions is an accepted fact. But within the particle range for emulsions, there are coarser and finer particles, so it is perfectly correct to call an emulsion, having predominantly fine particles, a fine emulsion, and one having predominantly coarse particles, a coarse emulsion.

The State of Aggregation

The second basis for the classification of the dispersed systems is the state of aggregation. Since both the dispersed particles and the dispersion medium may be solid, liquid or gaseous, we have to distinguish between dispersions such as solid in liquid, liquid in liquid, etc., in addition to making the previously explained classification into coarse, colloidal and molecular dispersions. Emulsions, accordingly, are to be classified as coarse dispersions of liquid in liquid, whereas a coarse dispersion of a solid in a liquid is called a suspension, and a coarse dispersion of a gas in a liquid, a foam.

There seems to be no place for ambiguous interpretations. Yet, we know that we have to deal in practice with emulsions—and very important ones, for that matter—which are not made up of two liquids in the true sense of the word. Milk, for instance, has a liquid external phase, but the internal phase, the butter fat, is a solid rather than a liquid. Oleomargarine is another example; here the external phase consists of more or less solid fats, whereas the internal phase is a liquid, either water or skim milk. A particularly puzzling picture is presented by an emulsion-polymerization batch. At the start, the liquid monomers, for example, butadiene and styrene, are emulsified as an internal phase; then, as polymerization proceeds, these liquids transform gradually into more and more viscous polymers, and the finished polymerization products are usually plastic solids. Wax emulsions and many of the bituminous emulsions are quite definitely dispersions of solids in liquids which, according to the orthodox classification, ought to be called suspensions.

The difficulty in deciding whether to classify systems like those mentioned in the preceding section as emulsions or suspensions arises from an inadequate definition of a liquid. The kinetic theory of matter gives a general conception of the three states of aggregation. The liquid state is, so to speak, an intermediate between the solid and the gaseous states. However, whereas the transition from gas to liquid is fairly sharp, there are innumerable intermediates between the liquid and the solid state. Highly viscous liquids, pastes, gels and plastic solids belong in this category. Any state of transition will show some properties of the adjacent states, and it is a matter of opinion, as well as of expedience, to classify such a system. Classifications are highly important, but they should never become so rigid as to be more embarrassing than helpful. Materials like milk, latex, wax or bituminous dispersions behave in most respects as emulsions, whereas typical suspensions, such as clay in water or pigment in oil, behave altogether differently. One of the typical differences is that on breaking an emulsion, the particles of the internal phase will show a tendency to flow together, very markedly if the internal phase consists of thin liquids, less noticeably with heavy liquids and plastic solids whereas the truly solid particles of a suspension show no such tendency.

It is thus correct to define an emulsion as a coarse dispersion of a liquid in a liquid, if the term *liquid* is understood to include such borderline states as plastic solids.

Immiscibility

The phases of an emulsion are generally considered in terms of "oil" and "water." This pair of liquids is the traditional symbol of immiscibility. In more technical terms, water and "water-friendly" substances are called hydrophilic, and oil and oil-like substances, hydrophobic. Yet, in examining the many different substances of both types used in emulsions, all degrees of miscibility and immiscibility are found. Here, again, is a range without sharp demarcation. It is exceedingly hard to state where immiscibility ends and miscibility begins, particularly in dealing with mixtures and solutions.

What is the physical meaning of immiscibility? The particles of a liquid are kept together by cohesive forces. They have a definite value for any given liquid and can be measured indirectly by means of a phenomenon related to the cohesive forces, the surface tension. Toward the particles of another liquid, the particles of the first will also exert an attraction known as adhesive forces. The net result of these two forces is expressed as the interfacial tension between the two liquids. If the cohesive forces, which tend to hold the liquid particles together, are stronger than the adhesive forces, which tend to pull the particles apart, then the interfacial tension will be high and the two liquids will not mix. If, however, the interfacial tension assumes very low values, or becomes actually zero, the liquids are miscible. A substance like octane, for instance, having an interfacial tension of 50.8 dynes/cm, toward water, is practically immiscible with water, ethyl ether (interfacial tension = 10.7 dynes/cm) is partially soluble in water (7.5 parts in 100 at 20°C.), and glycerol, which shows no measurable interfacial tension toward water is miscible with water in any proportion. It may be mentioned here that the solubility of one liquid in another is not solely dependent upon interfacial tension; other factors, such as the presence of polar and non-polar groups and their distribution within the molecule, have some influence too.

There will be no difficulty in predicting how substances at both ends of the range of miscibility will behave if their dispersion is attempted. Octane will produce an emulsion in water, if proper conditions are provided, and glycerol a solution. The partially miscible substances may form either an emulsion or a solution, depending upon the concentration. In the case of ethyl ether, for example, a solution will be formed if less than 7.5 parts of ether are mixed with 100 parts of water; if higher concentrations are used, part of the ether will be dissolved in the water and part of it will become emulsified, provided that suitable emulsifying agents are present. It is quite evident that only the immiscible portion can form an emulsion. Thus, in a broader sense, even those liquids that show partial miscibility will be included in the category of emulsions, if the statement is made that an emulsion is a dispersion of immiscible liquids.

Stability of Emulsions

Only two out of the ten definitions, listed previously, mention the factor of stability, and another one states merely that emulsions ". . . can be separated on standing, heating, etc. . . ." The other definitions avoid this important point altogether, and with good reason. There is hardly a more elusive concept than that of emulsion stability. If an emulsion is to be considered stable, it must not undergo major changes. But for how long, and under what temperature variations or mechanical and chemical influences must it remain unchanged? May an emulsion be considered stable if, as one manufacturer of a surface-active agent cheerfully announces: ". . . excellent emulsions can be produced by the use of XX so long as any sort of agitation is present. The emulsions break more or less completely when agitation ceases." Another student of emulsion stability measures the stability by indicating the height of the separated oil layer in a test tube after 2, 4, 6, etc., hours; if after 24 hours no oil separation is apparent, the emulsion is considered stable and the contents of the test tube go down the sewer. Both concepts of stability will hardly meet with the approval of a manufacturer of commercial emulsions.

On the other hand, may an emulsion be expected to remain stable indefinitely? The very fact that emulsions are mixtures of immiscible liquids, immiscibility varying widely with the different constituents, as emphasized before, explains why a certain degree of instability is involved in any emulsion system. Were the two liquids completely miscible, the resulting system— a solution—would be thermodynamically stable. Such systems remain stable over an infinite period of time, provided no outside forces disturb the stability. Emulsions are not thermodynamically stable. Even if outside influences are completely eliminated, the system is not entirely in equilibrium internally. In forming an emulsion, one liquid is forced into another with which it is immiscible, and to overcome the powerful forces opposing this operation, energy must be supplied. The higher the degree of immiscibility, the stronger the forces that resist the formation of an emulsion or, in physical terms, liquids of high interfacial tension are hard to emulsify. At a certain level of interfacial tension, the formation of a normal emulsion becomes practically impossible, regardless of how much energy is supplied. The resistance to emulsification is too high and the two phases will break apart as soon as the supply of energy is discontinued. In order to emulsify such liquids properly, the interfacial tension must first be reduced. This is done by the addition of emulsifying agents. Then, when the resistance to emulsification is sufficiently low, the emulsion can be easily produced. Yet, a certain degree of immiscibility, or better, of interfacial tension will always remain; even the best emulsifying agent will not bring the interfacial tension down to zero. At the surface of each one of the billion little droplets formed, a small amount of residual tension will be present. Although exceedingly small for each individual droplet, these forces, multiplied by the huge number of droplets, will add up to an appreciable amount of free energy within the emulsion system. This free energy is the cause of the internal instability of the emulsion. It tends continuously to bring the free surface to a minimum or, in other words, to force the droplets to flow together and break the emulsion.

Thus, it is correct to say that an emulsion is less stable than the more homogeneous systems, such as solutions or solids. It is incorrect, however, to call an emulsion unstable, since everyone knows that there are many natural and man-made emulsions of sufficient stability to perform satisfactorily within the limits of practical needs. It seems that the question of stability must be dealt with in a restricted sense. As pointed out previously, an emulsion may be called practically stable if it fulfills the purpose it is intended for.

There is still another approach to the problem. Maximum stability is, by no means, an advantage in all cases. Very often it is just the ease with which the two phases of a system can be separated that determines its practical value. It is, for example, much easier to break a finished emulsion-polymerization batch, than to separate the solvent from the polymer in a solution-polymerization. Here the lower degree of stability of the emulsion becomes an advantage. The same holds true for many coating emulsions, food preparations, etc., all of which must be easily decomposed in order to make the internal phase available. To summarize: The field of emulsions must be confined within certain limits. An emulsion is considered a coarse dispersion, coarse in the sense of a particle size above 0.1μ, of one liquid in another liquid wtih which it is immiscible, the term liquid to be taken in its broadest sense, as explained above.

Many of the earlier theories of emulsions deal merely with one of the many different aspects of the emulsion system; if they do succeed in explaining one particular emulsion phenomenon, they fail completely to account for others of equal importance or they are even contradictory to facts easy to observe. But, as Jules Henry Poincaré, the eminent French mathematician remarks: ". . . we must never believe that discarded theories have been either sterile or useless." There is always a grain of truth in the theoretical speculations of the honest investigator of facts. Thus, some of the earlier attempts to explain emulsions will be examined, even though, with the increased insight of today, better ones are known. At the time when these theories were developed, they were the best that could be offered and they led the way to the later and better theories. Indeed, no one can tell how the theories of today will be looked upon, fifty or one hundred years from now.

The Viscosity Theory

One of the oldest attempts to explain the formation of an emulsion was what may be called the viscosity theory. It was assumed that an emulsion is formed if two immiscible liquids are brought into intimate contact by stirring, triturating or grinding and the finished product is high in viscosity. This is the description of an undoubtedly correct observation, but it is not an explanation. The earliest emulsions made were salves and ungents for pharmaceutical and cosmetical use, and in these products, the high viscosity merely coincided with the formation of rather stable emulsions. But, as it is easy enough to prove, viscosity alone does not promote stability in emulsions. Very thin emulsions can be quite stable and very viscous ones most unstable. The main reason that induced the earlier investigators to confuse viscosity with stability seems to lie in the fact that many substances which impart high viscosity to the external phase are, at the same time, efficient emulsifying agents and protective colloids. Some of the early formulations used blends of waxes and oils as oil phase, whereas the aqueous phase contained gums of the water-soluble type and occasionally some alkali which formed soaps with the acidic constituents of the fats. This, indeed, is still a good formulation which includes all the necessary ingredients to give stable emulsions. However, the resulting high viscosity of the external phase is only incidental; it is an important factor in stability, but not the reason for stability.

The higher the viscosity of the external phase, the lower the general mobility of the dispersed particles and, therefore, the less the chance for the particles to meet and coalesce. If the external phase becomes exceedingly heavy, any kind of movement ceases and the particles are pinned down in fixed positions; in this way, more or less solid emulsions of great stability, but unfortunately of very limited usefulness, can be made.

As a theory of emulsions, the viscosity theory can be discarded.

The Surface-Film Theory

A major step in the right direction was made by assuming the existence of a film-like structure that surrounds and protects the globules of the internal phase. As early as 1862, W. Marcet, a physiologist, published a paper [*J. Chem. Soc.,* 15, 407 (1862)] "On the Chemistry of Digestion," in which he outlined, more clearly and more definitely than anyone before him, a new theory of emulsions. We quote from the original paper, which is a remarkable combination of keen observation and sound reasoning:

". . . I must now beg to make a few observations on the phenomena of fatty emulsions. When neutral fats or fatty acids in a fused condition are agitated with water, no emulsion is formed but large globules are seen to pervade the fluid; on standing, they immediately run into each other and rise to the surface, the aqueous fluid remaining perfectly clear. When fused neutral fats are agitated with a solution of neutral tribasic phosphate of soda, I have observed the same phenomena to take place as with pure water, but when fatty acids are treated with a solution of phosphate of soda an emulsion is formed, or in other words, the globules of fat lose the property of running into each other; they remain separate, the fluid assuming a milky appearance; consequently phosphate of soda does not act equally on neutral fats and on fatty acids. This subject appearing to me of great interest, I have given it much attention and I have found that the emulsion produced by acting on fatty acids with phosphates of soda is invariably accompanied by the formation of a certain quantity of soap. . . ."

"Emulsions of fat are also produced when bile and fused fatty acids are agitated together, or when pancreatic juice is shaken with both neutral or acid fats. . . . When fused fatty acids are shaken in a test tube with phosphate of soda or bile, the fat is instantly divided by a mechanical process into very minute globules, just as would happen if the fat was agitated with water; but at that moment each of these very small fat particles becomes surrounded with a layer of soap, from the surface of the globule being saponified by the phosphate of soda or bile. From this circumstance the globules of fat lose their property of running into each other . . ."

". . . the results of my inquiry were communicated to the Royal Society in 1858. Shortly afterwards I was informed that bile had already been observed by Lenz of Dorpat, to possess the above-mentioned property, and by referring to his valuable dissertation "On the Digestion of Fats" I found he was the first who discovered so far back as 1850 that bile emulsioned fatty acids, but not neutral fats . . ."

Little is to be added to Marcet's vivid description. The process that he describes, namely the formation of soap when fatty acids are brought into contact with aqueous alkalies during the emulsification, is referred to today as the formation of the emulsifying agent *in situ,* and is widely employed in modern formulations. The surface layer of soap was, later on, termed the *surface film,* and now it is, more correctly, referred to as the *interfacial film.*

Ever since, the formation of film-like structures around the droplets has been the accepted basis of any emulsion theory. However, many supplements and enlargements of the original surface-film theory were indispensable in accounting for the intricate properties of the emulsion system. In Marcet's case, the film originated at the surface of each droplet; thus no difficulty was encountered in explaining how it got there. Yet, we know that similar films will be produced if suitable agents are dispersed in either of the two phases. The failure to explain how the film is produced in these much more important cases is one of the defaults of the pure surface film theory. In addition, it is necessary to determine what keeps the film in position and what gives it permanence, and also why and under what circumstances the film gives way when the emulsion breaks and what the causes of phase reversal may be. These and numerous other questions remain unanswered by the theory in its original form, and it will be necessary to dig much deeper into the physics of surfaces and interfaces in order to get the answers. As Max Planck once said: "We see in all modern scientific advances that the solution of one problem unveils the mystery of another. Each hilltop we reach discloses to us another hilltop beyond."

The Surface-Tension Theory

The surface-tension theory or, as it is more correctly called, the interfacial-tension theory assumes that the reduction of the interfacial tension explains the formation of an emulsion. As it was shown in numerous papers by Plateau [*Ann. Phys.,* 141, 44 (1870)], Quincke [*Ann. Phys.,* 271, 580 (1888)], Donnan [Z. *phys. Chem.,* 31, 42 (1899)] and Hillyer [*J. Am. Chem. Soc.,* 25, 511 (1903)], it is undoubtedly true that a pair of immiscible liquids of high interfacial tension cannot be emulsified. If, however, the interfacial tension is lowered by suitable methods, the emulsification proceeds quite readily.

Yet, the surface-tension theory cannot be accepted as a general explanation for the formation of emulsions. To state that the reduction of the surface tension or the interfacial tension is the only cause of emulsion formation is incorrect. An example from another field will illustrate the point. At low temperatures, many chemical reactions will proceed infinitely slowly or not at all, whereas they will be swiftly completed at elevated temperatures. This fact, however, can enter the theory of the chemical reaction only as an incidental, though very important factor; many other factors, such as the chemical affinity, the thermodynamical equilibrium, etc., are also to be considered in explaining the reaction.

Similarly, the reduction of the interfacial tension is only an incidental factor in the formation of emulsions. The emulsion system as a whole cannot be explained by this alone. Typical emulsion phenomena, such as phase reversal, formation of multiple emulsions, the action of antagonistic ions, etc., have little or nothing to do with the interfacial tension and its reduction.

The surface-tension theory explains the rôle of the interfacial tension in the process of emulsification. However, if an attempt is made to interpret emulsions solely from this standpoint an impasse is reached. The following quotation from H. W. Hillyer's paper: "On the Cleansing Power of Soap" [*J. Am. Chem. Soc.,* **25**, 518 (1903)] will serve as an example. After explaining the fact that some of the typical properties of soap, such as the detergent action and foam formation, are due to the reduction of the surface tension of water, he proceeds to discuss the action of soaps as emulsifying agents:

"It would seem that this low surface tension of soap solutions must be a prime factor in their emulsifying power. Viscosity can have little to do with it, for solutions containing about one per cent of sodium oleate are excellent as emulsifying agents, but have a viscosity so low that careful measurement would be necessary to show that they are more viscous than water. Using the same reasoning as in the case of bubbles and foam, we may say that when two oil drops approach each other in water, they tend to coalesce and finally do so because the greater surface tension of the drops easily withdraws the mobile water from between them till they touch and coalesce. But when drops are in soap solution, the surface tension is so very much less that it is not able to withdraw the solution rapidly from between the drops, and they are kept separate. If the soap solution is notably viscous, the slight surface tension will have still greater difficulty in thinning the film to the point of rupture. A mass of droplets separated by films of low surface tension and notable viscosity will be a permanent emulsion."

Hillyer's explanation gives a fairly good idea how it has been attempted to explain the stability of the emulsion system by the surface-tension theory. It is very interesting to note that even the most ardent advocates of the pure surface-tension theory cannot avoid postulating the existence of a protecting film around the droplets. This is, of course, a factor which goes far beyond the mere reduction of the surface tension, and it shows that the pure surface-tension theory is not capable of giving a satisfactory explanation of all properties of the emulsion system. As it will be seen later, the surface-tension theory and the earlier surface-film theory merged into a new theory, the adsorption theory, which, for the first time, gives a real explanation of emulsions. Before examining this theory it is, however, necessary to mention an interesting speculation which became known as the phase-volume theory, although it does not exactly deserve that name.

The Phase-Volume Theory

It is now, in retrospect, rather astonishing that up to the early years of the 20th century, hardly anybody was aware of the fact that emulsions exist as two fundamentally different types, namely oil-in-water (O/W) and water-in-oil (W/O). Although occasionally mentioned before, the first definite statement was made by Walter Ostwald in a paper: "Beiträge zur Kenntnis der Emulsionen," * [*Kolloid Z.,* 6, 103 (1910)]. Engaged in the examination of emulsions for the impregnation of wood, he explained that not only oil could be emulsified in water, as is the case in most of the emulsions studied at that time, but also water could be emulsified in oil, which would evidently give systems with entirely different properties. Thus far, the merits of Ostwald's paper are indisputable. Yet, in the later part of the same paper he attempted to develop a theory of emulsions on the basis of the volume ratio of the two emulsion phases, an attempt which was definitely less successful. The theory was later termed the phase-volume theory. To quote from a review made by Bancroft [*J. Phys. Chem.,* 16, 178 (1912)]: "While his reasoning is inaccurate it is interesting to note how far one can go astray if one starts from slightly inaccurate premises."

The phase-volume theory asserts that the formation of either the O/W or the W/O type of emulsion depends upon the relative volumes occupied by the two phases, e.g., if the volume of the water phase is larger than that of the oil phase, an O/W emulsion will be more likely, and vice versa. If a certain maximum concentration is reached, namely at an internal phase of about 74 per cent by volume, the emulsion can no longer remain stable and reversal of the phases or breaking will occur. For this bold statement, the following explanation is offered. If a great many rigid spheres of equal size are packed as closely together as possible, the space occupied by the spheres is constant and independent of their size. It can be calculated that 74 per cent of the total volume will be occupied by the spheres, and the remaining 26 per cent will be left as interstices. Therefore, the maximum concentration of the internal phase is limited to 74 per cent by volume, since there is no more space available for it.

The fallacy of this theory is easy to prove, as it is entirely

---

* Contributions to the Understanding of Emulsions.

possible to produce emulsions of more than 74 per cent internal phase. The theory is based on two wrong assumptions. First, the dispersed droplets are not necessarily of equal size; on the contrary, in most emulsions the particle size of the droplets covers a rather wide range. Now, if the particles differ in size, it will always be possible to pack smaller particles into the interstices among the larger ones. Second, the emulsion globules are not rigid. If the packing becomes very close, so that the globules exert pressure upon one another, they are quite easily deformed. Then, of course, many more than the theoretical number corresponding to 74 per cent can be packed into a given space. These very concentrated emulsions may even remain quite stable, if the interfacial film offers sufficient resistance. Thus the phase-volume theory can be discarded.

Yet, in spite of the apparent defects of this theory, there is a grain of truth in it. As stated before, the resistance offered by the interfacial film is an important factor in maintaining the stability of very concentrated emulsions. There is no doubt that the close packing in this type of emulsions exerts a great strain upon the interfacial film which, as will be discussed later, is a very delicate structure hardly withstanding great pressure. In fact, the very concentrated emulsions have a dangerous tendency to reverse phases or to break. In recognition of this fact, the careful formulator avoids introducing too much internal phase in his emulsion formula.

The Solid Particle Theory

Another theory of emulsions is the so-called solid particle theory. Though it is not a theory of great importance, it also contributed to the correct conception of emulsion systems. In 1907, S. U. Pickering published a paper on emulsions [*J. Chem. Soc.,* **91**, 2001 (1907)] in which he presented abundant experimental evidence for the peculiar behavior of finely dispersed solids in emulsions. In particular, he investigated freshly precipitated metal hydroxides, carbonates and sulfides, as well as specific basic salts, and found that many of them are capable of promoting emulsification. He drew the following conclusions from his experiments (*l. c.,* pp. 2014 and 2015):

"The view the writer was eventually led to adopt as to emulsification was that it depends solely on the size of the particles constituting the precipitate. When the oil is broken up into globules . . . and these globules find themselves in the presence of a number of very much more minute solid particles, the latter will be attracted by the globules and will form a coating or pellicle over the globules preventing them from coming into contact and coalescing with their neighbours. Whether gravitation alone is sufficient to account for such result or whether other forces come into play, must be left for others to determine, but that the solid particles do congregate closely round the globules, there can be no doubt for they can often be seen under a powerful microscope. With basic copper sulphate this is so, although the particles are so nearly ultramicroscopic that they cannot be resolved sufficiently to admit of any estimate being made as to their actual size."

"Further evidence that the globules must be enveloped in some covering is found in the fact that these emulsions do not make the containing vessel oily; indeed, this forms a very good distinctive test between a true emulsion and a quasi- or imperfect emulsion."

Pickering quite clearly anticipates the adsorption theory, but he stresses the fact that it must be solid particles that accumulate at the interface. He offers no explanation of how this accumulation occurs. Thus, the merits of his paper lie mainly in the discovery that solid particles, if in a state of finest subdivision, can act as emulsifying agents. Finely-dispersed solids are quite frequently employed as cheap and fairly effective emulsifying agents in modern emulsions.

As will be seen later, the theory of oriented adsorption adopts the idea of individual particles at the interface and throws some light upon the role of finely-divided solids as emulsion promoters.

The Adsorption Theory

None of the theories examined so far gives sufficient explanation of the why and how of emulsions. The adsorption theory is the first acceptable explanation of emulsion phenomena. It is usually linked with the name of W. D. Bancroft, who made the most important contribution to its conception, although many other authors had their share in its development.

In 1899, F. G. Donnan published a paper entitled: "Über die Natur der Seifenemulsionen" * [Z. phys. Chem., 31, 42 (1899)] in which he makes the following statements:

> "In view of all these observations and of my own experiments the following outline of a theory of soap emulsions (and possibly of all emulsions) seems to be on safe grounds."
>
> "The soap becomes concentrated in the surface layer between the oil and the aqueous liquid.** The equilibrium can be conceived in the following way: Due to its capacity of reducing the surface tension, the soap has the tendency to concentrate at the surface, because that causes a decrease in the free energy of the system. . . . By the accumulation at the surface the effectiveness of the active substance is greatly increased. In this way the work necessary for an enlargement of the common surface is reduced to a much lower value and thus the formation of small droplets made easier. One has to visualize each one of these small droplets as surrounded with a more concentrated surface layer."

Here the formation of the surrounding film and the reduction of the surface tension are clearly traced back to the accumulation of soap particles at the common surface of the two phases, the interface. This phenomenon is now commonly referred to as

---

* On the Nature of the Soap Emulsions.
** Related phenomena are probably the accumulation of gases at glass surfaces or the removal of dissolved substances from solutions by charcoal, kieselguhr, etc.

adsorption, and therefore, the theory is called the adsorption theory.

Adsorption is a very common occurrence in nature. It is, in its widest meaning, the accumulation of particles at a surface. The adsorption at liquid surfaces, which is the most interesting case in dealing with emulsions, is just a special case of adsorption. Adsorption at solid surfaces is necessarily restricted to particles captured from the regions adjacent to the solid surface, i.e., from the outside. Adsorption at liquid surfaces is not subject to such restrictions. Particles, originally dissolved or dispersed in the liquid, may migrate toward the surface from the inside and become adsorbed at the surface. In fact, this case is of the utmost significance in emulsions. Most of the emulsions are prepared by dispersing the emulsifying agent in one of the phases before emulsification. Then the adsorptive forces will accumulate the particles at the interface.

Particles that accumulate at the liquid surface invariably act as reducers of the surface tension. The process is usually called positive adsorption. The inverse phenomenon, namely that of thinning out at the surface and accumulating in the interior of the liquid, is called negative adsorption, and causes an increase of the surface tension. Any substance that becomes dissolved or dispersed in a liquid must possess a certain affinity for the dispersion medium. If the affinity is very strong, the substance will be easily soluble in or may be wetted by the dispersion medium; it will be pulled into the interior of the liquid, i.e., negatively adsorbed. Many of the inorganic salts, acids and bases and some of the lower organic compounds are readily soluble in water and negatively adsorbed; in fact, they usually increase the surface tension of the water. Some of the organic compounds, such as soaps, certain proteins and esters, on the other hand, are positively adsorbed and thus reduce the surface tension of the water. They are generally called surface-active agents, and emulsifying agents belong to this group.

Positive adsorption at the interface is the explanation given by the adsorption theory for the reduction of the interfacial tension and for the formation of the interfacial film. Donnan in his paper, quoted above, is still on the ground of the surface tension theory and only cautiously feels his way toward the new theory. Bancroft considers the adsorption of particles at the interface as an established fact. After discussing some of the earlier theories in a series of papers entitled: "The Theory of Emulsification" [*J. Phys. Chem.*, 16, 177, 345, 475, 739 (1912)], he explains his own conception as follows [*J. Phys. Chem.*, 17, 514, 515 (1913)]:

"Donnan considers the surface film in the case of soap as part of the water phase though differing in concentration from it. All the difficulties disappear if we consider the surface film as a separate phase, so that we have drops of oil, a surface film and surrounding water. We must do something of this sort in the case of foams or soap bubbles, because there it is absurd to consider the film as part of the enclosed air or of the external air . . ."

"With a real emulsion the conditions are different because we have two distinct liquids. It seems to me that it is easy to modify Donnan's theory so that it will fit the facts. Let us imagine a flexible, verticle diaphragm which separates two liquids A and B, and which is wetted by each. Since the diaphragm by definition absorbs each of the liquids, the surface tension of the two sides of the wetted diaphragm will not be the same as a rule. Owing to the difference in the surface tensions, the diaphragm will bend so that the side with the higher surface tension becomes concave. This change tends to envelope the liquid on that side. Consequently we conclude that liquid A will form drops in the emulsion in case liquid B lowers the surface tension of the diaphragm more than does liquid A."

In later publications, Bancroft modifies his ideas to some extent. In his book, *Applied Colloid Chemistry* (3rd Ed. McGraw-Hill Book Co., New York, 1932, p. 363), he says:

"If we call the two liquids "water" and "oil" and the emulsifying agent "soap" the emulsifying film has a minimum thickness of three molecules, one molecule of water, one molecule of soap, and one molecule of oil. There will be two surfaces to the emulsifying film, the one towards the water and the one towards the oil. If the surface tension of the water-soap interface is less than that of the oil-soap interface, the film will tend to curl so as to be convex on the water side and we shall have a tendency to emulsify oil in water. If the surface tension at the water-soap interface is greater than that of the oil-soap interface, the film will tend to curve so as to become concave at the water side and we shall have a tendency to emulsify water in oil."

In several important points, the adsorption theory goes far beyond any previous theory. First, it explains how the interfacial tension is reduced, namely, by positive adsorption of particles or molecules at the interface. Second, it tells how the protecting film is formed, again by adsorption of particles at the interface. Third, it shows why only a specific type of substances, the emulsifying agent, is capable of producing permanent emulsions, because only these substances can be adsorbed at the interface. Fourth, it offers a possible explanation for the formation of either O/W or W/O emulsions that is not contrary to observed facts or natural laws. The correctness of this explanation has been much disputed since then; some other explanations were proposed by later workers, but none of them so far is altogether satisfactory.

The merits of the adsorption theory are unquestionable; it is, in fact, the basis of most of the modern speculations on the formation and properties of emulsions. Still, several questions are left open. No adequate explanation is given for the structure of the interfacial film and for the phenomena of breaking and phase reversal. Very little is revealed about the rôle of the emulsifying agents. The mere statement that they are positively adsorbed gives no clue to their true nature. However, no theory of emulsions may be called satisfactory unless it covers all the phases of emulsification.

Among the later theories, the so-called hydration theory stands alone in contesting the achievements of the adsorption theory.

It attempts to explain the emulsion system from a different view-point and actually questions the existence of an interfacial film. In doing so it becomes entangled in serious contradictions.

The Hydration Theory

In 1917, M. H. Fischer and M. O. Hooker in their book on *Fats and Fatty Degeneration* (John Wiley & Sons, Inc., New York, 1917) set forth a new theory of emulsions, which takes a course different from that of any of the theories examined before. The authors claim (*l. c.*, p. 5) the following:

"In reviewing the empirical instructions available for the preparation of emulsions, and in our own attempts to formulate such as would always yield permanent results, we were struck with the fact that their production is always associated with the discovery of a method whereby the water (or other medium) which is to act as the dispersing agent is all used in the formation of a colloid hydration (solvation) compound. In other words, when it is said that the addition of soaps favors the formation and stabilization of a division of oil in water, it really means that soap is a hydrophilic colloid which, with water, forms a colloid hydrate with certain physical characteristics and that oil is divided in this. The resulting mixture cannot, therefore, be looked at as a subdivision of oil in water, but rather as one of oil in a hydrated colloid."

The basic difference between the hydration theory and all the previous theories lies in the assumption that substances are capable of acting as emulsifying agents only because they bind the dispersion medium with formation of colloidal hydrates in water, or solvates in other dispersion media, and not because these substances reduce the interfacial tension and form protecting films around the droplets (adsorption theory). Furthermore, the hydration theory asserts that an O/W emulsion will be produced if a colloidal hydrate is formed in the water phase, and a W/O emulsion, if a colloidal solvate is formed in the oil phase.

The existence of hydrated or solvated compounds is now generally accepted: They are responsible for the high viscosity of many colloidal solutions, the formation of gels and several other phenomena occurring in colloidal dispersions. It is assumed that a specific class of substances, called lyophilic colloids, i.e., "solvent-loving" colloids, form voluminous structures with their dispersion medium, which must be regarded as intermediates between physical mixtures and chemical compounds. The dispersion medium is not only the vehicle for the lyophilic colloid, but it is linked to it by secondary valence forces, and the resulting hydrated or solvated complexes are new individuals, different in physical and chemical properties from their two constituents. The hydration theory is also known as the lyophilic colloid theory.

There is no doubt that many of the substances used as emulsifying agents do produce hydrated or solvated complexes. All the agents investigated by Fischer and Hooker, i.e., soap, casein and other proteins, starch, egg yolk, etc., belong to this class. However, they are also potent reducers of surface tension, and they impart high viscosity to the external phase. Accordingly, their emulsifying action can be explained, just as well, by the adsorption theory. In addition, numerous synthetic agents, which were unknown when the hydration theory was developed, do not form hydrated complexes, or, form these to an extent insufficient for supporting Fischer's viewpoint.

The main objection to the hydration theory is the lack of an adequate explanation of the equilibrium within the emulsion system. As pointed out before, if a liquid is forced into another liquid toward which it shows high interfacial tension, the resulting system must be internally unstable. Whereas the adsorption theory explains in a satisfactory manner how the internal free energy of the system is balanced, the hydration theory has nothing to offer in this respect. It is, thus, at best, only a partial theory of emulsions.

It is likely that the hydrated or solvated colloids, whenever they occur in sufficient quantity in emulsions, will become partly adsorbed at the interface, where they will act according to the adsorption theory; the balance of these colloids will remain in the external phase, increasing the viscosity and so improving the stability, as was claimed by the old viscosity theory.

One fact, however, should not be overlooked. Even if the hydration theory overestimated the part played by the hydrated colloids in emulsions, they are important owing to their capacity for binding the water. Many emulsion failures are due to the reactivity of water which, as is well known, dissociates electrolytes and hydrolyzes many other inorganic and organic compounds, destroying constituents essential for the maintenance of stability. Bound in the form of hydrated complexes, the water is much less aggressive. Thus, the hydrated colloids contribute indirectly to the stability of emulsions.

The Oriented Adsorption Theory

The theory of oriented adsorption is not an independent theory. It follows closely the principles outlined by the earlier adsorption theory. Yet, it introduces a new viewpoint which improves the older theory to a great extent. The oriented adsorption theory agrees with the former explanation up to the point that adsorbed particles at the interface reduce the interfacial tension and form a protecting film around the globules. However, whereas the pure adsorption theory merely stated that specific particles are adsorbed, the new theory adds: in oriented positions. By introducing the concept of molecular orientation, an explanation of the rôle of emulsifying agents was offered.

The discovery of the phenomenon of molecular orientation is the outcome of the efforts of a number of investigators who worked independently on the same problem and came to almost the same conclusion almost simultaneously. In 1916, Irving Langmuir published a note on the subject [*Met. Chem. Eng.,* 15, 468 (1916)], followed a year later by a more detailed paper [*J. Am. Chem. Soc.,* 39, 1848 (1917)]. Independently of his work,

William D. Harkins and his coworkers published in 1917 the results of their investigations on molecular orientation [*J. Am. Chem. Soc.,* **39**, 354, 451 (1917)]. Therefore, the theory of oriented adsorption is generally referred to as the Langmuir-Harkins theory.

The kinetic theory of matter was considered a model theory in its time. Yet, in one respect, it had a rather detrimental influence upon the trend of thought of the scientific world of the 19th and early 20th century. For simplicity, the classic kinetic theory had to assume that matter is composed of particles which act as if they were hard and elastic spheres, somewhat similar to minute golf balls. It was frequently overlooked that this was but a useful simplification, which should not be confused with established facts.

In gases, where the particles are at great distances from one another and in swift motion, the assumption of rigid and elastic particles leads to a satisfactory explanation of the system. In the case of denser systems, i.e., liquids and solids, the golf ball conception will not work. The molecules, packed closely together, will attract and repell one another, which golf balls definitely will not do. To explain the properties of liquids and solids, it was assumed that the molecules are surrounded by a spherical field of forces which is very strong near the surface of the molecule, but rapidly diminishes with increasing distance from this surface. This field of forces accounts for many of the properties of liquid systems, e.g., the surface tension. Yet, it does not explain other properties of liquids, for instance, the behavior of the emulsifying agents at the interface.

The concept of molecular orientation offers an explanation of these properties. The first step was to revise the ideas about the shape and size of the molecules. The structural formulas of organic chemistry had prepared the way. Organic chemists had represented the molecules of aliphatic hydrocarbons as elongated, chain-like structures, and those of aromatic hydrocarbons as flat, disk-like configurations, and recent X-ray investigations .proved the correctness of this conception.

As soon as the old concept of spherical particles was discarded, many aspects of the theory changed automatically. The sphere is an ideally balanced body, uniform in all directions. If a number of spheres is arranged in space, none of them can possibly have a preferred position with regard to the others; all directions are equivalent. Any other geometrical body is less well balanced. The greater the deviation from the spherical shape, the more the mutual position of the particles will influence the properties of the system as a whole. Non-spherical structures, such as sticks, cylinders or disks may be arranged in space in two different ways. If no forces act on the particles, the arrangement will be one of complete disorder in random positions. However, adequate forces acting on the particles may result in an orderly arrangement. These arranging forces are generally called orienting forces and under their influence non-spherical particles may assume oriented positions in space.

The orienting forces originate in the special structure of the molecule. A molecule consists of atoms which are centers of positive and negative electrical energy. The arrangement of these centers within the molecule governs its electrical behavior toward the outside. If the centers are well balanced, which is the case if the molecule is symmetrical, the molecule is electrically neutral toward the outside, e.g., the molecules of diatomic elements, O_2,

$$
\text{or } H_2, \text{ or organic molecules like } H\!-\!\overset{\displaystyle H}{\underset{\displaystyle H}{\vert\,\text{C}\,\vert}}\!-\!H \text{ or } H\!-\!\overset{\displaystyle H}{\underset{\displaystyle H}{\vert\,\text{C}\,\vert}}\!-\!\overset{\displaystyle H}{\underset{\displaystyle H}{\vert\,\text{C}\,\vert}}\!-\!H.
$$

If, however, the centers of electrical energy are unevenly distributed within the molecule, as is the case with asymmetrically built molecules, such as HCl, H_2O, or NH_3, then the molecule will have electrical activity toward the outside. It is called a polar molecule, whereas the former type is referred to as non-polar.

A polar molecule behaves like a small rod with $+$ and $-$ charges on either end. If placed in an electrical field it will orient itself with its positive pole toward the cathode and its negative pole toward the anode. Polar molecules have a strong affinity for other polar molecules and, accordingly, polar substances will have a strong tendency to dissolve in polar solvents, such as water. Non-polar substances, on the other hand, will show better solubility in non-polar solvents, e.g., octane or benzene.

Of particular interest for the emulsion chemist are those organic substances which contain both polar and non-polar groups. As is well known, most organic compounds are composed of several groups. Some of them may be non-polar, such as $-CH_3$, $-C_2H_5$, and their higher homologs; others may be polar, such as $-OH$, $-COOH$, $-SO_3H$, $-Cl$, etc. If groups of both types are present in one molecule, compounds of dual behavior are formed. They are called molecules of the mixed non-polar—polar type. Molecules of this sort unite the properties of a non-polar and a polar compound. If the polar group is dominant, then the molecule will be predominantly polar. Such compounds will be water-soluble, as a rule. If, however, the non-polar portion is dominant, the molecule will be predominantly non-polar, and, accordingly, soluble in non-polar solvents.

If molecules of the mixed type are placed at the interface between water and oil, those having a dominant polar group will be immediately pulled into the water in spite of the resistance of the weak non-polar portion. On the other hand, a molecule having a dominant non-polar portion will immediately dissolve in the oil phase. Neither type can remain at the interface. If, however, the polar and the non-polar portion are of approximately equal strength the molecule will remain at the interface where the double nature will have a marked influence upon the behavior of these molecules. The polar group, having a strong tendency to enter the water phase, will attempt to get as near as possible to the water, and the non-polar group will act in the opposite direction. As a result, the molecules will be oriented at the interface in specific positions, with the polar end pointing toward the water and the non-polar end toward the oil. This is the explanation offered by the oriented adsorption theory for the behavior of emulsifying agents which are polar—non-polar compounds.

If a great many molecules accumulate at the interface in oriented positions, a continuous film will develop which has the strange property of being polar at one side—namely the one formed by the polar ends of the molecules and pointing toward the water—and non-polar at the other side. This concept of the interfacial film throws a new light upon the emulsion system. The film is no longer an accumulation of some particles in complete disorder, but a structure of easily-predictable properties. The observation that water-repellant oil droplets (in an O/W emulsion) become water-compatible when emulsifying agents are added, is no longer a mystery. The oil droplet itself is incompatible with water, but in the presence of a suitable emulsifying agent, the oil droplet is not in contact with the water at all; it is in contact with the non-polar ends of the oriented molecules of the emulsifying agent for which it has strong affinity. The water, in turn, is not in contact with the oil either, but with the polar ends of the oriented molecules. Consequently, the old droplets appear to have hydrophilic properties, the hydrophobic core being shielded from the water. In this light, the interfacial film appears to fulfil a double task: one the one hand, it separates the two incompatible phases and keeps the droplets from coalescing, and on the other hand, it acts as a buffer or a link between them. As Harkins puts it (in an article in: Alexander's *Colloid Chemistry,* Vol. I, p. 221; The Chemical Catalog Co., Inc., New York, 1926): ". . . at any surface or interface the change which occurs is such as to make the transition to the adjacent phase less abrupt."

The peculiar properties of the interfacial film can now be explained. The film was found to be tough and elastic when it resisted the stress of close packing in concentrated emulsions, but easily destroyable when the emulsion broke. According to the oriented adsorption theory the film consists of individual particles, held in position by the polar forces. Therefore, pressure and consequent deformation can do little harm, so long as the polar forces are undisturbed. If, however, these forces are weakened by some change in the system, for instance, by chemical decomposition of the emulsifying agent, then the particles will fall apart, i.e., the interfacial film is destroyed and the emulsion breaks.

Thus, the theory of oriented adsorption explains the properties of the emulsifying agents. They consist of elongated molecules of the mixed non-polar—polar type, e.g., in sodium oleate: $CH_3(CH_2)_7CH=CH(CH_2)_7COONa$, the non-polar portion is represented by the long hydrocarbon chain, whereas the polar —COONa group balances the molecule. In the vast majority of emulsifying agents, long hydrocarbon chains, usually of 12 to 18 carbon atoms, are present. These hydrocarbons may be obtained from fats and oils of animal, vegetable and mineral origin. Because of their elongated, chain-like structure, they are ideally suited as the non-polar constituent. Occasionally, however, other organic compounds are used, such as aromatic hydrocarbons or terpenes. The polar portion can be represented by a still greater variety of radicals. Any polar group, of which a few examples were given before, or combinations of two or more of them, may be introduced into the hydrocarbon molecule. The most important polar groups in emulsifying agents are the —COOH group and the substituted carboxylic group of organic salts, esters, amides, etc.; the —OH group (one or more); the —SO_3H group and its metal-substituted derivatives; a penta-valent nitrogen atom linked with a variety of organic radicals, and many others. Thus, an almost infinite variety of natural and synthetic emulsifying agents is available.*

The emulsifying action of finely-dispersed solids may be ac-

---

* A selection of commercially available emulsifying agents is assembled in a list at the end of this chapter.

counted for as follows. Even if very small, these solid particles consist of an enormous number of molecules; consequently it cannot be molecular orientation that determines their behavior at the interface. Yet, in many respects, small solid particles have an action similar to that of the molecules of organic emulsifiers. Firstly, they show a very definite preference for either the water or the oil phase, i.e., they are easier to wet with either water or oil. If the solid particles are wetted by water, they will not be able to act as emulsifiers, just as water-soluble compounds of the mixed non-polar—polar type cannot remain at the interface but will travel into the water. Particles, wetted by oil, on the other hand, will not perform at the interface, either. However, if their "wettability" is between the two extremes, then the small solid particles will act at the interface as the building stones of an interfacial film, in the same way as well-balanced molecules of the mixed type do. Secondly, these small solid particles often adsorb large quantities of the dispersion medium with the formation of colloidal solvated complexes, identical with the solvated complexes produced by the more familiar lyophilic colloids.

From the emulsion chemist's viewpoint, finely-divided solids can be classified into two groups. Hydrophilic solid particles, such as clay, in particular, colloidal clay (bentonite), metal hydroxides, etc., will act as promoters of O/W emulsions; hydrophobic solid particles, on the other hand, such as carbon black or graphite, will have a tendency to produce W/O emulsions.

It has been suggested earlier that any good theory of emulsions should give a satisfactory explanation of all the major and minor emulsion phenomena. The theory of oriented adsorption is better in this respect than any previous attempt. The formation of the emulsion, its stability, as well as its breaking and the influence of chemical and physical factors are well accounted for.

In one respect, however, the theory does not offer a satisfactory explanation, namely, why and on what conditions either the O/W or the W/O type of emulsion is formed. Closely connected with this question is the phenomenon of phase reversal. Empirically, both problems are fairly well under control; experience shows that hydrophilic agents, i.e., those which are fairly water-soluble, promote O/W emulsions, whereas hydrophobic agents, which are oil-soluble, favor the formation of the W/O type. Furthermore, it is known that the phase-volume ratio and the order of incorporating the constituents have an important bearing upon the type of emulsion formed. Yet, a real explanation of the phenomena involved is not provided by the oriented adsorption theory.

A hint as to the cause of the formation of either O/W or W/O emulsions is found in the first paper published by Langmuir on molecular orientation [*Chem. Met. Eng.,* 15, 468 (1916)].

"If a film of closely packed oleic acid molecules covers the surface of water to which sodium hydroxide has been added, OH groups are adsorbed by the COOH radicals, causing an expansion of the lower side of the film without a corresponding expansion of the upper side. This results in a bulging of the film downwards in spots so that it finally detaches itself in the form of particles, the outer surface of which consists of COOH groups together with adsorbed OH, while the interior consists of the long hydrocarbon chains."

Though here a water surface is considered, and not an interface between water and oil, the fundamental principle is given in that a one-sided increase in bulkiness of a thin film causes the film to curve. At an interface the conditions are essentially the same. Molecules of the mixed type, in which the polar and the nonpolar portion are well balanced, are adsorbed in oriented positions. If the two portions are in absolute equilibrium, there is *no* curving tendency, since both sides of the film are equally strong. Agents of this type are of ambiguous character; they are neither hydrophilic nor hydrophobic, and, thus, they show neither real preference for the O/W nor for the W/O type of emulsion. In an agent of definite hydrophilic character, the polar portion of the molecule must be slightly stronger than the non-polar portion; then the agent will act as a promoter of O/W emulsions. To produce hydrophobic agents, which will show a preference for the W/O type, the non-polar section of the molecule must be made slightly stronger than the polar portion.

Applying the principles outlined by Langmuir to the interface, the following interpretation can be given: An agent with a slightly dominant polar group will show a somewhat stronger tendency to adsorb polar particles (ions or molecules); this will cause a somewhat greater bulkiness of the interfacial film at the polar (water) side, and, therefore, a tendency to curve convexly toward the water and concavely toward the oil. Accordingly, the film will tend to envelop the oil droplets. The inverse reasoning can be applied to the W/O type emulsifying agents. It is quite wrong, however, to attribute the spherical shape of the emulsion droplets to the tendency of the interfacial film to curve. As was mentioned before, liquid particles, dispersed in a medium, will assume a spherical shape under the influence of surface tension. The interfacial film has no influence on the shape of the liquid particles.

Assuming now that in the early stages of emulsification, droplets of both oil and water are temporarily formed, only those droplets that are protected by an interfacial film will be stable. When a hydrophilic agent is present, producing an interfacial film with a tendency to curve concavely to the oil, only the oil droplets will become stabilized, whereas the water droplets will lack protection and will flow together at once. Thus, an O/W emulsion will be formed. As J. H. Hildebrand [*J. Phys. Chem.,* 45, 1303 (1941)] points out:

". . . there is reason to believe that curvature in one direction yields lower energy than curvature in the other; hence this direction is, undoubtedly, a factor in determining which liquid shall be the enclosed phase."

The phenomenon of phase reversal may be explained as the

result of a slight alteration in the balance of the molecular structure of the agent, caused, for instance, by a chemical reaction. If
by such action an agent which had initially a slightly dominant
polar group is transformed into an agent having a slightly
dominant non-polar group, the equilibrium at the emulsion
interface is disturbed. A state of higher free energy is created,
which is less stable. Then the conditions for phase reversal are
given and if, in addition, the phase-volume ratio is more favorable
for the formation of the opposite type of emulsion, the phases
will be reversed; again establishing a state of lower free energy.

This explanation is not contrary to physical laws, but it is not
quite satisfactory. There is little experimental evidence in favor
of the curvature hypothesis. It cannot be proved, for instance,
that the film at the interface is actually monomolecular; if more
than one layer of molecules participate in its architecture, the
hypothesis loses much ground. As some critics point out, the
forces producing curvature are exceedingly weak, probably too
weak to account for the establishment of an equilibrium at the
interface. Moreover, the fact that many emulsifying agents dissociate and electrical charges and potential differences occur at
the interface is not duly considered. To quote Hildebrand once
more (*l. c.,* p. 1305):

> "The various factors which contribute to the stability of one
> type of emulsion rather than the inverse type are supplemental
> rather than rival. The direction of film curvature for minimum
> energy has probably been overemphasized at the expense of the
> more mechanical forces operating during emulsification."

The Oriented Wedge Theory

The oriented wedge theory is essentially a theory for a special
group of emulsifying agents, the soaps. As pointed out before,
the oriented adsorption theory describes an emulsifier molecule
as a structure of non-spherical shape, e.g., a small rod having a

polar and non-polar end. The oriented wedge theory goes farther. It asserts that the molecules have cross-sections of different sizes at both ends, i.e., they are not cylindrical but have the shape of small cones or wedges. An alkali soap, for example, is represented by the general formula:

$$RCOOM_I$$

where R stands for a long hydrocarbon chain and M_I for a monovalent cation, such as Na^+, K^+, or NH_4^+; the polar group —$COOM_I$ is assumed to have a larger cross-section than the non-polar hydrocarbon chain. The metallic soaps, on the other hand, are represented by the following formulas:

$$\begin{matrix} RCOO \\ RCOO \end{matrix} > M_{II} \qquad\qquad \begin{matrix} RCOO \\ RCOO—M_{III} \\ RCOO \end{matrix}$$

where M_{II} stands for a divalent cation, such as Ca^{++}, Mg^{++}, or Zn^{++}, and M_{III} for a trivalent cation, for instance Al^{+++}. In this type of soaps the non-polar end of the molecule is supposed to have a larger cross-section, because the di- or trivalent metals have two or three acid radicals attached to each metal atom. The soap molecules are thus described by the theory as little wedges which, because of their peculiar shape, force the interfacial film to curve. If an alkali soap molecule becomes adsorbed at the interface, the film will be bulkier at the water side, since the polar heads are bulkier than the non-polar tails. Therefore, the film will curve concavely toward the oil and promote the formation of O/W emulsions. Molecules of a metallic soap, on the other hand, having a bulkier non-polar portion, will curve the film concavely toward the water, causing the formation of an emulsion of the W/O type. In this way, the oriented wedge theory accounts for the well-known fact that alkali soaps are

O/W emulsifiers, whereas metallic soaps promote the formation of W/O emulsions.

This theory was first presented by Harkins and his coworkers [*J. Am. Chem. Soc.,* **39**, 595 (1917)] as a part of the general theory of molecular orientation. Later on, it was developed into an independent theory by Finkle. and his coworkers [*J. Am. Chem. Soc.,* **45**, 2780 (1923)]. A summary of the oriented wedge theory was presented by Finkle and his coworkers at the First Colloid Symposium, at the University of Wisconsin [Colloid Symposium Monograph, I, 196 (1923)] in which some more specific statements were made:

> ". . . if the polar group, in the water, occupies more space than is necessary for the closest packing of the hydrocarbon chain, the latter can be packed more closely if the film is convex on the water side. . . . It is obvious that the direction and degree of curvature, if this hypothesis is correct, should vary first with the atomic volume of the metal, being more convex the larger this volume, and second with the number of hydrocarbon chains attached to a single metallic atom, according to its valence. Zinc soap . . . should make the interface convex toward the "oil" side, while an aluminum soap should give still more curvature and more stable emulsions of water in oil. Where the cross-section of the hydrocarbon chain and of the metallic end are of the same magnitude, there will be no tendency to curvature, and no very stable emulsion, in spite of the high adsorption at the interface, which is still possible."

The oriented wedge theory has been much disputed since. Though it is certainly an interesting speculation, it is just another attempt to explain the type of emulsion formed on the basis of film curvature. In addition, there is only very little experimental evidence for the wedge shape of the molecules. It is probably correct to assume that in sodium or potassium oleate, the cross-section of the polar end is larger than that of the hydrocarbon chain. But the same must be true, even to a larger extent, of the soaps of heavy monovalent metals, e.g., the silver salt of fatty acids, since the atomic volume of silver is larger than that of sodium or potassium; yet, silver soaps promote the formation of W/O emulsions. It appears, therefore, that the actual shape of the molecule has less bearing upon the type of emulsion formed than the balance between the polar and the non-polar portions. Silver, though monovalent, is but weakly hydrophilic; the non-polar hydrocarbon chain is dominant in the molecule and, accordingly, silver oleate is hydrophobic and promotes the formation of W/O emulsions.

One of the main objections to the oriented wedge theory is the fact, that it deals solely with the soap type of emulsifying agents. Even if the explanation given for soaps is accepted, no explanation is given for the action of other emulsifying agents, such as the cation-active compounds, or the agents of the non-ionic type. In particular, the latter class has numerous members of both the W/O and O/W promoting type, yet there is no trace of evidence that their different action is due to the different shape of the molecules.

Electrokinetic Theories

In all previous discussions, the fact that electrical charges occur in emulsions has been neglected. The rôle of these charges is by no means clear. Whereas some authors credit them with having very little influence on the emulsion system, others claim that they are a factor of paramount importance. In the following, a brief survey will be given of the electrical phenomena observed in emulsions.

The term, electrokinetic phenomenon, refers to (1) the motion of suspended particles caused by electric charges, or to (2) the appearance of electrical charges owing to the motion of suspended particles. The most important of these phenomena observed in emulsions is that of electrophoresis. If an electric current passes through an emulsion, the droplets of the internal phase move toward one of the electrodes. This must be due to the fact that the droplets carry electrical charges of a sign opposite to that of the electrode toward which they travel. In most O/W emulsions, the oil globules were found to be negatively charged, whereas the water droplets in a W/O emulsion are positively charged. However, there are many exceptions to this rule.

Without going into details, it may be said that charges are probably derived from the adsorption of electrically charged ions at the surface of the particle, either by electrolytic disassociation of molecules at the surface or by the capture of ions from the aqueous phase. If a globule preferentially adsorbs ions of one kind, e.g., negative ions, the particle, as a whole, will have a negative charge. Such a charged particle has been compared to a giant polyvalent ion, with a view to the analogy between the electrophoretic migration of dispersed particles and the electrolytic motion of ordinary ions.

If a large number of electrically charged particles float freely in a dispersion medium, as is the case with an emulsion, the charges will prevent the particles, to some extent, from approaching one another, since like charges repel. In this way, the electrical charges have a stabilizing effect on the emulsified droplets, preventing them from coming in contact and flowing together. If the particles are exceedingly small, as in the previously-mentioned oil-hydrosols, then the repellency of the charged surface will become a decisive factor in the maintenance of stability. These very dilute dispersions of minute oil particles in water remain stable without any emulsifying agent. It is well known, however, that the normal types of emulsions which have considerably larger particles and a high concentration of the internal phase, cannot be produced without the help of emulsifying agents; evidently, the repellent action of the surface charges alone is insufficient to keep the globules apart. Unfortunately, many of the investigations on the rôle of the electrical charges in emulsions were made with the oil-hydrosol type and the conclusions obtained, undoubtedly true for minute particles at high dilution, are not valid for con-

centrated emulsions having larger particles. A general theory
of emulsions, based solely upon the presence of electrical charges
has, therefore, little chance to succeed.

Another factor which has an important bearing upon the
structure of the interfacial film is the electrokinetic potential; it
is a direct consequence of the peculiar arrangement of the electrical charges at the particle surface. If an emulsion droplet is
negatively charged, i.e., if a layer of negative charges or ions is
adsorbed at its surface, there will be a compensating number of
positive charges or ions arranged in a loose shell around the
droplet. These two shells of charges of opposite sign are called
the electric double layer and the potential difference across the
double layer is referred to as the electrokinetic potential, or zeta
potential.

The presence of a potential difference at the surface of the
emulsion droplet throws a new light upon the formation of the
emulsion and the maintenance of stability.

In 1932, C. H. M. Roberts published a paper entitled: "A New
Theory of Emulsions" [*J. Phys. Chem.*, **36**, 3087 (1932)], in
which he attempts to integrate the principles of adsorption,
orientation and electrokinetics into a general theory of emulsions.
The formation of a W/O emulsion proceeds according to Roberts
as follows (*l. c.*, p. 3096):

"At the instant of formation of an interface, the opposed surfaces of the respective phases will have the same average concentration of compounds as any cross-section within the respective
volumes; that is, no adsorption has yet taken place. At this instant
also, the electrokinetic potentials on both sides will have their
maximum dynamic values. Ions and molecules immediately begin
to move toward the interface, but the ions arrive first because of
their higher mobility . . ."

"Neglecting molecular adsorption for the moment, we can consider that equilibrium of ionic adsorption is attained, at which in-

stant the electrokinetic potential will have attained maximum values. While this equilibrium is being reached, the interfacial tension will fall with extreme rapidity, while the electrokinetic potential will increase with corresponding rapidity."

"From this stage of the process we must consider the relatively slow moving molecules, which are beginning to concentrate in the interface and crowd out the more mobile ions . . . on the oil side, the replacement of ions by polar molecules oriented with their most polar ends toward the water, will proceed continuously. When the point is reached where there is electrical equivalence between the ions and polar molcules on the oil side, the corresponding electrokinetic potential will be zero, while the rate of change of the interfacial tension on the oil side will have reached a low value."

"As the age of the interfacial film continues to increase beyond that point, there will be an increasing preponderance of molecules over ions in the interfacial film, until the static condition of a complete monomolecular layer of polar molecules in the primary layer is reached. At this time, the electrokinetic potential on the oil side will have attained a low steady value of opposite sign to that in the early stages of the process and the interfacial tension will have attained its minimum static value."

Robert's theory certainly brings up numerous interesting factors, but it will require much additional evidence to evaluate the true rôle of the electrical charges in the emulsion system.

An attempt was made to describe the development of the theory of emulsions. This survey is far from complete; many other theories and hypotheses could have been mentioned. Yet, it was the intention of the author to discuss only those theories in particular, which will help the worker in the field of emulsions to understand this intricate subject. For information on some of the other theories the reader is referred to *The Theory of Emulsions and Their Technical Treatment,* by W. Clayton (The Blakiston Co., Philadelphia, 1943) and *Emulsions and Foams,* by S. Berkman and G. Egloff (Reinhold Publishing Corp., New York, 1941).

LIST OF EMULSIFYING AGENTS

As pointed out previously, emulsifying agents are needed for emulsion manufacture. If a comparison is made between a list of emulsifying agents, compiled some 10 or 15 years ago, and the list which is included in this chapter, the enormous increase in the number and types of emulsifying agents will be apparent.

The commercially available emulsifying agents have been classified into eight groups with some subdivisions, as follows:

ANION-ACTIVE AGENTS

Group 1. Soaps
    a. Alkali Soaps
    b. Metallic Soaps
Group 2. Organic Amino Compounds Producing Soaps with Fatty Acids
Group 3. Sulfated Compounds
    a. Sulfated Oils
    b. Sulfated Alcohols
Group 4. Sulfonated Compounds
    a. Aliphatic Sulfonates
    b. Aromatic Sulfonates (also with aliphatic side-chains)

CATION-ACTIVE AGENTS

Group 5. Cation-Active Agents

NON-IONIC AGENTS

Group 6. Ester and Ethers
    a. Hydrophobic Esters
    b. Hydrophilic Esters

MISCELLANEOUS AGENTS

Group 7. Natural and Modified Natural Agents
Group 8. Finely-Dispersed Solids

The agents of groups 1 to 4 are anion-active; they are usually salts of organic acids, which dissociate as any other salt into anions and cations. In the class of anion-active agents, the "active" group, which characterizes the emulsifying agent, is in the anionic portion of the molecule. For example:

$$CH_3(CH_2)_7CH{=}CH(CH_2)_7COONa \rightarrow$$
Sodium oleate

$$CH_3(CH_2)_7CH{=}CH(CH_2)_7COO^- + Na^+$$
Anion containing the active group   Cation

or:

$$CH_3(CH_2)_7CH{=}CH(CH_2)_7CH_2OSO_3Na \rightarrow$$
Sodium oleyl sulfate

$$CH_3(CH_2)_7CH{=}CH(CH_2)_7CH_2OSO_3{}^- + Na^+$$
Anion containing the active group   Cation

The agents of group 5 are cation-active. On dissociation the active group remains in the cation, as the following example shows:

$$\left[\begin{array}{c} CH_3CH_3 \\ \diagdown\diagup \\ N \\ \diagup\diagdown \\ CH_3(CH_2)_{14}CH_2CH_3 \end{array}\right]Cl \rightarrow \left[\begin{array}{c} CH_3CH_3 \\ \diagdown\diagup \\ N \\ \diagup\diagdown \\ CH_3(CH_2)_{14}CH_2CH_3 \end{array}\right]^+ + Cl^-$$
Anion

Cetyl-trimethyl   Cation containing the
ammonium chloride   active group

The agents of group 6 are non-ionic, or non-dissociating compounds, mostly esters, in which the dissociating —COOH group is blocked by esterification, e.g.:

$$C_{11}H_{23}COOC_2H_4OC_2H_4OH$$
Diethylene glycol monolaurate

In group 7, a number of agents are assembled in a rather arbitrary way. These are natural, refined or slightly modified substances hard to classify into any of the groups 1 to 6.

Finally, group 8 embraces the solids which act as emulsifying agents when in a state of finest dispersion.

The value of this arrangement into groups lies not only in the ease of survey, but, much more, in the fact that the agents within one group or sub-group act in emulsions rather similarly and are, to some extent, interchangeable.

General Formula: RCOOM

Chemical Designation: Alkali salts of higher fatty acids,* also of other higher organic acids.

Type of Emulsion: O/W

Description: Pastes or solids, occasionally chips, flakes or powders of white or yellowish color and of alkaline reaction; not calcium-tolerant; somewhat affected by hydrolysis.

Suggested Use: Cheap general-purpose emulsifying agents, effective only in alkaline emulsions.

Commercial Name	Chemical Name or Formula	Remarks	Manufacturer
Ammonium laurate	$C_{11}H_{23}COONH_4$	Volatile alkali component; recommended for coating emulsions.	Glyco
Ammonium linoleate	$C_{17}H_{31}COONH_4$	Volatile alkali component; recommended for coating emulsions.	Various
Ammonium stearate	$C_{17}H_{35}COONH_4$	Anhydrous solid or aqueous paste.	"
Dresinate	Sodium resinate	Dry powder or aqueous paste.	Hercules
Liquid soap	—	Aqueous soap solution with approx. 40% soap.	Various
Miscibol	Potassium oleo-abietate	—	Glyco

* Most commercial soaps are made from natural fats and oils, which are mixed triglycerides of various fatty acids. The resulting soaps are then also mixtures of different fatty acid salts.

329

Commercial Name	Chemical Name or Formula	Remarks	Manufacturer
Potassium oleate	$C_{17}H_{33}COOK$	Potassium soaps are generally softer and more water-soluble than the corresponding sodium soaps.	Various
Potassium palmitate	$C_{15}H_{31}COOK$		"
Protalene L	Salts of protein-fatty acid condensates	—	Touraine
Rosoap	Sodium oleo-abietate	—	Glyco
Soap flakes	—	Usually more alkaline than ordinary soap.	Various
Sodium oleate	$C_{17}H_{33}COONa$	—	"
Sodium palmitate	$C_{15}H_{31}COONa$	—	"
Sodium resinate	$C_{19}H_{29}COONa$	—	"
Sodium stearate	$C_{17}H_{35}COONa$	—	"
Soft soap	Mainly potassium oleate	—	"

METALLIC SOAPS
(anion-active)

General Formula:
$$RCOO{-}M_{II} \quad \text{or} \quad (RCOO)_{3}M_{III}$$

Type of Emulsion: W/O

Chemical Designation: RCOO Fatty acid salts or di- or trivalent light metals.

Description: Fine white powders of fatty odor; form highly viscous solutions or gels in hydrophobic solvents.

Suggested Use: Bodying agents for the oil phase and auxiliary emulsifying agents.

Commercial Name	Chemical Formula	Remarks	Manufacturer
Aluminum stearate	$(C_{17}H_{35}COO)_{3}Al$	Available with varying content of free fatty acid.	Various

330

Commercial Name	Chemical Name or Formula	Remarks	Manufacturer
Calcium linoleate	$(C_{17}H_{31}COO)_2Ca$	Usually aqueous pulp	Various
Calcium stearate	$(C_{17}H_{35}COO)_2Ca$	—	"
Magnesium stearate	$(C_{17}H_{35}COO)_2Mg$	—	"
Zinc stearate	$(C_{17}H_{35}COO)_2Zn$	—	"

AMINO COMPOUNDS PRODUCING SOAPS WITH FATTY ACIDS
(resulting soaps: anion-active)

General Formula:

$$\underset{H}{\overset{R'}{N}}{-}H \qquad \underset{H}{\overset{R'}{N}}{-}R'' \qquad \underset{R'''}{\overset{R'}{N}}{-}R'' \qquad also \qquad HN\underset{R'}{\overset{R'}{\diagup}}O$$

Chemical Designation: Primary, secondary, or tertiary aliphatic amino compounds.

Type of Emulsion: O/W

Description: Water-white or yellowish liquids or crystalline solids, of strongly alkaline reaction; odorless or of typical amino-odor; form soaps when reacted with fatty acids (e.g., $RCOONHR'_3$); not calcium-tolerant.

Suggested Use: The soaps, called "amino soaps," are outstanding emulsifying agents for technical emulsions, cosmetics, soluble oils, etc.; those amines with low boiling point are especially useful in coating emulsions; not to be used in acidic medium.

Commercial Name	Chemical Formula	Remarks	Manufacturer
2-Amino-1-butanol	CH₃—CH₂—CH—CH₂OH NH₂	Boiling point 178°C.	Commercial
2-Amino-2-methyl-1-propanol	CH₃—C—CH₂OH NH₂ CH₃	Boiling point 165°C.	

331

Commercial Name	Chemical Name or Formula	Remarks	Manufacturer Commercial
2-Amino-2-methyl-1, 3-propanediol	$CH_2OH-C-CH_2OH$ with NH_2 above and CH_3 below	—	—
2-Amino-2-ethyl-1, 3-propanediol	$CH_2OH-C-CH_2OH$ with NH_2 above and C_2H_5 below	—	"
Diethanolamine	$NH(C_2H_4OH)$	Boiling point 133.5°C.	Carbide
Dimethyl amino-ethanol	$N-CH_3$ with CH_3 above and C_2H_4OH below	Boiling point 133.5°C.	"
N-Ethyl morpholine	morpholine ring with C_2H_4N, CH_2-CH_2, CH_2-CH_2, O	Boiling point 138.0°C.	"
Methyl diethanolamine	CH_3N with C_2H_4OH and C_2H_4OH		"

332

Commercial Name	Chemical Name of Formula	Remarks	Manufacturer
N-Methyl morpholine	CH_3N structure with CH_2—CH_2 / CH_2—CH_2 ring and O	Boiling point 115.4°C.	Carbide
Morpholine	HN ring with CH_2—CH_2 / CH_2—CH_2 and O	Boiling point 128.9°C; most versatile volatile agent.	"
Triethanolamine	C_2H_4OH / N—C_2H_4OH / C_2H_4OH	Most popular all-purpose agent of the group.	Various
Trigamine	—	—	Glyco
Tris (hydroxymethyl) aminomethane	CH_2OH—C—CH_2OH with NH_2 and CH_2OH	—	Commercial
Tris isopropanol amine	$CH_2CHOHCH_3$ / N—$CH_2CHOHCH_3$ / $CH_2CHOHCH_3$	—	Carbide

(anion-active)

General Formula:

Chemical Designation: R—CH(OSO$_3$M)—R'COOM

Sulfated fatty acids and their alkali salts; i.e., fatty acids containing the group —CH(OSO$_3$M)— somewhere in the middle of the chain.

Type of Emulsion: O/W

Description: Oily, water-soluble liquids of reddish-brown color; not calcium-tolerant.

Suggested Use: Mainly designed as detergents and wetting agents; also fairly efficient emulsifying agents for fat-liquors; soluble oils, etc.

Commercial Name	Chemical Name	Remarks	Manufacturer
Aquasol AR 75	Sulfated castor oil	25% water content.	Cyanamid
Monopol oil	Sulfated castor oil	—	Various
Monosulph	Sulfated castor oil	—	National Oil
Nopco 1471	Sulfated vegetable oil	—	"
Nopcob	Sulfated vegetable oil	—	
Sulfated castor oil	Sodium salt of castor oil sulfuric acid ester	Most popular agent of the group; contains varying amounts of water, if not specifically declared "anhydrous."	Various
Sulfated neatsfoot oil	Sodium salt of sulfated neatsfoot oil	Special for fat-liquors.	"
Sulfated olive oil	Sodium salt of sulfated olive oil	—	"
Turkey red oil	Sulfated castor oil	—	"

SULFATED ALCOHOLS AND ESTERS
(anion-active)

General Formula:

RCH$_2$OSO$_3$M or RCOOR'OSO$_3$M

(R = long chain hydrocarbon, R' = di- or trivalent alcohol)

334

Chemical Designation:	
Type of Emulsion:	O/W
Description:	Sulfuric acid esters of long-chain alcohols, or esters of their alkali salts. Liquids, pastes or wax-like solids with many similarities to soaps; thoroughly calcium-tolerant and little affected by hydrolysis.
Suggested Use:	Good general-purpose emulsifiers, especially recommended for soluble oils, cleansing emulsions, polishes and cosmetics.

Commercial Name	Chemical Name or Formula	Remarks	Manufacturer
Arctic Syntex M	$CH_3(CH_2)_{16}COOCH_2CHOHCH_2OSO_3Na$	Available as flakes or beads.	Colgate
Arctic Syntex M (liquid)	$CH_2(CH_2)_{16}COOCH_2CHOHCH_2OSO_3NH_4$	—	"
Duponol C	Technical sodium lauryl sulfate	Controlled for lead and arsenic content.	du Pont
Duponol D Paste	Special alcohol sulfate	Available in form of paste or powder.	"
Duponol ES	Technical sodium oleyl sulfate	—	"
Duponol G	Oil-soluble alcohol sulfate	—	"
Duponol LS	Technical sodium oleyl sulfate	—	"
Duponol ME	Technical sodium lauryl sulfate	Minimum electrolyte content.	"
Duponol OS	Oil-soluble alcohol sulfate	—	"
Duponol WA	Technical sodium lauryl sulfate	—	"
Duponol WS	Oil-soluble alcohol sulfate	Wax soluble.	"
Orvus WA	Sodium lauryl sulfate	—	Procter
Sodium cetyl sulfate	$C_{15}H_{31}CH_2OSO_3Na$	—	Various
Sodium lauryl sulfate	$C_{11}H_{23}CH_2OSO_3Na$	—	"
Sodium oleyl sulfate	$C_{17}H_{33}CH_2OSO_3Na$	—	"
Tergitol wetting agent 08	Sodium sulfate of 2-ethyl hexanol	40% aqueous solution.	Carbide
Tergitol wetting agent 4	Sodium sulfate of 7-ethyl 2-methyl undecanol-4	25% aqueous solution.	"
Tergitol wetting agent 7	Sodium sulfate of 3,9-diethyl-tride-canol-6	25% aqueous solution.	"

Commercial Name	Chemical Name or Formula	Remarks	Manufacturer
Triton 720	Sodium salt of alkyl phenoxyethyl sulfate	—	Rohm
Triton 770	Sodium salt of alkyl phenoxyethyl sulfate	Supplied in water—isopropanol mixture.	"
Triton 773	Sodium salt of alkyl phenoxyethyl sulfate	Supplied in aqueous mixture.	"

ALIPHATIC SULFONATES
(anion-active)

General Formula: RSO_3M or $RCOOR'SO_3M$ or $RCONHR'SO_3M$ (R = long chain hydrocarbon, R' = lower hydrocarbon)

Chemical Designation: Sulfonates of long-chain aliphatic hydrocarbons or of aliphatic esters or amides.

Type of Emulsion: O/W

Description: Mostly odorless, wax-like or crystalline solids; thoroughly calcium-tolerant and stable over a wide range of pH.

Suggested Use: Outstanding emulsifying and wetting agents for many purposes.

Commercial Name	Chemical Name or Formula	Remarks	Manufacturer
Aerosol OT	Dioctyl sodium sulfosuccinate	Available in 100% strength or dissolved in water and a mutual solvent.	Cyanamid
Aerosol MA	Dihexyl sodium sulfosuccinate	—	"
Aerosol AY	Diamyl sodium sulfosuccinate	—	"

Commercial Name	Chemical Name or Formula	Remarks	Manufacturer
Aerosol IB	Dibutyl sodium sulfosuccinate	—	Cyanamid
Arctic Syntex A	$CH_3(CH_2)_7CH_2CH=CH(CH_2)_7COOC_2H_4SO_3Na$	Available as powder or flakes.	Colgate
Arctic Syntex T	$CH_3(CH_2)_7CH=CH(CH_2)_7CON(CH_3)C_2H_4SO_3Na$	Available as flakes or aqueous pastes and gels.	"
Emarsol	Sulfoacetate of mono- and diglycerides mixed with mono- and diglycerides	Edible agent and anti-splatterer.	Emulsol
Igepon A	$CH_3(CH_2)_7CH=CH(CH_2)_7COOC_3H_5O_2Na$	—	General
Igepon T	$CH_3(CH_2)_7CH=CH(CH_2)_7CON(CH_3)C_2H_4SO_3Na$	—	"
MP-189	Petroleum hydrocarbon sodium sulfonate	—	du Pont
MP-646 S Paste	Petroleum hydrocarbon sodium sulfonate	—	"
Petrosul C50	Petroleum sulfonate	Approx. 50% sulfo acids.	Pennsylvania
Petrosul C75	Petroleum sulfonate	Approx. 75% sulfo acids.	"
Petrosul C90	Petroleum sulfonate	Approx. 90% sulfo acids.	"
Sulfatate	Sodium salt of sulfonated hydrocarbon	—	Glyco

AROMATIC SULFONATES
(anion-active)

General Formula: RSO_3M or $R'RSO_3M$
(R = aromatic, R' = aliphatic)

Chemical Designation: Sulfonates of aromatic hydrocarbons, also with aliphatic side chains.

Type of Emulsion: O/W

Description: Crystalline or wax-like odorless solids of white or brownish color; thoroughly calcium-tolerant and stable over a wide range of pH.

Suggested Use: Mainly as wetting and dispersing agents, also as auxiliary emulsifying agents.

337

Commercial Name	Chemical Name	Remarks	Manufacturer
Aerosol AS	Isopropyl naphthalene sodium sulfonate	Solution of Aerosol OS in water and a mutual solvent.	Cyanamid
Aerosol OS	Isopropyl naphthalene sodium sulfonate	Contains 5% inorganic salts.	"
Albatex	Sulfonate of an alkylated benzimidazole	—	Ciba
Alkanol B	Alkyl naphthalene sodium sulfonate	—	du Pont
Alkanol S	Sodium tetrahydro-naphthalene sulfonate	—	"
Areskap	Monobutyl phenylphenol sodium monosulfonate	Available as liquid and as dry powder.	Monsanto
Aresket	Monobutyl diphenyl sodium monosulfonate	Available as liquid and as dry powder.	"
Aresklene	Dibutyl phenylphenol sodium disulfonate	Available as paste and as dry powder.	"
Beaconol A	Monoethyl phenylphenol sodium monosulfonate	—	Beacon
Beaconol M	Monoethyl phenylphenol potassium monosulfonate	—	"
Beaconol S	Monoethyl phenylphenol amino monosulfonate	—	"
Beaconol T	Monoethyl phenylphenol guanidine monosulfonate	—	"
Darvan 1	Sodium salt of alkyl naphthalene sulfonic acid	Short alkyl chain.	Vanderbilt
Darvan 2	Sodium salt of alkyl naphthalene sulfonic acid	Long alkyl chain.	"
Daxad 11	Sodium salt of alkyl naphthalene sulfonic acid	Short alkyl chain.	Dewey
Daxad 23	Sodium salt of alkyl naphthalene sulfonic acid	Long alkyl chain.	"
Invadine B	Sodium alkyl phenylene sulfonate	—	Ciba

Commercial Name	Chemical Name or Formula	Remarks	Manufacturer
Invadine C	Alkyl naphthalene sulfonic acid	—	Ciba
Invadine N	Sodium alkyl naphthalene sulfonate	—	"
Nacconol NR	Sodium alkyl benzene sulfonate	Alkyl radical between C_{10}–C_{20}.	National Aniline
Nacconol NRSF	Sodium alkyl benzene sulfonate	Salt-free.	"
Nekal A	Isopropyl naphthalene sodium sulfonate	—	General
Nekal BX	Isobutyl naphthalene sodium sulfonate	—	"
Neomerpin N	Alkyl naphthalene sulfonic acid	—	du Pont
Santomerse D	Decylbenzene sodium sulfonate	—	Monsanto
Santomerse S	Decylbenzene sodium sulfonate	30% aqueous solution of Santomerse D.	"
Santomerse 1	Alkyl aryl sodium sulfonate	Neutral.	"
Santomerse 2	Alkyl aryl sodium sulfonate	Alkaline.	"
Santomerse 3	Dodecylbenzene sodium sulfonate	Available as powder or paste.	"
Twitchell reagent	Sulfonaphthyl stearic acid	—	Various
Ultravon K	Heptadecyl benzimidazol monosulfonate	—	Ciba
Ultravon W	Heptadecyl benzimidazol disulfonate	—	"

General Formula:

$$R \underset{R'''}{\overset{R'}{\underset{\diagdown}{\overset{\diagup}{N}}}} R''$$

y

(R = long chain, R', ", R'' = short groups, y = acidic group)

Chemical Designation: Salts of quaternary ammonium compounds or of heterocyclic compounds containing a pentavalent nitrogen atom.

Type of Emulsion: Mainly O/W

Description: From thin, colorless liquids to tan, wax-like solids; thoroughly calcium-tolerant; somewhat sensitive to hydrolysis.

Suggested Use: Valuable agents for use in neutral or acidic emulsions, especially in combination with non-ionic agents; not to be used in combination with anion-active agents.

Commercial Name	Chemical Name or Formula	Remarks	Manufacturer
Ammonyx	Quaternary ammonium halide	—	—
Cationic amine 220	1-Hydroxyethyl-2-heptadecenyl glyoxalidine	—	Carbide
Cetyl pyridinium chloride	$\left[C_nH_{2n+1}-N \begin{smallmatrix} CH=CH \\ \\ CH=CH \end{smallmatrix} CH \right] Cl$	—	Merrill
Emulsept	N(acyl colamino formyl methyl) pyridinium chloride	10% aqueous solution; marked antiseptic action.	Emulsol
Intracol	Long-chain fatty acid amide	—	Synthetic
Isonol CL 1	Higher quaternary ammonium halide	W/O agent.	Onyx
Isonol DL 1	Higher quaternary ammonium halide	—	"
Sapamine A	Diethylamino ethyloleylamide acetate	—	Ciba
Sapamine CH	Diethylamino ethyloleylamide hydrochloride	—	"
Sapamine KW	Methosulfate of a quaternary ammonium compound	—	"
Sapamine MS	Diethylamino ethyloleylamide methosulfate	—	"
Secal	Higher fatty acid glycerol ester containing an amine salt	Combination of a non-ionic agent with a cation-active agent.	Emulsol
Steary sapamine base	Diethylamino ethylstearylamide	—	
Triton K 60	Cetyl dimethyl benzyl ammonium chloride	—	Ciba

General Formula: RCOOR'

Chemical Designation: Fatty acid esters of lower polyvalent alcohols.

Type of Emulsion: W/O

Description: Viscous, odorless liquids or wax-like solids of amber to dark-brown color; oil-soluble and water-insoluble; little affected by hydrolysis; small additions of soaps facilitate the dispersion in water, producing so-called "self-dispersible" agents.

Suggested Use: General-purpose agents for the water-in-oil type of emulsions; added in small proportions to O/W emulsions, giving improved stability and creamy consistency.

Commercial Name	Chemical Name or Formula	Remarks	Manufacturer
Arlacel C	Sorbitan monooleate	Special agent for cosmetic emulsions.	Atlas
Arlacel A, B	Anhydrohexitol monooleic esters		
Diethyleneglycol monolaurate	$C_{11}H_{23}COOC_2H_4OC_2H_4OH$	Also available in self-dispersible grade.	Glyco
Diethyleneglycol monooleate	$C_{17}H_{33}COOC_2H_4OC_2H_4OH$·	"	"
Diethyleneglycol monostearate	$C_{17}H_{35}COOC_2H_4OC_2H_4OH$	"	"
Glaurin	Diethyleneglycol monolaurate		
Glyceryl monooleate	$C_{17}H_{33}COOCH_2.CHOHCH_2OH$	Also available in edible grade.	Various
Glyceryl monoricinoleate	$C_{17}H_{32}OHCOOCH_2.CHOHCH_2OH$	—	"
Glyceryl monostearate	$C_{17}H_{35}COOCH_2.CHOHCH_2OH$	Also available in edible grade.	"
Nonaethyleneglycol diricinoleate	$C_{17}H_{32}OHCOOCH_2$	—	Glyco

$$C_{17}H_{32}OHCOOCH_2 \left.\begin{array}{c} \\ \\ \end{array}\right\} (CH_2OCH_2)_9$$

341

Commercial Name	Chemical Name or Formula	Remarks	Manufacturer
Nopco 1073 B	Oleic amine ester	—	National Oil
Pentamul 6	Pentaerythritol monostearate	—	Heyden
Pentamul 87	Pentaerythritol mono soybean fatty acid ester	—	"
Pentamul 126	Pentaerythritol monooleate	—	"
Pentamul 147	Pentaerythritol monolaurate	—	"
Pentamul 149	Pentaerythritol monocaprate	—	"
Prolaurin	Propyleneglycol laurate	Self-emulsifiable.	Glyco
Prolein	Propyleneglycol oleate	Self-emulsifiable.	"
Prostearin	Propyleneglycol stearate	Self-emulsifiable.	"
Span 20	Sorbitan monolaurate	—	Atlas
Span 40	Sorbitan monopalmitate	—	"
Span 60	Sorbitan monostearate	—	"
Span 80	Sorbitan monooleate	—	"
Span 85	Sorbitan trioleate	—	"
Tegin	Glyceryl monostearate	Special agent for cosmetic emulsions.	Goldschmidt
Tegin P	Propyleneglycol monostearate	—	"

Hydrophilic Esters
(non-ionic)

General Formula:

RCOOR'(OCH₂)ₙOH

$RCOOR'(OCH_2)_nOH$

Chemical Designation:

Fatty acid esters of higher polybasic alcohols or alcohol-ethers.

Description:

Viscous, odorless liquids or wax-like solids of amber to dark-brown color; water-soluble; thoroughly calcium-tolerant and little affected by hydrolysis.

Suggested Use:

Excellent all-purpose emulsifying agents; particularly recommended in combination with other agents of the anionic or cationic type.

342

Commercial Name	Chemical Name or Formula	Remarks	Manufacturer
Advawet	—	Non-ionic surface-active compounds.	Advance
Dodecaethyleneglycol monorici-noleate	$C_{17}H_{32}OHCOOCH_2(CH_2OCH_2)_{12}CH_2OH$	Recommended for essential oil emulsions.	Glyco
Emargol	Mono- and diglycerides mixed with sulfoacetate of mono- and diglycerides	Recommended for food emulsions and as anti-splattering agent.	Emulsol
Emcol CA	Selected blend of mono- and diglycerides of higher fatty acids plus soaps	Mixture of non-ionic agent with anion-active agent.	"
Emcol DL 50, DO 50, etc.,	Monodiethyleneglycol fatty acid esters	—	"
Emcol EL 50, EO 50, etc.,	Monoethyleneglycol fatty acid esters		"
Emcol L	Hydrophilic fatty acid ester of a polyhydric alcohol	Recommended for food, cosmetic, and pharmaceutical emulsions.	"
Emcol MS	Blend of hydrophilic glycerol fatty acid esters	Recommended for food, cosmetic, and pharmaceutical emulsions.	"
Emcol PL 50, PO 50, etc.,	Monopropyleneglycol fatty acid esters	—	"
Emulphor AG, ELA	Ethyleneoxide condense with fatty acids	—	General
Emulphor O	Polyethyleneglycol condensate	—	"
Igepal	Ethyleneoxide polymer	—	"
Intral 224, 229, 384	Long-chain fatty acid esters	—	Synthetic
Janusol	Mixture of lauryl and myristil esters	—	"
Mulsor	Long-chain fatty acid ester	—	"
Neutronyx	Non-ionic surface active compound	—	Oynx
Nonaethyleneglycol monooleate	$C_{17}H_{33}COOCH_2(CH_2OCH_2)_9CH_2OH$	Recommended for essential oil emulsions.	Glyco
Nonaethyleneglycol monostearate	$C_{17}H_{35}COOCH_2(CH_2OCH_2)_9CH_2OH$	Recommended for paste-type emulsions.	"

343

Commercial Name	Chemical Name or Formula	Remarks	Manufacturer
Secal	Higher fatty acid glycerol ester containing an amine salt	Mixture of a non-ionic agent with a cation-active agent.	Emulsol
Tetraethyleneglycol monostearate	$C_{17}H_{35}COOCH_2(CH_2OCH_2)_4CH_2OH$	Recommended for paste-type emulsions.	Glyco
Triton NE	Polyalkylene ether alcohol	—	Rohm
Tween 20	Polyoxyalkylene derivative of sorbitan monolaurate	—	Atlas
Tween 40	Polyoxyalkylene derivative of sorbitan monopalmitate	—	"
Tween 60, 61	Polyoxyalkylene derivative of sorbitan monostearate	—	"
Tween 80, 81	Polyoxyalkylene derivative of sorbitan monooleate	—	"
Tween 85	Polyoxyalkylene derivative of sorbitan triolein	—	"

General Characteristics:

Type of Emulsion: Mostly O/W, some W/O

Description: Mostly amorphous solids, forming viscous solutions in proper dispersion medium, usually in water.

Suggested Use: Bodying agents for the external phase and auxiliary emulsifying agents and protective colloids.

NATURAL AND MODIFIED NATURAL AGENTS

The agents of this group belong to different classes of chemical compounds, comprising alcohols, esters, salts, amino compounds, etc.; while there is little chemical similarity, the physical behavior is rather analogous.

Commercial Name	Chemical Name or Formula	Remarks	Manufacturer
Algin	Sodium alginate	Available in various grades of viscosity.	Algin
Amerchol C, LB	Free sterols and sterol esters	W/O emulsifier.	Cholesterol

344

Commercial Name	Chemical Name or Formula	Remarks	Manufacturer
Amerchol S	Free cholesterol, free sterols and free higher alcohols	W/O emulsifier.	Cholesterol
Bile salts	Sodium glycocholate and sodium taurocholate	Extracted from animal bile.	Various
Carboxymethyl cellulose	$[C_6H_7O_2(OH)_2OCH_2COOH]_n$	Available in various grades of viscosity.	Dow
Casein	Phospho protein	Available in many grades of refinement and grain size.	Various
Cellosize WS	Hydroxyethyl cellulose	Available as dry powder or as 8 or 10% aqueous solution.	Carbide
Cephalin	Phospho lipid	One of the active constituents of egg yolk.	—
Cholesterol	$C_{27}H_{45}OH$	W/O emulsifier.	Various
Colloresin	Methylcellulose	Available in various grades of viscosity.	Drug
Egg yolk	Lecithin and cephalin as active ingredients	—	—
Gum acacia	Natural product	Available in various grades of refinement.	Various
Gum arabic	"	"	"
Gum karaya	"	"	"
Gum tragacanth	"	"	"
Irish moss			"
Kelgin	Sodium alginate		"
Keltex	Sodium alginate	—	Kelco
Keltone	Sodium alginate	—	"
Lanoline	Cholesterol as active ingredient	—	"
Lecithin	Phospho lipid	W/O agent. One of the active constituents of egg yolk, also in soyabeans, etc.	Various "

Chemical Name	Chemical Name or Formula	Remarks	Manufacturer
Locust bean gum	Natural product	Available in various grades of refinement.	Various
Methocel	Methyl cellulose	Available in various grades of viscosity.	Dow
Methyl cellulose	$[C_6H_7O_2(OH)_2OCH_3]_n$	"	
Protovac	Modified casein	Soluble in water without addition of alkali.	Casein
α Soya protein	—	Pure protein.	Various
β Soya protein	—	With natural impurities.	"
Superloid	Ammonium alginate	—	Algin
Yelkin C, TTS	Lecithin preparations	—	Ross

FINELY DISPERSED SOLIDS

General Characteristics: Most finely dispersed solids, insoluble in both phases, may act as emulsifying agents; those which are more easily wetted by the water phase will promote O/W emulsions, those more easily wetted by the oil phase, W/O emulsions.

Type of Emulsion: O/W and W/O

Description: Finest inorganic or organic powders, of a particle size within the colloidal range.

Suggested Use: In practice only the so-called "colloidal clays" are employed as fairly efficient emulsifying and bodying agents for technical O/W emulsions, e.g., bituminous emulsions, cosmetics, polishes, etc.

Commercial Name	Chemical Name	Remarks	Manufacturer
Bentonite	Colloidal clay	Available in various grades of purity and fineness.	Various
Colloidal Clay	Impure aluminum silicate	—	"
Volclay KWK 33	Colloidal clay	Recommended for easy and quick mixing with water.	Colloid

In the preceding list of emulsifying agents, the names of the manufacturers are abbreviated as follows:

Advance — Advance Solvents and Chemical Corp.
Algin — Algin Corporation of America
Atlas — Atlas Powder Co.
Beacon — Beacon Co.
Carbide — Carbide and Carbon Chemicals Corp.
Cascin — Cascin Company of America
Cholesterol — American Cholesterol Products, Inc.
Ciba — Ciba Co., Inc.
Colgate — Colgate-Palmolive-Peet Co.
Colloid — American Colloid Co.
Commercial — Commercial Solvents Corp.
Cyanamid — American Cyanamid and Chemical Corp.
Dewey — Dewey & Almy Chemical Co.
Dow — The Dow Chemical Co.
Drug — General Drug Corp.
du Pont — E. I. du Pont de Nemours & Co., Inc.
Emulsol — Emulsol Corp.
General — General Dyestuff Corp.
Glyco — Glyco Products Co., Inc.
Goldschmidt — Goldschmidt Chemical Corp.
Hercules — Hercules Powder Co.
Heyden — Heyden Chemical Corp.
Kelco — Kelco Co.
Merrill — William Merrill Co.
Monsanto — Monsanto Chemical Co.
National Aniline — National Aniline Division of Allied Chemical & Dye Corp.
National Oil — National Oil Products Co., Inc.
Onyx — Onyx Oil and Chemical Co.
Pennsylvania — Pennsylvania Refining Co.

347

Procter   Procter & Gamble Co.
Ross   Ross & Rowe, Inc.
Rohm   Rohm & Haas Co.
Synthetic   Synthetic Chemicals, Inc.
Touraine   Touraine Chemical Co.
Vanderbilt   R. T. Vanderbilt Co., Inc.

INDEX

A

Absolute viscosity equation, 266
Acidic emulsions, emulsifying agents for, 340
Activated carbon, preparation of, 40
N(Acyl colamino formyl methyl) pyridinium chloride, 340
Adsorption of soap in emulsions, 269
  negative, 305
  positive, 305
  theory, 304
Advawet, 343
Aerosol, 336, 338
Agar, 69
Agar emulsion, preparation of, 76
Agent-in-oil emulsifying method, 21
Agent-in-water emulsifying method, 20
Aggregation, state of, 289
Aging, effect of, on emulsion, 24
Agitators, 90
Agricultural spray emulsions, 127
Albatex, 338
Albumen, 70
Alcohol sulfate, oil-soluble, 335
Alcohols, fatty acid esters of higher polybasic, 342
  fatty acid esters of lower polyvalent, 341
  sulfated, 334
Algin, 344
Alginates, 69
Aliphatic amides, sulfonates of, 336
  amino compounds, 331
  esters, sulfonates of, 336
  sulfonates, 336
Alkali soaps, 329
Alkaline emulsions, emulsifying agents for, 329
Alkanol, 338

Alkyl aryl sodium sulfonate, 339
  naphthalene sodium sulfonate, 338
  naphthalene sulfonic acid, 339
  phenoxyethyl sulfate sodium salt, 336
Alkylated benzimidazole, sulfonate of, 338
Alteration of colloidal properties, 158
Alternate addition emulsifying method, 23
Aluminum hydroxide, 73
  silicate, impure, 346
  stearate, 330
Amerchol, 344, 345
Amino compounds producing soaps with fatty acids, 331
Amino soaps, 331
2-Amino-1-butanol, 331
2-Amino-2-ethyl-1, 3-propanediol, 332
2-Amino-2-methyl-1, 3-propanediol, 332
2-Amino-2-methyl-1-propanol, 331
Ammonium alginate, 346
  laurate, 329
  linoleate, 329
  stearate, 329
Ammonyx, 340
Amount of emulsifier, 17
Anhydrohexitol monooleic esters, 341
Anion-active agents, 329
Antioxidants, 205
Antitoxins, oil-in-water emulsion, 33
Application of emulsifying methods, 20
Aquasol AR 75, 334
Aracel, 341
Arachis oil with potassium oleate emulsion, 124
Arctic Syntex, 335, 337
Areskap, 338
Aresket, 338
Aresklene, 338

Aromatic hydrocarbons, sulfonates of, 337

Asphaltic bitumen, acid content of, 261

bitumen content of road emulsions, 263

bitumen emulsions, methods of manufacture of, 258

bitumen emulsions, stability of, 275

bitumen, physical properties of dispersions of, 253

B

Batch churn, 93

Beaconol, 338

Bentonite, 73, 346

Bile salts, 345

Bituloid, 40

Bitumen, water-soluble substances in, 272, 273

Bituminous emulsions, 59

Black powder, preparation of, 41

Blood albumin, 135

Bordeaux oil emulsion, 136

"Bound" water in emulsions, 271

Breakdown test for road emulsions, 275, 279

Breaking emulsions, 54

latex, 240

Bronzing emulsions, 43, 44

Brush homogenizer, 111, 112

"Building up" emulsifying method, 76

Butterfat-containing mixes, 85

C

Caffein, removal of, from coffee, 41

Calcium linoleate, 331

stearate, 331

Carbolineums, "water-soluble," 130, 138

Carbon black paste, colloidal, 85

Carboxymethyl cellulose, 345

Carrageen, 69

Casein, 69, 345

methods for solubilizing, 217

modified, 346

substitutions, 222

Caseinates, 135

Castor oil emulsion, 80

oil, sulfated, 334

oil sulfuric acid ester, sodium salt of, 334

Cataphoresis experiments, 207

Cation-active agents, 339

Cationic Amine 220, 340

Cellosize WS, 345

Cephalin, 345

Cetyl dimethyl benzyl ammonium chloride, 340

pyridinium chloride, 340

Character of surface in removal of oil by emulsification, 195

Characteristics of emulsions, comparative, 8

of emulsions, desirable, 9

Charlotte mill, 104

Chemical interaction between oil and emulsifier, 157

nature of asphaltic bitumen, 255

Chemistry of digestion, 396

Choice of emulsifying agents, 70

Cholesterol, 179, 345

and lecithin, effect on emulsion systems of, 180

free, 345

Churns, 93

Classification of emulsifying agents, 326

Clays, colloidal, 346

Clear emulsions, 72

Coagulation of asphaltic bitumen emulsions, 254

of rubber latex, 244, 245

of rubber latex by "dipping," 251

Coarse emulsions, 288

Cod liver oil emulsion, 79

liver oil emulsion, preparation of, 76

Cold-mix emulsions, 133

Colloid mills, 90, 94, 260

mills, rough surface, 104

Colloidal clays, 135, 346

hydrates, 308

solvates, 308

Colloresin, 345

Commercial asphaltic bitumen emulsions, conclusion about, 278

asphaltic bitumen emulsion, requirements of, 256

Commercial bulletins on emulsions, 30
emulsions, manufacture of satisfactory, 29
soaps, 330
Compatibility charts, 136
of mineral oil emulsions with other spray substances, 136
Components of emulsions, 8
Compounded latex, 250
Concentration, adjustment of emulsion, 25
of dispersed phase and emulsion viscosity, 32
of rubber latex, 247
Consistency, measurement of, 184
Continuous churn, 94
Corrosion-preventing emulsion, 43
Creaming, direction of, 163
of spray emulsions, 150
Crepe rubber, 249
Cresylic acid-oil emulsion, 136
Crude oil-field emulsions, breaking of, 55–57
Currying of leather, 231

D

Darvan, 338
Daxad, 338
De Laval homogenizer, 114, 115
Decylbenzene sodium sulfonate, 339
De-emulsifying, 54
effect of ultrasonics, 3
Defatting fish meal, 41
Definitions of emulsions, 285
Degree of dispersion. See particle size.
Deinking paper, 41
Design of emulsifying machines, 88
Detergents and emulsifying agents, new, 202
Determination of emulsion type, 162
Diamyl sodium sulfosuccinate, 336
Diatomaceous earth, 135
Dibutyl phenylphenol sodium disulfonate, 338
sodium sulfosuccinate, 337
Diethanolamine, 332

Diethylamino ethyloleylamide, 340
ethyloleylamide acetate, 340
ethyloleylamide hydrochloride, 340
ethyloleylamide methosulfate, 340
ethylstearylamide, 340
Diethyleneglycol monolaurate, 341
monooleate, 341
monostearate, 341
3,9-Diethyl-tridecanol-6 sodium sulfate, 335
Differences in partition of emulsifier, 159
Digestion, chemistry of, 296
Diglycerides of higher fatty acids, 343
Dihexyl sodium sulfosuccinate, 336
Dimethyl amino-ethanol, 332
Dineric interface, arrangement of the molecules in the, 49
Dioctyl sodium sulfosuccinate, 336
Dispersants, 78
Dispersion, degree of. See particle size.
state of, 287
Dispersions, 74
Distribution of polar compounds between wool-oil and oil-water interfaces, 199
Dodecaethyleneglycol monoricinoleate, 343
Dodecylbenzene sodium sulfonate, 339
Dormant emulsions, 133
sprays, mineral oil emulsion, 136
Dresinate, 329
Drop test, 163
Drum-stuffing, 231
Dry "roll-up," 25
Dual emulsions, 154
systems, stability in, 153
type systems, possible explanation of, 157
Duo-Visco Valve, 110
Duponol, 335
Dust allaying emulsion, 39

E

Edible emulsifiers, 67, 68
emulsions, 47
Egg yolk, 179, 345

Einstein's equation of emulsion viscosity, 25
Electrical conductance method, 163
Electrodepositing rubber from latex, 251
Electrokinetic potential effect on structure of interfacial film, 324
theories, 322
Electrolytes, stabilizing emulsions to, 26
Emargol, 337, 343
Emcol, 343
Emulphor, 343
Emulsept, 340
Emulsifiable mineral oils, 201
Emulsification, mechanism of, 1
purpose of, 66
special techniques of, 72
Emulsifying agents, 48, 75, 78, 326
agents for agricultural sprays, 135
agents, anion-active, 329
agent, characteristics of, 13
agents, classification of, 326
agent, choice of, 14, 67, 70
agent consumption, effect of colloid mill on, 19
agents and detergents, new, 202
agent, differences in partition of, 159
agents, edible, 67, 68
agent and interfacial tension, 12
agents, list of, 15, 16, 329
agent and method of emulsification, 17
agents for mineral oil emulsions, 134
agents, modified natural, 344
agents, natural, 344
agents, non-ionic, 341
agents, oriented adsorption theory of properties of, 315
agents in the paint industry, 217
agent, protective layer of, 207-8
agent, required amount of, 17
aids, mechanical, 71
bowls, 105
capacity of emulsifying agents, 49
effect of mustard, 182
machines, design of, 88
machines and their manufacturers, 118
machines, types of, 90

Emulsifying methods, 19, 75
methods, application of, 20
Emulsion technology, 326
Emulsions and emulsification in the wool textile industry, 193
failures, 79
formulae, 79
of insecticidal solutions, 141
in the leather industry, 230
manufacture, important considerations in, 26
in medicine, highly-dispersed, 33
paints, 214
paints, pigment/liquid relationship in, 211, 212
paints, preparation of, 210, 211, 217, 218, 228
paint vehicle, preparation of, 216
in the patent literature, 39
phases, comparative characteristics of, 8
stability of, 292
in thin films, stability of, 207
of true oils and other liquids, 140
type, determination of, 162
type, effect of the relative volume of phases on, 181
as weed killers, 146
Equilibrium between liquid homogeneity and heterogeneity, 168
Esters as emulsifying agents, 50
hydrophilic, 342
hydrophobic, 341
sulfated, 334
Ethers as emulsifying agents, 50
2-Ethyl hexanol sodium sulfate, 335
7-Ethyl 2-methyl undecanol-4 sodium sulfate, 335
N-Ethyl morpholine, 332
Ethyleneoxide condensate with fatty acids, 343
polymer, 343
Evaluation of emulsifying agents, 66
Experimental procedure of emulsification, 120

F

Failures of emulsions, 79
Fat-liquor, breaking of, 238

Fat-liquoring leather, 237
 properties of sulphated neatsfoot oil
  on chrome-tanned calfskin, 237–8
 vegetable-tanned leather, 239
Fatty acid esters of higher polybasic
  alcohols, 342
 acid esters of lower polyvalent alcohols, 341
Finely dispersed solids, 346
Finishing the emulsion, 24
Fire-fighting, emulsions in, 41
Foliage emulsions, 133
 sprays, mineral oil emulsion, 137
Food emulsions, 47
 emulsion, typical, 176
Formation of interfacial film, oriented
  adsorption theory for, 314
 of water-in-oil emulsions, 324
Formulae of emulsions, 79
Formulation, general, 68
 industrial emulsion, 66
Foundry molds, emulsions for the treat-
  ment of, 39
Free emulsions, 166
Fresh fruit preservation, emulsion for,
  40
Fruit flavoring, 83
Fuel, emulsion for reducing dusting of,
  40
Fungicidal action of emulsions and
  wetting power, 144
Fur removal in boilers, 43
Furniture polish, 87

G

Garthe's whisk, 93
Gas, effect of, on emulsification, 2, 3, 4
Gaulin's emulsifying machine, 106
Gels, 75
Gelatin, 68
 and glue, 135
Gibbs, laws of adsorption, 18
Glaurin, 341
Glycerol ester of higher fatty acid con-
  taining amine salt, 340, 344
Glyceryl monooleate, 341
 monoricinoleate, 341
 monostearate, 341, 342
Grashof's whisk, 92

Gravity separation of emulsions, 54
Gum, 135
 acacia, 345
 arabic, 68, 345
 karaya, 70, 345
 tragacanth, 70, 345

H

Hand machines, 117
Hand-stuffing, 231
Hatschek's equation, 25, 271
Hatt-Dussek "homogenizer," 102, 103
Heat-coagulation of rubber latex, 250
Heptadecyl benzimidazol disulfonate,
  339
 benzimidazol monosulfonate, 339
Hevea, manihot, ficus rubbers, com-
  parison of, 248
Higher alcohols, free, 345
 fatty acid glycerol ester containing
  amine salt, 340, 344
 polybasic alcohol fatty acid esters, 342
History of agricultural sprays, 128
Homogeneity of asphaltic bitumen
  emulsions, 257
Homogenization of mayonnaise emul-
  sion, 181
Homogenizers, 90, 106, 107, 112
Homogenizing pressure and motor current, relation of, 109, 110
Hurrell mill, 99, 101
Hydration theory, 308
Hydrocarbons, purification of, 40
Hydrophilic esters, 342
 glycerol fatty esters, blend, 343
 polyhydric alcohol fatty acid ester,
  343
 solid particles, 316
Hydrophobic esters, 341
 solid particles, 316
Hydroxyethyl cellulose, 345
1-Hydroxyethyl-2-heptadecenyl glyox-
  alidine, 340

I

Igepal, 343
Igepon, 337
Immiscibility, 291

Important considerations, 26
Impregnation of leather, 231
Impulsor homogenizer, 115, 116
Indications of the type' of emulsion, 163–5
Indicator method, 162
Industrial emulsion formulation, 66
Insecticidal emulsions, 44–46, 131
    solutions, emulsions of, 141
Insecticides, classifying, 127, 128
Interaction between emulsifier and the liquids, 155
Interdependence of viscosity and asphaltic bitumen content, 266
Interfacial film, 298
    film, effect of electrokinetic potential on structure of, 324
    film, oriented adsorption theory of formation of, 314
    layer, properties of, 209, 210
    tension, 291
    tension determination, 16
    tension and emulsification, 11, 12
    -tension theory. See surface-tension theory.
Intracol, 340
Intral, 343
Invadine, 338, 339
Inversion of spray emulsions, 154
Irish moss, 345
Isobutyl naphthalene sodium sulfonate, 339
Isonol, 340
Isopropyl naphthalene sodium sulfonate, 338, 339

J

Janusol, 343

K

Karaya gum, 345
Kek mill, 104, 105
Kelgin, 345
Keltex, 345
Keltone, 345

L

Langmuir-Harkins theory. See oriented adsorption theory.

Lanolin, 345
Latex, 240
    analysis of total solids in, 243
    compounding, 42
    concentration of, 58
    gelling or setting of, 245
    particles, size of, 240
Lauryl and myristil esters, mixture of, 343
Lead arsenate suspension-lubricating oil emulsion, 136
Leather industry, emulsions in the, 46, 230
Lecithin, 345
    and cholesterol, effect on emulsion systems of, 180
    dual emulsions of, 160
    emulsions, 48
    preparation, 346
Length of the molecule in scouring, 196
"Liability" of asphaltic bitumen emulsions, 256
    test, 279
Liberation of free oil from sprays, 151
Life of road emulsions, 265
Linseed oil, vulcanization of, 42
Lipin, 135
Liquid petrolatum and agar emulsion, 84
Liquid soap, 329
List of emulsifying agents, 329
Locust bean gum, 346
Long-chain alcohol alkali salts, sulfuric acid esters of, 335
    alcohols, sulfuric acid esters of, 335
    aliphatic hydrocarbons, sulfonates of, 336
    fatty acid amide, 340
    fatty acid esters, 343
Lower polyvalent alcohol fatty acid esters, 341
Lubricant emulsions, 43
Lyophilic colloid theory. See hydration theory.

M

Magnesium hydroxide, 73
Magnesium stearate, 331

Manufacture of practical emulsions, 7
  of satisfactory commercial emulsions, 28, 29
Manufacturers of emulsifying agents, 329
  of emulsifying machines, 118
Manufacturing methods of asphaltic bitumen emulsions, 258
Marix's emulsifying machine, 89
Mayonnaise, 80, 81
  definition of, 177
  homogenization of, 181
  method, 163
  pH of, 190
  stability of, 178, 184
  time of beating, 189
  typical commercial formula for, 178
  viscosity of, 190, 191
Measurement of viscosity of road emulsions, 265
Mechanical emulsifying aids, 71
Mechanics of application of oil emulsions, 144
Mechanism of emulsification, 1
Medicinal emulsions, 47
Mercury, emulsification of, 2
Metallic soaps, 330
Methocel, 346
Methods of application of asphaltic bitumen emulsions, 257
  of cracking emulsions, 148
  of preparing soap-stabilized emulsions, 119
  of preparing spray emulsions, 148
Methyl cellulose, 345, 346
  diethanolamine, 332
N-Methyl morpholine, 333
Microscopical examination of particle size, 24
Milk, converting, into froth, 54
Mineral oil and agar emulsion, 81
  oils, emulsifiable, 201
  oil emulsions, 130
  oil emulsions, action on plants, 132
  oil emulsions, compatibility with other spray substances, 136
  oil emulsion dormant sprays, 136
  oil emulsions, emulsifiers for, 134
  oil emulsions for insects attacking animals and man, 137

Mineral oil emulsion, pharmaceutical, 85
  oil emulsion, preparation of, 76
  oil emulsions, sale of, 133
  oil emulsion summer sprays, 137
  oil salad dressing, 83
  oils, toxicity of, to the insect, 131
  and tar oils, mixed, 139
Miscellaneous patents, 57
Miscible oils, 133, 166
  oils, requirements of, 169
Miscibol, 329
Mixed sprays, 136
Mixing equipment used in paint industry, 220
  process for mayonnaise, 185
  processes, slow-speed, 261
Mobilometer, 184
Modified natural emulsifying agents, 344
Molecular orientation, 310
Molecule, mixed non-polar—polar, 313
  non-polar, 312
  polar, 312
Monobutyl diphenyl sodium monosulfonate, 338
  phenylphenol sodium monosulfonate, 338
Monodiethyleneglycol fatty acid esters, 343
Monoethyl phenylphenol amino monosulfonate, 338
  phenylphenol guanidine monosulfonate, 338
  phenylphenol potassium monosulfonate, 338
  phenylphenol sodium monosulfonate, 338
Monoethyleneglycol fatty acid esters, 343
Monoglycerides of higher fatty acids, 343
Monomolecular film of soap, 18
Monopol oil, 334
Monopropyleneglycol fatty acid esters, 343
Monosulph, 334
Morpholine, 333
Mosses, 69
MP-189, 337

MP-646 S Paste, 337
Mulsor, 343
Mustard, emulsifying effect of, 182
  stabilizing effect on mayonnaise, 185

N

Nacconol, 339
Nascent soap, effect of, 125
  soap emulsifying method, 23
Natural emulsifying agents, 48, 344
  organic stabilizers, 25
Nature of emulsions, 8
Neatsfoot oil, sulfated, 334
Negative adsorption, 305
Nekal, 339
Neomerpin N, 339
Neutral emulsions, emulsifying agents
  for, 340
Neutronyx, 343
Nicotine-oil emulsion, 136
  sulphate-oil emulsion, 136
Nitrogenous compounds as emulsifying
  agents, complex, 51
Nonaethyleneglycol diricinoleate, 341
  monooleate, 343
  monostearate, 343
Non-fattening salad dressing, 83
Non-ionic emulsifying agents, 341
Non-polar molecule, 312
Non-polar—polar molecule, 313
Nopco, 334, 342
Nopcob, 334

O

Oil content of scoured fabric, determination of, 195
  reextracted from leather, 235
  retained by the foliage, 142
  tannage, 230
Oil-in-water emulsions, emulsifying
  agent for, 16
  emulsions, explanation for formation
  of, 307
  emulsions, phase-volume theory for,
  300
  emulsions used as antitoxin, 33

Oils, sulfated, 334
Oil-soluble alcohol sulfate, 335
Oleic amine ester, 342
Oleoresinous component of the emul-
  sion, 226
  emulsion interior flat wall paint, 215
  emulsion paint vehicle, formula for,
  216
Olive oil with sodium oleate emulsion,
  124
  oil, sulfated, 334
Optimum pH for scouring, 203
Orange syrup, 82
Orientation theory of emulsification, 17
Oriented adsorption theory, 310
  wedge theory, 319
Orthokinetic coagulation, 4
Orvus WA, 335
Oxidation products as emulsifying
  agents, 51
Ovicidal emulsions, 131
Ozomulsion, 85

P

Paint emulsions, 207, 214
  microbicidal, 44
Paraffin wax emulsion, preparation of,
  22
Particle size, 287
  size, coarse, 288
  size of pigment in emulsion paints,
  227
  size, range of, 21
  size in road emulsions, 263
  size of stable emulsions, 24
Patent literature, emulsions in the, 39
Penetrants, 78
Penetration test for asphaltic bitumen,
  254
Pentaerythritol mono soybean fatty acid
  ester, 342
  monocaprate, 342
  monolaurate, 342
  monooleate, 342
  monostearate, 342
Pentamul, 342
Peptones, 135

Petroleum hydrocarbon sodium sulfonate, 337
oil conversion, 41, 42
sulfonate, 337
Petrosul, 337
Pfaudler whisk, 91
pH, adjustment of, 26
of casein water paints, 226, 227
of mayonnaise, 190
of rubber latex, 244
of scouring wool, 193, 203
Pharmaceutical mineral oil emulsion, 85
Phase reversal, 317
Phases of emulsions, 76
Phase-volume ratio, altering the, 155
theory, 300
Phosphatides in egg fat, 179
Phospho lipid, 345
Phospho protein, 345
Photomicrographs of resin-oil emulsion with various substitutions for casein, 223–4
taken at different stages of emulsification, 221
Physical properties of dispersions of asphaltic bitumen, 253
Pigments, dispersion of, 74
Pigment/liquid relationship in emulsion paints, 211, 212
Pigmented emulsion, 227
Plauson's emulsifying machine, 90
Polar character of the oil, 197
compounds between wool-oil and oil-water interfaces, distribution of 199
molecule, 312
and non-polar groups and emulsifying agents, 49
Polyalkylene ether alcohol, 344
Polyethyleneglycol condensate, 343
Polyhydric alcohol, hydrophilic fatty acid ester, 343
Polysulphide-light petroleum lubricating oil emulsion, 136
Positive adsorption, 305
Potassium oleate, 330
oleo-abietate, 330
palmitate, 330

Powdered solids in breaking emulsions, 55
Practical emulsion manufacture, 7
Precautions with mineral oil emulsions for plants, 138
Premier colloid mill, 96–99
paste mill, 99, 100
Preparation of emulsion paint vehicle, 216
Preservation of rubber latex, 244, 245
Pressure measurement, 108
Preventing creaming of spray emulsions, 151
Primary aliphatic amino compounds, 331
Principles of emulsification, 11
Prolaurin, 342
Prolein, 342
Properties of commercial asphaltic bitumen emulsions, 263
of various paint emulsions, 225
Propyleneglycol laurate, 342
oleate, 342
stearate, 342
Prostearin, 342
Protalene L, 330
Protective colloids for rubber latex, 250
Proteins, 135
Protein-fatty acid condensates, salts of, 330
Protovac, 346
Purpose of emulsification, 66

Q

Quaternary ammonium compound methosulfate, 340
ammonium compounds, salts of, 339
ammonium halide, 340

R

Ramsden phenomenon, 54
Rannie homogenizer, 114
Rate of phase separation and diameter of droplets, relation of, 31
References, 29, 30, 38, 59–65, 118, 171–5, 192, 206, 213, 239, 252, 278

Refining of oil, 42
Refractive index, adjustment of, 73
Relation between degree of emulsification and consistency, 219
Relative volume of the phases, effect on emulsion type of, 181
Removal of grease from wool by emulsification, 193
of oil residues from fruit, 142
Required amount of emulsifier, 17
Requirements of a commercial asphaltic bitumen emulsion, 256
of miscible oils, 169
of satisfactory commercial emulsion, 28, 29
of stabilization, 10
Resinates as emulsifiers, 134
Road emulsions, 253
Rosoap, 330
Rough surface colloid mills, 104
Rubber content of latex, 243
latex, 205, 240

S

Salad dressing, 177
dressing, non-fattening, 83
dressing with starch, 83
Salt organosols, preparation of, 40
Salts of protein-fatty acid condensates, 330
Santomerse, 339
Sapamine, 340
Saponin, 135
Scientific aspects of the physical properties of asphaltic bitumen emulsions, 265
Scouring, optimum pH for, 203
and polar compounds, 197
processes, thin oil films in, 194
wool, 193
Secal, 340, 344
Secondary aliphatic amino compounds, 331
Sedimentation of road emulsions, 264
Selection of emulsifier, 14
of emulsifying method, 19
Sewage, clarification of, 41
Shipping conditions, 28
Shock-absorbing emulsions, 43
Silica gel, 73

Size-frequency analysis, 120
curve of a bitumen emulsion, 259
distribution, 124
Slow-speed mixing processes, 261
Soap, alkali, 329
flakes, 330
metallic, 330
particles, accumulation at interface, 304
Soap-producing amino compounds, 331
Soaps, 70, 343
adsorption in emulsions, 269
as emulsifiers, 134
emulsifying method, nascent, 23
incompatibility of, 134, 135
monomolecular film of, 18
and the new detergents, 203
stabilized emulsions, 119
Soapy emulsions, 133
Sodium alginate, 344, 345
alkyl benzene sulfonate, 339
alkyl naphthalene sulfonate, 339
alkyl phenylene sulfonate, 338
cetyl sulfate, 335
glycocholate, 345
lauryl sulfate, 335
oleate, 330
oleo-abietate, 330
oleyl sulfate, 335
palmitate, 330
resinate, 330
salt of castor oil sulfuric acid ester, 334
stearate, 330
taurocholate, 345
tetrahydro-naphthalene sulfonate, 338
Soft soap, 330
water and emulsification, 26
Solid content of emulsions, 24
particles, hydrophilic, 316
particles, hydrophobic, 316
particle theory, 302
particles, accumulation at interface, 301
Solids, finely dispersed, 346
Solidification of liquid hydrocarbons, 59
Sorbitan monolaurate, 342
monolaurate polyoxyalkylene derivative, 344

Sorbitan monooleate, 341, 342
  monooleate polyoxyalkylene deriva-
    tive, 344
  monopalmitate, 342
  monopalmitate polyoxyalkylene de-
    rivative, 344
  monostearate, 342
  monostearate polyoxyalkylene deriva-
    tive, 344
  trioleate, 342
  triolein polyoxyalkylene derivative,
    344
Soya protein, 346
Span, 342
Special alcohol sulfate, 335
  systems, consideration of, 160
  techniques of emulsification, 72
Specific gravity of asphaltic bitumen,
  254
Spontaneous emulsification, 75
  emulsion droplets, effect of γ (De
    Nouy) on diameter of, 30
Spray emulsions, analysis of, 147
  emulsions, creaming of, 150
  emulsions, ease of formation of, 148
  for insects attacking animals and
    man, 137
Stability of asphaltic bitumen emulsions, 256, 275
  criteria of, 209
  in dual systems, 153
  of emulsion, 76, 292
  of emulsions in thin films, 207
  of mayonnaise, 178
  of spray emulsions, 151
Stabilizing adjustments, final, 24
  emulsions, 10
  emulsions to electrolytes, 26
  role of emulsifying agent in, 12
Starch, 135
State of aggregation, 289
  of dispersion, 287
Stearyl sapamine base, 340
Sterol esters, 344
Sterols, free, 344, 345
Stimulating effect of emulsions on
  plants, 141
Stock emulsions, 166
Sterile emulsion, preparation of, 34
Stokes' equation, modified, 10

Storage conditions, 28
Sulfatate, 337
Sulfated alcohols, 334
  castor oil, 334
  esters, 334
  neatsfoot oil, 334
  olive oil, 334
  oils, 334
  vegetable oil, 334
Sulfite lye, 135
Sulfonaphthyl stearic acid, 339
Sulfonated compounds as emulsifying
  agents, 52
  hydrocarbon sodium salt, 337
Sulfonates, 336
  of aliphatic esters, 336
  of aromatic hydrocarbons, 337
  of long-chain aliphatic hydrocarbons,
    336
Sulfonation test, 133
Sulfuric acid esters of long-chain alcohol alkali salts, 335
  acid esters of long-chain alcohols, 335
Summer sprays, mineral oil emulsion,
  137
Superloid, 346
Surface characteristics in removal of
  oil from wool by emulsification,
  195
Surface tension, adsorption theory for
  lowering of, 304
Surface-active agents, 75
  compounds, anionic, 329
  compounds, cationic, 339
  compounds, non-ionic, 343
Surface-film theory, 296
Synthetic rubber, preparation of, 42

T

Tar distillate emulsions, 138
Tegin, 342
Temperature of emulsion formation, 27
Tergitol wetting agent, 335
Tertiary aliphatic amino compounds,
  331
Test for determining the relative stabil-
  ity of mayonnaise, 184, 185
  for rate of break of emulsions on
    the road, 279

Testing the emulsion, 24
Tetraethyleneglycol monostearate, 344
Textile industry, emulsions and emulsification in the wool, 193
Theory of emulsifying agents, 283
of emulsions, 283
Thickness of adsorbed emulsifier film, 208
Thin films of oil in scouring processes, 194
Thomas' equation, 11
Time of beating mayonnaise, 189
Toxaemic conditions treated by highly-dispersed emulsions, 33
Toxicity of mineral oils to the insect, 131
of soap in agricultural sprays, 140
Tragacanth, gum, 345
Transparent emulsions, 72
emulsions, preparation of, 58
Triethanolamine, 333
Trigamine, 333
Tris (hydroxymethyl) aminomethane, 333
Tris isopropanol amine, 333
Triton, 336, 340, 344
True oils and other liquids, emulsions of, 140
Turkey red oil, 334
Tween, 344
Twitchell reagent, 339
Two-stage homogenization, 109
Types of emulsion, indications of, 163–5
of emulsifying machines, 90
of latices, 240, 241

U

Ultrasonic waves, 1–5
waves, demulsifying effect of, 3
Ultravon, 339
Uses of emulsions, 39

V

Vaccines, emulsions in the administration of, 37

Vegetable oil, sulfated, 334
Viscoliser, 114
Viscosity of agricultural sprays, 148
of the emulsion, 25, 163
of mayonnaise, 190, 191
of road emulsions, 257, 263, 264
Viscosity/concentration curves, 274
Viscosity theory, 295
Viscosity-shear curve of bitumen emulsion, 267
Volck, 145
analysis of, 147
Volklay KWK 33, 346
Volume and composition of the aqueous liquid used in mayonnaise, 187, 188
of cream as test for emulsion type, 163

W

Water absorption of bitumen, 272, 273
repellent, 82
Water-in-oil emulsions, 300
emulsions, emulsifying agent for, 16, 341
emulsions, formation of, 324
emulsions, phase-volume theory of, 300
"Water-soluble" carbolineums, 130, 138
Wax emulsions in carding and finishing wool, 193
Weed killer emulsions, 146
Weir homogenizer, 112, 113, 114
Wetting power and fungicidal action of emulsions, 144
Whisks, 91
Winter spraying, 139
Wood preservation, emulsion for, 40
Wood's metal, emulsification of, 2
Wool textile industry, emulsions and emulsification in, 193

Y

Yelkin, 346

Z

Zinc stearate, 331